GARDENERS' WORLD
DIRECTORY

Compiled by

Geoff Hamilton

BBC BOOKS

Published by BBC Books,
a division of BBC Worldwide Publishing,
BBC Worldwide Limited, Woodlands, 80 Wood Lane
London W12 0TT

First Published 1993
Reprinted 1993
This Revised Edition Published 1995

ISBN 0 563 37154 4

Maps by Rodney Paull
Drawings by Peter Bailey

Printed and bound in Great Britain by Redwood Books Ltd, Trowbridge

Cover printed by Clays Ltd, St Ives PLC

Chapters which include this rosette contain products which have been tried and
tested at Barnsdale

Contents

Introduction

The *Gardeners' World* office receives hundreds of letters every single week of the year. Most of them are seeking advice and information. Where can I buy the product you showed last week? How far apart should I sow my carrots? Will little Johnnie be ill if he eats laburnum seeds? Where can I get further information about allotments? Gardeners are hungry for information and we are delighted to try to help.

Alas, because we get so many requests, we sometimes take quite a long time to provide the information. We apologize for that and hope that this little book will go some way to rectifying the problem.

In it you will find all those handy facts and figures you so often need to get your gardening just right and to make it that much more successful. But we also hope it will give you some inspiration.

If you want to know what to plant in that shady corner, you will find dozens of suitable plants listed. If you get hooked on a particular species of plant and want to find out more, well the addresses of the relevant society or perhaps the National Plant Collection will enable you to do so. And, if you want to know where to buy unusual plants, we can help there too.

This is also a very personal book. At Barnsdale I test dozens of new products each year and I have my own favourite old ones too. While I in no way want to suggest that the tools, equipment and sundries I use are the only satisfactory ones, at least you can be sure that those listed have done the job for me over the years. And as you can imagine, most of the gear used at Barnsdale gets a pretty rugged trial. I have marked the chapters which contain the relevant products with a Barnsdale Recommended rosette.

Mind you, I know jolly well that there are some first rate gardeners amongst our viewers so I wouldn't dream of inflicting my own preferences on you to the exclusion of all else. So, if you want to control whitefly you'll find my favourite organic control, but you'll also be able to look up the appropriate chemical.

Finally, may I ask a favour? We intend to update our directory regularly so there is constant room for improvement. If there are facts missing that you'd like included, I'd be grateful if you would spare a minute to drop me a line to let me know.

I hope you'll find the *Gardeners' World Directory* useful.

Geoff Hamilton

Television and Radio Stations

M ost programmes welcome letters from their viewers, whether it be queries, complaints, or even praise! If you want to get in touch, write to the producer or the presenter of the programme. But do bear in mind that, if other programmes receive the same amount of mail as there is in the *Gardeners' World* postbag, you may wait some time for a reply.

BBC TV Addresses

London
Television Centre, Wood Lane,
London W12 7RJ
Tel: (0181) 743 8000

Birmingham
BBC Broadcasting Centre, Pebble
Mill Road, Birmingham B5 7SA
Tel: (0121) 414 8888

Edinburgh
Broadcasting House, Queen St,
Edinburgh EH2 1JF
Tel: (0131) 225 3131

Norwich
St Catherine's Close, All Saints
Green, Norwich NR1 3ND
Tel: (01603) 619331

Plymouth
Broadcasting House, Seymour Road,
Mannamead, Plymouth PL3 5BD
Tel: (01752) 229201

ITV Company Addresses

Anglia Television Ltd
Anglia House, Norwich NR1 3JG
Tel: (01603) 615151
AND
48 Leicester Square, London
WC2H 7FB
Tel: (0171) 321 0101

Border Television plc
The Television Centre, Harraby,
Carlisle CA1 3NT
Tel: (01228) 25101

Carlton Television Ltd
101 St Martin's Lane, London
WC2N 4AZ
Tel: (0171) 615 1515

Central Independent Television plc
Central House, Broad St,
Birmingham B1 2JP
Tel: (0121) 643 9898
AND
Television House, Lenton Lane,
Nottingham NG7 2NA
Tel: (0115) 986 3322
AND
35–38 Portman Square, London
W1A 2HZ
Tel: (0171) 486 6688

Channel Television
Television Centre, La Pouquelaye, St Helier, Jersey JE2 3ZD, Channel Islands
Tel: (01534) 68999

GMTV
The London Television Centre, Upper Ground, London SE1 9LT
Tel: (0171) 827 7000

Grampian Television plc
Queen's Cross, Aberdeen AB9 2XJ
Tel: (01224) 646464

Granada Television Ltd
Granada Television Centre, Quay St, Manchester M60 9EA
Tel: (0161) 832 7211
AND
36 Golden Square, London W1R 4AH
Tel: (0171) 734 8080

HTV Ltd
HTV Wales, The Television Centre, Culverhouse Cross, Cardiff CF5 6XJ
Tel: (01222) 590590
AND
The Television Centre, Bath Road, Brislington, Bristol BS4 3HG
Tel: (0117) 977 8366

London Weekend Television Ltd
London Television Centre, Upper Ground, London SE1 9LT
Tel: (0171) 620 1620

Meridian Broadcasting Ltd
Television Centre, Northam, Southampton SO9 5HZ
Tel: (01703) 222 5555
AND
48 Leicester Square, London WC2H 7FB
Tel: (0171) 839 2255

Scottish Television plc
Cowcaddens, Glasgow G2 3PR
Tel: (0141) 332 9999

Tyne Tees Television Ltd
The Television Centre, City Road, Newcastle upon Tyne NE1 2AL
Tel: (0191) 261 0181
AND
15 Bloomsbury Square, London WC1A 2LJ
Tel: (0171) 405 8474

Ulster Television plc
Havelock House, Ormeau Road, Belfast BTT 1EB
Tel: (01232) 328122

Westcountry Television Ltd
Western Wood Way, Plympton, Plymouth PL1 3EW
Tel: (01752) 333333

Yorkshire Television Ltd
The Television Centre, Leeds LS3 1JS
Tel: (01132) 438283
AND
Television House, 32 Bedford Row, London WC1R 4HE
Tel: (0171) 242 1666

Channel 4 Television
124 Horseferry Road, London SW1P 2TX
Tel: (0171) 396 4444

BBC NATIONAL RADIO

BBC Broadcasting House, Portland Place, London W1A 1AA
Tel: (0171) 580 4468

RADIO 2
FM 88.0 – 90.2

RADIO 4
FM 92.4 – 94.6
LW 198 kHz (1515 m)

RADIO 5
MW 909, 693 kHz (330, 433 m)

BBC Local Radio

CHANNEL ISLANDS

BBC RADIO GUERNSEY
FM 93.2
MW 1116 kHz
Commerce House, Les Banques,
St Peter Port, Guernsey
Tel: (01481) 728977
Phone-in: (01481) 728888

BBC RADIO JERSEY
FM 88.8
MW 1026 kHz
Broadcasting House, Rouge
Bouillon, St Helier, Jersey
Tel: (01534) 70000
Phone-in: (01534) 20255

SOUTH WEST

BBC RADIO BRISTOL
FM 95.5 Bristol 94.9 Bath 104.6
MW Avon: 1548 kHz
Tyndall's Park Road, Bristol BS8 1PP
Tel: (0117) 974 1111
Phone-in: (0117) 923 8877

Key to radio stations

Channel Islands
1 BBC Radio Jersey
2 BBC Radio Guernsey

South
3 BBC Radio Cornwall
4 BBC Radio Devon (Plymouth)
5 BBC Radio Devon
6 BBC Somerset Sound
7 BBC Radio Bristol
8 BBC Wiltshire Sound
9 BBC Radio Solent
10 BBC Radio Oxford
11 BBC Berkshire
12 BBC Three Counties Radio
13 Greater London Radio
14 BBC Radio Kent
15 BBC Southern Counties Radio

Midlands and Eastern Counties
16 BBC Essex
17 BBC Radio Suffolk
18 BBC Radio Norfolk
19 BBC Radio Cambridgeshire
20 BBC Radio Peterborough
21 BBC Radio Lincolnshire
22 BBC Radio Northampton
23 BBC Radio Leicester
24 BBC Radio Nottingham
25 BBC CWR
26 BBC Radio Derby
27 BBC Radio Gloucestershire
28 BBC Radio Hereford and Worcester
29 BBC Radio WM
30 BBC Radio Stoke
31 BBC Radio Shropshire

Wales
32 BBC Radio Wales
33 BBC Radio Cymru
34 BBC Radio Clwyd

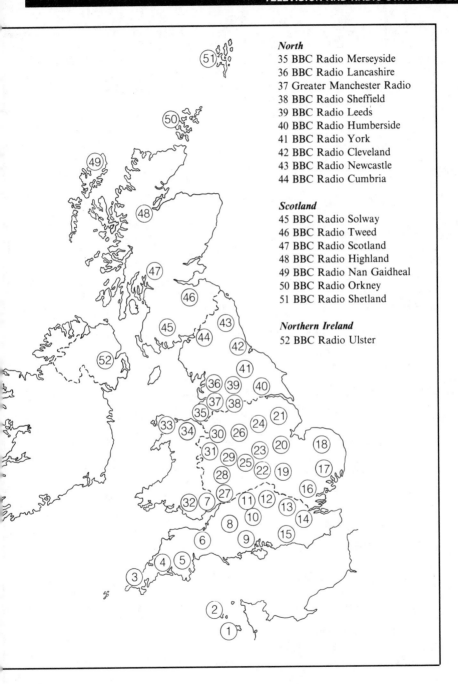

North
35 BBC Radio Merseyside
36 BBC Radio Lancashire
37 Greater Manchester Radio
38 BBC Radio Sheffield
39 BBC Radio Leeds
40 BBC Radio Humberside
41 BBC Radio York
42 BBC Radio Cleveland
43 BBC Radio Newcastle
44 BBC Radio Cumbria

Scotland
45 BBC Radio Solway
46 BBC Radio Tweed
47 BBC Radio Scotland
48 BBC Radio Highland
49 BBC Radio Nan Gaidheal
50 BBC Radio Orkney
51 BBC Radio Shetland

Northern Ireland
52 BBC Radio Ulster

BBC RADIO CORNWALL
FM Mid & West 103.9 North & East
95.2 Sally 96
MW Mid & West 630 kHz North &
East 657 kHz
Phoenix Wharf, Truro TR1 1UA
Tel: (01872) 75421
Phone-in: (01872) 222222

BBC RADIO DEVON
FM Exeter 95.8 Plymouth 103.4 N
Devon 94.8 & 103.4
Torbay 103.4 Okehampton 96.0
MW Exeter 990 kHz Plymouth
855 kHz N Devon 801 kHz
Torbay 1485 kHz
PO Box 100, St David's Hill, Exeter
EX4 4DB
Tel: (01392) 215651
Phone-in: (01392) 269611
ALSO
PO Box 5, Plymouth PL1 2AD
Tel: (01752) 260323
Phone-in: (01752) 269611

BBC RADIO GLOUCESTERSHIRE
FM 104.7 Stroud 95.0 Cirencester
95.8
London Road, Gloucester GL1 1SW
Tel: (01452) 308585
Phone-in: (01452) 307575

BBC RADIO PLYMOUTH
for transmission and address details
see Radio Devon

BBC SOMERSET SOUND
MW 1323 kHz
14–16 Paul Street, Taunton TA1 3PF
Tel: (01823) 252437
Phone-in: (01823) 251641

BBC WILTSHIRE SOUND
FM N Wilts 103.6 W Wilts 104.3
Salisbury 103.5

MW N Wilts: 1368 kHz
W Wilts 1323 kHz
PO Box 1234, Salisbury SP1 3DX
Tel: (01722) 411280
Phone-in: (01793) 513366

SOUTH

BBC RADIO SOLENT
FM 96.1
MW 999 kHz Bournemouth
1359 kHz
Broadcasting House, Havelock Road,
Southampton SO1 OXR
Tel: (01703) 631311
Phone-in: (01703) 631316

**BBC SOUTHERN COUNTIES
RADIO**
FM 104.6
Broadcasting Centre, Guildford
GU2 5AP
Tel: (01483) 306113
AND
FM C&S Sussex 95.3 E Sussex 104.5
N Sussex 104
MW C&S 1485 kHz E Sussex 1161
kHz N Sussex 1368
Broadcasting Centre, Marlborough
Place, Brighton BN1 1TU
Tel: (01273) 680231
Phone-in (01273) 570057

SOUTH EAST

BBC ESSEX
FM N&C Essex 103.5 S Essex 95.3
MW 765 kHz
PO Box 765, Chelmsford, Essex
CM2 9XB
Tel: (01245) 262393
Phone-in: (01245) 495050

BBC RADIO KENT
FM 96.7, 104.2
MW 1035, 1602, 774 kHz
Sun Pier, Chatham, Kent ME4 4EZ
Tel: (01634) 830505
Phone-in: (01634) 811111

SOUTH CENTRAL

BBC RADIO BERKSHIRE
FM W Berks 104.1 E Berks 95.4
42a Portman Road, Reading
RG3 1NB
Tel: (01734) 567056

GREATER LONDON RADIO
FM 94.9
35c Marylebone High Street, London
W1A 4LG
Tel: (0171) 224 2424
Phone-in: (0171) 224 2000

BBC RADIO OXFORD
FM 95.2
MW 1485 kHz
269 Banbury Road, Oxford
OX2 7DW
Tel: (01865) 311444
Phone-in: (01865) 311111

BBC THREE COUNTIES RADIO
FM S Beds, Herts, Bucks 103.8 N
Bucks 104.5
N Beds, N Herts 95.5
MW Beds, Herts, Bucks 630 kHz N
Beds 1161 kHz
PO Box 3CR, Hastings Street, Luton
LU1 5XL
Tel: (01582) 441000
Phone-in: (01582) 455555

WEST

BBC RADIO SHROPSHIRE
FM 96.0 Ludlow 95.0
MW 75.6 kHz Ludlow 1584 kHz
PO Box 397, Shrewsbury SY1 3TT
Tel: (01743) 248484
Phone-in: (01743) 248321

MIDLANDS/ANGLIA

BBC RADIO CAMBRIDGESHIRE
FM 96.0
MW 1026 kHz
PO Box 96, Cambridge CB2 1LD
Tel: (01223) 315970
Phone-in: (01223) 315444

BBC RADIO CWR
FM Coventry & Warwick 94.8
FM Warwick, Leamington, Stratford
& S Warks 103.7
FM Nuneaton & Atherstone 104
25 Warwick Road, Coventry
CV1 2WR
Tel: (01203) 559911
Phone-in: (01203) 231231

BBC RADIO DERBY
FM 104.5, 94.2, 95.3
MW 1116 kHz
PO Box 269, Derby DE1 3HL
Tel: (01332) 361111
Phone-in: (01332) 616161

BBC RADIO LEICESTER
FM 104.9
MW 837 kHz
Epic House, Charles Street, Leicester
LE1 3SH
Tel: (0116) 251 6688
Phone-in: (0116) 242 2222

BBC RADIO LINCOLNSHIRE
FM 94.9
MW 1368 kHz
PO Box 219, Newport, Lincoln
LN1 3XY
Tel: (01522) 511411
Phone-in: (01522) 511219

BBC RADIO NORFOLK
FM 95.1
MW E Norfolk 855 kHz W Norfolk
873 kHz
Norfolk Tower, Surrey Street,
Norwich NR1 3PA
Tel: (01603) 617411
Phone-in: (01603) 617321

BBC RADIO NORTHAMPTON
FM 104.2, 103.6
MW 1107 kHz
PO Box 1107, Abingdon Street,
Northampton NN1 2BE
Tel: (01604) 239100
Phone-in: (01604) 234455

BBC RADIO NOTTINGHAM
FM 103.8, 95.5
MW 1584 kHz
York House, Mansfield Road,
Nottingham NG1 3JB
Tel: (0115) 941 5161
Phone-in: (0115) 934 3434

BBC RADIO PETERBOROUGH
FM 95.7
MW 1449 kHz
PO Box 957, Peterborough PE1 1YT
Tel: (01733) 312832
Phone-in: (01733) 315444

BBC RADIO STOKE
FM 94.6
MW 200 kHz
Cheapside, Hanley, Stoke-on-Trent
ST1 1JJ *Tel*: (01782) 208080

BBC RADIO SUFFOLK
FM E Suffolk 103.9 W Suffolk 104.6
Lowestoft 95.5
Broadcasting House, St Matthew's
Street, Ipswich IP1 3EP
Tel: (01473) 250000
Phone-in: (01473) 212121

BBC RADIO WM
FM 95.6
MW 1548 kHz
PO Box 206.
Birmingham B5 7QQ
Tel: (0121) 414 8484
Phone-in: (0121) 432 2000

NORTH EAST

BBC RADIO CLEVELAND
FM 95.0 Whitby 95.8
MW 1548 kHz
PO Box 954B, Broadcasting House,
Newport Road, Middlesbrough
TS1 5DG
Tel: (01642) 225211
Phone-in: (01642) 225511

BBC RADIO HUMBERSIDE
FM 95.9
MW 1485 kHz
9 Chapel Street, Hull HU1 3NU
Tel: (01482) 23232
Phone-in: (01482) 27744 from N of
Humber
Phone-in: (01472) 353501 from S of
Humber

BBC RADIO LEEDS
FM 92.4, 95.3
MW 774 kHz
Broadcasting House, Woodhouse
Lane, Leeds LS2 9PN
Tel: (0113) 244 2131
Phone-in: (0113) 244 3222

BBC RADIO NEWCASTLE
FM 95.4
MW 1458 kHz
BBC Broadcasting Centre, Barraack
Road, Newcastle upon Tyne
NE99 1RN
Tel: (0191) 232 4141
Phone-in: (0191) 232 6565

BBC RADIO SHEFFIELD
FM Sheffield 88.6 Chesterfield 94.7
all other areas 104.1
MW 1035 kHz
Ashdell Grove, 60 Westbourne Road,
Sheffield SIO 2QU
Tel: (0114) 268 6185
Phone-in: (0114) 268 2682

BBC RADIO YORK
FM C 103.7 E 95.5 W & NW 104.3
MW C & E 1260 kHz W & NW
655 kHz
20 Bootham Row, York YO3 7BR
Tel: (01904) 641351
Phone-in: (01904) 641641

NORTH WEST

BBC RADIO CUMBRIA
FM N 95.6 W 95.6 S 96.1 Kendal
95.2 Windermere 104.2
MW N 756 kHz W 1458 kHz S 836
kHz
Hilltop Heights, London Road,
Carlisle CA1 2NA
Tel: (01228) 31661
Phone-in: (01228) 38484

BBC RADIO LANCASHIRE
FM C&W 103.9 E 95.5 N 104.5
MW C&W&E 855 kHz N 1557 kHz
Darwen St, Blackburn BB2 2EA
Tel: (01254) 262411
Phone-in: (01254) 583583

GREATER MANCHESTER RADIO
FM 95.1
PO Box 951, Oxford Road,
Manchester M60 1SJ
Tel: (0161) 200 2000
Phone-in: (0161) 228 2255

BBC RADIO MERSEYSIDE
FM 95.8
MW 1485 kHz
55 Paradise St, Liverpool L1 3BP
Tel: (0151) 709 9333

IRELAND

BBC RADIO ULSTER
FM 92.4–95.4
MW 1341 kHz Enniskillen 873 kHz
Broadcasting House, Ormeau
Avenue, Belfast BT2 8HQ
Tel: (01232) 338000
Phone-in: (01232) 325757

WALES

BBC RADIO CLWYD
FM 97.1, 103.4
MW 1260 kHz
AM 657 kHz
The Old School House, Glanrafon
Road, Mold CH7 1PA
Tel: (01352) 700367
Phone-in: (01352) 700367

BBC RADIO CYMRU
FM 92.4–94.6, 96.8 & 103.5–105
BBC Bryn Meirion, Meirion Road,
Bangor, Gwynedd LL57 2BY
Tel: (01248) 370880

BBC RADIO WALES
AM 882 kHz
Broadcasting House, Llandaff,
Cardiff CF5 2YQ
Tel: (01222) 572888

SCOTLAND

BBC RADIO HIGHLAND
FM 92–95, 103.5–105
7 Culduthel Road, Inverness
IV2 4AD
Tel: (01463) 720720

BBC RADIO NAN GAIDHEAL
FM 103–105
52 Church Street, Stornoway,
Isle of Lewis PA87 2LS
Tel: (01851) 705000

BBC RADIO ORKNEY
FM 93.7
Castle Street, Kirkwall, Orkney
KW15 1DF
Tel: (01856) 873939

BBC RADIO SCOTLAND
FM 92.4
MW 810 kHz
5 Queen Street, Edinburgh EH2 1JF
Tel: (0131) 225 3131

BBC RADIO SHETLAND
FM 92.7
Brentham House, Harbour Street,
Lerwick, Shetland ZE1 0LR
Tel: (01595) 694747

BBC RADIO SOLWAY
MW 585 kHz
Elmbank, Lover's Walk, Dumfries
DG1 1NZ
Tel: (01387) 68008

BBC RADIO TWEED
FM 93.5
Municipal Buildings, High Street,
Selkirk IO7 4BU
Tel: (01750) 21884

Organizations

Trade organizations are mainly concerned with assisting their members in several ways, but can also be a source of useful information for gardeners. Generally, they'll be the administrators of a code of conduct which controls the quality and service expected from members. If, for example, you're thinking of having your garden landscaped, you'd be very well advised to use a member of the British Association of Landscape Industries from whom you can expect a decent job. And if, by any chance, you don't get it, well you can complain to the Association who will take action.

Other organizations too will be happy to give you advice concerning their particular speciality. You may fear problems over the security of your allotment site. In that case the National Society of Allotment and Leisure Gardeners will be able to help. If you think you've bred a winning rose, then the British Rose Growers Association may want to hear, while a complaint about bad landscaping should be directed at the British Association of Landscape Industries.

Official Organizations

Arboricultural Association
Ampfield House, Ampfield, Romsey,
Hampshire SO51 9PA
Tel: (01794) 768717

Botanical Gardens Conservation International
Descanso House, 199 Kew Road,
Richmond, Surrey TW9 3BW
Tel: (0181) 940 0047

Botanical Society of the British Isles
c/o Dept of Botany, The Natural
History Museum, Cromwell Road,
London SW7 5BD
Tel: (0171) 938 8701

Botanical Society of Scotland
c/o Royal Botanical Garden,
Edinburgh, Lothian EH3 5LR
Tel: (0131) 552 7171

British Agricultural & Garden Machinery Association
14/16 Church Street, Rickmansworth,
Hertfordshire WD3 1RQ
Tel: (01923) 720241

British Agrochemicals Association Ltd
4 Lincoln Court, Lincoln Road,
Peterborough PE1 2RP
Tel: (01733) 349225

British Association of Landscape Industries (BALI)
Landscape House, 9 Henry Street, Keighley, West Yorkshire BD21 3DR
Tel: (01535) 606139

British Association Representing Breeders
9 Portland Street, King's Lynn, Norfolk PE33 1PB
Tel: (01553) 840364

British Bedding and Pot Plant Association
22 Long Acre, London WC2E 9LY
Tel: (0171) 235 5077

British Bonsai Association
Daisy Cottage, 131 Nine Mile Ride, Wokingham, Berkshire RG11 4HY
Tel: (01734) 328634

British Dahlia Growers Association
c/o Halls of Heddon, West Heddon Nurseries, Heddon-on-the-Wall, Newcastle upon Tyne NE15 0JS
Tel: (01661) 852445

British Dried Flowers Association
c/o Eathorpe Park Hotel, The Fosse, Eathorpe, Leamington Spa, Warwickshire CV33 9DQ
Tel: (01926) 632632

British Orchid Council
A J Hainsworth, 52 Weaste Lane, Thelwall, Cheshire WA4 3JR
Tel: (01925) 261791

British Rose Growers Association
46 Alexandra Road, St Albans, Hertfordshire AL1 3AZ
Tel: (01727) 833648

British Trust for Ornithology
The Nunnery, Nunnery Place, Thetford, Norfolk IP24 2PU
Tel: (01842) 750050

Bulb Information Desk
43 King Street, London WC2E 8RJ
Tel: (0171) 240 4705

Centre for the Conservation of Historic Parks & Gardens
Institute of Advanced Architectural Studies, University of York, York YO1 2EP
Tel: (01904) 433966

Conservatory Association
2nd Floor, Godwin House, George Street, Huntingdon, Cambridgeshire PE18 6BU
Tel: (01480) 458278

Council for the Protection of Rural England
Warwick House, 25 Buckingham Palace Road, London SW1W 0PP
Tel: (0171) 976 6433

Department of the Environment
2 Marsham Street, London SW1
Tel: (0171) 276 3000

English Vineyards Association
38 West Park, London SE9 4RH
Tel: (0181) 857 0452

Federation to Promote Horticulture for the Disabled
Thorngrove, Common Mead Lane, Gillingham, Dorset SP8 4RE
Tel: (01747) 822242

Fertiliser Manufacturers Association
Greenhill House, Thorpe Wood, Peterborough PE3 6GF
Tel: (01733) 331303

Forestry Commission
231 Corstorphine Road, Edinburgh EH12 7AT
Tel: (0131) 334 0303

Friends of Brogdale
The Brogdale Horticultural Trust,
Brogdale Farm, Faversham, Kent
ME13 8XS
Tel: (01795) 535286

Fruit Group of the RHS
Mrs M Sweetingham, RHS, Vincent
Square, London SW1P 2PE
Tel: (0171) 834 4333

Garden History Society
5 The Knoll, Hereford HR1 1RU
Tel: (01432) 354479

**The Gardener's Royal Benevolent
Society**
Bridge House, 139 Kingston Road,
Leatherhead, Surrey KT22 7NT
Tel: (01372) 373962

Gardening for the Disabled Trust
Hayes Farm House, Hayes Lane,
Peasmarsh, East Sussex TN31 6XR
Write for information

Good Gardeners Association
Two Mile Lane, Highnam,
Gloucester GL2 8DW
Tel: (01452) 305814

Health & Safety Executive
St Hughes House (Room 414),
Trinity Road, Stanley Precinct,
Bootle, Merseyside L20 3QY
Tel: (0151) 951 4225

**Henry Doubleday Research
Association**
National Centre For Organic
Gardening, Ryton-on-Dunsmore,
Coventry, West Midlands CV8 3LG
Tel: (01203) 303517

Horticultural Development Council
18 Lavant Street, Petersfield,
Hampshire GU32 3EN
Tel: (01730) 263736

Horticultural Therapy
Goulds Ground, Vallis Way, Frome,
Somerset BA11 3DW
Tel: (01373) 464782

Horticultural Trades Association
Horticultural House, 19 High Street,
Theale, Reading, Berkshire
RG7 5AH
Tel: (01734) 303132

Horticulture Research International
Wellesbourne, Warwickshire
CV35 9EF
Tel: (01789) 470382

Institute of Groundmanship
19–23 Church Street, The Agora,
Wolverton, Buckinghamshire
MK12 5LG
Tel: (01908) 312511

The Institute of Horticulture
PO Box 313, 80 Vincent Square,
London SW1P 2PE
Tel: (0171) 976 5951

**Institute of Leisure & Amenity
Management**
Lower Basildon, Reading, Berkshire
RG8 9NE
Tel: (0491) 874222

International Bee Research Society
18 North Road, Cardiff CF1 3DY
Tel: (01222) 372409

**International Plant Propagators
Society**
Thelma Swash, Longfield Nursery,
Oreton, Shropshire DY14 0TS
Tel: (0174) 632605

International Tree Foundation
Sandy Lane, Crawley Down, West
Sussex RH10 4HS
Tel: (01342) 712536

Joint Council for Landscape Industries
Mr K Frazer, Olam House, Lower
Basildon, Berkshire RG9 9NE
Tel: (01491) 874222

The Landscape Institute
6/7 Barnard Mews, London
SW11 1QU
Tel: (0171) 738 9166

**London Association of Recreational
Gardeners**
45 The Ridgeway, Kenton, Harrow,
Middlesex HA3 0LN
Tel: (0181) 907 2040

**Ministry of Agriculture, Fisheries &
Food (MAFF)**
(Pesticides Safety Division),
Rothamsted, Harpenden,
Hertfordshire AL5 2SS
Tel: (01582) 763133

Mushroom Growers Association
2 St Paul's Street, Stamford,
Lincolnshire PE9 2BE
Tel: (01780) 66888

**National Association of Flower
Arrangement Societies of Great
Britain**
21 Denbigh Street, London
SW1 2HF
Tel: (0171) 828 5145

**National Council for the Conservation
of Plants and Gardens**
The Pines, Wisley Garden, Woking,
Surrey GU23 6QB
Tel: (01483) 211465

National Gardens Scheme
Hatchlands Park, East Clandon,
Guildford, Surrey GU4 7RT
Tel: (01483) 211535

**National Institute of Medical
Herbalists**
9 Palace Gate, Exeter, Devon
EX1 1JA
Tel: (01392) 426022

**National Institute of Agricultural
Botany**
Huntingdon Road, Cambridge
CB3 0LE
Tel: (01223) 276381

**National Society of Allotment &
Leisure Gardeners Ltd**
Odell House, Hunters Road, Corby,
Northamptonshire NN17 5JE
Tel: (01536) 266576

The National Trust
36 Queen Anne's Gate, London
SW1H 9AS
Tel: (0171) 222 9251

**An Taisce – National Trust for
Ireland**
The Jailor's Hall, Back Lane, Dublin
8, Eire
Tel: (00353) 1 541786

National Trust for Northern Ireland
Rowallane House, Saintfield,
Ballynahinch, Co. Down BT24 7LH
Tel: (01238) 510721

National Trust for Scotland
Gardening Advice Centre,
Greenbank House, Clarkston,
Glasgow G76 8RB
Tel: (0141) 639 3281

Northern Horticultural Society
Harlow Carr Botanical Gardens,
Crag Lane, Harrogate, North
Yorkshire HG3 1QB
Tel: (01423) 565418

Nuffield Orthopedic Centre NHS Trust
Windmill Road, Headington, Oxford
OX3 7LD
Tel: (01865) 741155

Organic Growers Association
86 Colston Street, Bristol
BS1 5BB
Tel: (0117) 929 9800

Plant Variety Rights Office
White House Lane, Huntingdon
Road, Cambridge CB3 0LF
Tel: (01223) 277151

Professional Gardeners Guild
Oak House, Sutton Park, Sutton
Green, Nr Guildford, Surrey
GU4 7QN
Tel: (01483) 39126

Royal Caledonian Horticultural Society
21 Newbattle Abbey Crescent,
Dalkeith, Midlothian EH23 3LN
Tel: (0131) 663 1192

Royal Forestry Society of England, Wales & Northern Ireland
102 High Street, Tring, Hertfordshire
SG4 8UT
Tel: (0144) 282 2028

Royal Gardener's Orphan Fund
48 St Albans Road, Codicote,
Hitchin, Hertfordshire SG4 8UT
Tel: (01438) 820783

Royal Horticultural Society
80 Vincent Square, London
SW1P 2PE
Tel: (0171) 834 4333

Royal Horticultural Society of Ireland
Swanbrook House, Bloomfield
Avenue, Donnybrook, Dublin 4, Eire
Tel: (00353) 1 6684358

Royal Horticultural Society's Garden
Wisley, Woking, Surrey GU23 6QB
Tel: (01483) 224234

Royal Society for the Protection of Birds
The Lodge, Sandy, Bedfordshire
SG19 2DL
Tel: (01767) 680551

Scotland's Garden Scheme
31 Castle Terrace, Edinburgh
EH1 2EL
Tel: (0131) 229 1870

Society of Floristry
The Old Schoolhouse, Payford,
Redmarley, Gloucestershire
GL19 3HY
Tel: (01531) 820809

Society of Garden Designers
6 Borough Road, Kingston upon
Thames, Surrey KT2 6BD
Tel: (0181) 974 9483

Soil Association
86 Colston Street, Bristol BS1 5BB
Tel: (0117) 929 0661

Somerset Trust for Nature Conservation
Fyne Court, Broomfield, Bridgwater,
Somerset TA5 2EQ
Tel: (01823) 451587

Sports Turf Research Institute
Bingley, West Yorkshire BD16 1AU
Tel: (01274) 565131

Thatching Advisory Service
Rose Tree Farm, 29 Mile Ride,
Finchampstead, Wokingham,
Berkshire RG11 4QD
Tel: (01734) 722361

The Tradescant Trust
Museum of Garden History,
St-Mary-at-Lambeth, Lambeth
Palace Road, London SE1 7JU
Tel: (0171) 261 1891

Tree Council
35 Belgrave Square, London
SW1X 8QN
Tel: (0171) 235 8854

The Tree Register of the British Isles
Tilgates, Bletchingley, Surrey
RH1 4QF
Tel: (01883) 843219

Women's Farm & Garden Association
175 Gloucester Street, Cirencester,
Gloucestershire GL7 2DP
Tel: (01285) 658339

Woodland Trust
Autumn Park, Dysart Road,
Grantham, Lincolnshire NG31 6LL
Tel: (01476) 74297

The Worshipful Company of Gardeners
25 Luke Street, London EC2A 4AR
Tel: (0171) 739 8200

Societies

A s gardeners' interests in plants grow, they often become hooked on one particular group of plants. I've met alpine enthusiasts for whom the plant world starts at about ten thousand feet, and there are gardeners whose gardens grow nothing at all but ferns, and the fuchsia enthusiasts who – well, need I go on?

There are also much more general societies like the Hardy Plant Society, the Cottage Garden Society and, of course, the Royal Horticultural Society. I belong to all three of those and look forward greatly to their monthly or quarterly bulletins and the many events they stage.

But perhaps the greatest advantage of joining a society is that, without exception, they are filled with gardeners who have unrivalled specialist knowledge which they're eager to share with fellow enthusiasts. You'll learn a lot by joining one and you'll make a lot of new friends too.

Specialist Societies

Alpine Garden Society
AGS Centre, Avon Bank, Pershore,
Worcestershire WR10 3JP
Tel: (01386) 554790

British & European Geranium Society
Norwood Chine, 26 Crabtree Lane,
Sheffield, South Yorkshire S5 7AY
Tel: (01142) 426200

British Bonsai Association
c/o Inglenook, 36 McCarthy Way,
Wokingham, Berkshire RG11 4UA

British Cactus & Succulent Society
E A Harris, 49 Chestnut Glen,
Hornchurch, Essex RM12 4HI
Tel: (01708) 447778

British Clematis Society
The Tropical Bird Gardens, Rode,
Bath, Avon BA3 6QW
Tel: (01373) 830326

British Fuchsia Society
20 Brodawel, Llannon, Llanelli,
Dyfed SA14 6BJ
Tel: (01269) 843798

British & European Geranium Society
85 Sparrow Farm Road, Ewell,
Surrey KT17 2 LP
Tel: (0181) 393 4229

British Gladiolus Society
24 The Terrace, Mayfield,
Ashbourne, Derbyshire
DE6 2JL
Tel: (01335) 45443

British Hosta & Hemerocallis Society
Cleave House, Sticklepath,
Okehampton, Devon EX20 2NN
Tel: (01837) 840482

British Iris Society
43 Sea Lane, Goring-by-Sea, West
Sussex BN12 4QD
Tel: (01903) 241993

British Ivy Society
14 Holly Grove, Huyton, Merseyside
L36 4JA
Tel: (0151) 489 1083

British National Carnation Society
3 Canberra Close, Hornchurch, Essex
RM12 5TR
Tel: (01708) 441786

**The British Orchid Growers
Association**
c/o Plested Orchids, 38 Florence
Road, College Town, Camberley,
Surrey GU15 4QD
Tel: (01276) 32947

**British Pelargonium & Geranium
Society**
134 Montrose Avenue, Welling, Kent
DA16 2QY
Tel: (0181) 856 6137

British Pteridological (Fern) Society
'Croziers', 16 Kirby Corner Road,
Canley, Coventry, West Midlands
CV4 8GD
Tel: (01203) 715690

Carnivorous Plant Society
94 Uplands Road, Woodford Bridge,
Essex IG8 8JW
Tel: (0171) 481 5574

Cottage Garden Society
Hirstfield House, 244 Edleston Road,
Crewe, Cheshire CW2 7EJ
Tel: (01270) 250776

Cyclamen Society
Tile Barn House, Standen Street,
Iden Green, Benenden, Kent
TN17 4LB
Tel: (01580) 240221

Daffodil Society
32 Montgomery Avenue, Sheffield,
South Yorkshire S7 1NZ
Tel: (0114) 255 0559

Delphinium Society
5 Woodfield Avenue, Carshalton
Beeches, Surrey SM5 3JB
Tel: (0181) 647 9623

European Palm Society
c/o The Palm Centre, 563 Upper
Richmond Road West, London
SW14 7ED
Tel: (0181) 876 3223

Ferns *see* **British Pteridological
Society**

**Fruit Group of the Royal
Horticultural Society**
see **Organizations**

Garden History Society
5 The Knoll, Hereford HR1 1RU
Tel: (01432) 354479

Hardy Plant Society
Little Orchard, Great Comberton,
Nr Pershore, Worcestershire
WR10 3DP
Tel: (01386) 710317

Heather Society
Denbeigh, All Saints Road, Creeting
St Mary, Ipswich, Suffolk IP6 8PJ
Tel: (01449) 711220

Hebe Society
Rosemergy, Hain Walk, St Ives,
Cornwall TR26 2AF
Tel: (01736) 795225

The Herb Society
134 Buckingham Palace Road,
London SW1W 9SN
Tel: (0171) 823 5583

International Camellia Society
41 Galveston Road, East Putney,
London SW15 2RZ
Tel: (0181) 870 6884

International Dendrology Society
School House, Stannington,
Morpeth, Northumberland
NE61 6HF
Tel: (01670) 789287

International Violet Association
11 Myddlewood, Myddle,
Shrewsbury, Shropshire SY4 3RY
Tel: (01939) 290877

International Water Lily Society
Stapeley Water Gardens, Nantwich,
Cheshire CW5 7LH
Tel: (01270) 623868

Irish Garden Plant Society
c/o National Botanic Gardens,
Glasnevin, Dublin 9, Eire
Tel: (00353) 1 8374388

Japanese Garden Society
45 Moorland Drive, Abbott's Lodge,
Runcorn, Cheshire
WA7 6HI
Tel: (01928) 718759

Lily Group of the Royal Horticultural Society
14 Marshalls Way, Wheathampstead,
St Albans, Hertfordshire AL4 8HY
Tel: (01582) 766715

Mammillaria Society
26 Glenfield Road, Banstead, Surrey
SM7 2DG
Tel: (017373) 54036

National Auricula & Primula Society
(Southern Section), 67 Warnham
Court Road, Carshalton Beeches,
Surrey SM5 3ND
Tel: (ex-directory)

National Auricula & Primula Society
(Midland & West Section), 6 Lawson
Close, Saltford, Bristol, Avon
BS18 3LB

National Auricula & Primula Society
(Northern Section), 146 Queens
Road, Cheadle Hulme, Cheshire
SK8 5HY

National Begonia Society
7 Springwood Close, Thurgoland,
Sheffield, South Yorkshire S30 7AB
Tel: (0114) 288 2801

National Bonsai Society
24 Bidston Road, Liverpool L4 7XJ
Tel: (0151) 263 5259

National Chrysanthemum Society
2 Lucas House, Craven Road, Rugby
CV21 3HY
Tel: (01788) 569039

National Dahlia Society
19 Sunnybank, Marlow,
Buckinghamshire SL7 3BL
Tel: (016284) 73500

National Pot Leek Society
8 Nelson Avenue, Nelson Village,
Cramlington, Northumberland
Tel: (01670) 715264

National Sweet Pea Society
3 Chalk Farm Road, Stokenchurch,
Buckinghamshire HP14 3TB
Tel: (01494) 482153

National Vegetable Society
56 Waun-y-Groes Avenue, Rhiwbina,
Cardiff, South Glamorgan CF4 4SZ
Tel: (01222) 627994

National Vegetable Society
(Scottish Branch), Rose Cottage,
74 Strathaven Road, Kirkmuirhill,
Lanark ML11 9RW
Tel: (01555) 893288

National Viola & Pansy Society
28 Carisbrooke Road, Edgbaston,
Birmingham B17 8NW
Tel: (0121) 429 4065

**North of England Rose, Carnation
and Sweet Pea Society**
16 Grenville Drive, Brunton Park,
Newcastle upon Tyne NE3 5PA

Orchid Society of Great Britain
120 Crofton Road, Orpington, Kent
BR6 8HZ
Tel: (01689) 829777

**Royal Caledonian Horticultural
Society** *see* **Organizations**

Royal Horticultural Society *see*
Organizations

Royal Horticultural Society's Garden
see **Organizations**

Royal National Rose Society
Chiswell Green, St Albans,
Hertfordshire AL2 3NR
Tel: (01727) 850461

Saintpaulia & Houseplant Society
33 Church Road, Newbury Park,
Ilford, Essex IG2 7ET
Tel: (0181) 590 3710

Scottish Begonia Society
126 Sheephouse Hill, Fauldhouse,
Bathgate, West Lothian EH47 9EL
Tel: (01501) 70265

Scottish Gladiolus Society
63 Gardiner Road, Blackhall,
Edinburgh EH4 3RL
Tel: (0131) 332 3681

**Scottish National Sweet Pea, Rose &
Carnation Society**
72 West George Street, Coatbridge,
Lanarkshire ML5 2DD
Tel: (01236) 429166

Scottish Orchid Society
20 Ancrum Road, Dundee
DD2 2HZ
Tel: (ex-directory)

Scottish Rhododendron Society
Stron Ailne, Colintraive, Argyll and
Bute, Strathclyde PA22 3AS
Write for information

Scottish Rock Garden Club
Groom's Cottage Flat, Kirklands,
Ancrum, Jedburgh TD8 6UJ
Tel: (01835) 830354

Sedum Society
12 Langdale Road, Gateshead, Tyne
& Wear NE9 5RN
Tel: (0191) 48 78706

The Sempervivum Society
11 Wingle Tye Road, Burgess Hill,
West Sussex RH15 9HR
Tel: (01444) 236848

**Tulip Society of Wakefield &
Northern England**
70 Wrenthorpe Lane, Wrenthorpe,
Wakefield, West Yorkshire
WF2 0PT
Tel: (01924) 375843

Wild Flower Society
68 Outwoods Road, Loughborough,
Leicestershire LE11 3LY
Tel: (01509) 215598

Allotment Gardeners

The National Society of Allotment and Leisure Gardeners Ltd
Registered Office:
Odell House, Hunters Road, Corby,
Northamptonshire NN17 5JE
Tel: (01536) 266576

The Scottish Allotments and Gardeners Society
14/1 Hoseason Gardens, Edinburgh,
Lothian EH4 7HQ
Tel: (0131) 539 5888

Organic Gardeners

Henry Doubleday Research Association (HDRA)
National Centre for Organic Gardening
Ryton on Dunsmore
Coventry CV8 3LG
Tel: (01203) 303517

Horticultural Courses

I f you're really interested in horticulture, at whatever level, there are great opportunities for learning more. If you just want to become a more successful amateur gardener, enrol for evening classes which are available in most areas.

If you, or one of your family, wish to make horticulture your career then you must decide first of all at which level you think you'll be successful, and which will suit your aspirations most.

There are plenty of courses to suit those people who would prefer to work with their hands, from the National Vocational Qualifications courses right up to the Advanced National Certificate.

Should you prefer a management qualification, you will find plenty of opportunities at several levels in the National Diploma, Higher National Diploma and degree courses. If it's a research career you're after, start by checking out the degree courses.

All colleges are keen to have candidates with the necessary qualifications and you'll find them extremely helpful. Just drop them a line detailing your requirements.

Information about part-time, evening, and day-release courses can be obtained from libraries, schools and colleges and local newspapers.

Information available at the library is dependent on that received from schools and colleges, therefore smaller libraries may not hold a vast amount of information. Main libraries also hold a Directory of Further Education which contains names and addresses of colleges which can be contacted for further details.

Schools and colleges generally publish a prospectus for courses commencing in September or October of each year, some of which are distributed locally through your door.

The local press may also advertise forthcoming courses at schools and colleges within your area.

Abbreviations used are as follows:

ANC	Advanced National Certificate (1 year)	NC	National Certificate (1 year)
ANCH	Advanced National Certificate in Horticulture (SCOTVEC) (1 year)	NCH	National Certificate in Horticulture (1 year)
BTEC	Business and Technical Education Council	ND	National Diploma (3 year sandwich course)
First D	First Diploma (1 year)	NDH	National Diploma in Horticulture (3 year sandwich course)
First DH	First Diploma in Horticulture (1 year)		
HND	Higher National Diploma (3 year sandwich course)	NVQ	National Vocational Qualification (3 year day release course)
HNDH	Higher National Diploma in Horticulture (3 year sandwich course)	SCOTVEC	Scottish Vocational Educational Council (equivalent to BTEC)

Royal Horticultural Society

Centres offering courses leading to the RHS General Examination in Horticulture:

England

Avon
Norton Radstock College of Further Education
Bristol University Botanic Gardens

Berkshire
Berkshire College of Agriculture

Buckinghamshire
Aylesbury College

Cambridgeshire
Cambridgeshire College of Agriculture & Horticulture
The Oundle Area Adult Education Centre

Cheshire
Cheshire College of Agriculture

Cleveland
Guisborough Agricultural Centre
Stockton and Billingham College of Further Education

Cornwall
Duchy College of Agriculture & Horticulture

Cumbria
Cumbria College of Agriculture & Horticulture

Dorset
Dorset College of Agriculture & Horticulture

Durham
Durham College of Agriculture & Horticulture

East Sussex
Brighton College of Technology
Plumpton Agricultural College

Essex
Southend Adult Education Centre

Gloucestershire
Hartpury College

Greater Manchester
City College Manchester
Tameside College of Technology

Hampshire
Farnborough College of Technology

Hertfordshire
Cassio College

Isle of Wight
Isle of Wight College of Arts &
 Technology

Kent
Hadlow College of Agriculture &
 Horticulture

Lancashire
Myerscough College

Leicestershire
Brooksby College

Lincolnshire
De Montfont University Lincoln
Riseholme Hall

London
Hampstead Garden Suburb Adult
 Education Centre
Merton Institute of Adult Education
South London College
Southwark College
See also Middlesex

Merseyside
Hughbard College
The Kennels Horticultural Centre

Middlesex
Capel Manor Horticulture &
 Environmental Centre
Frays Adult Education Centre
Norwood Hall School of
 Horticulture & Floristry
Richmond Adult and Community
 College
Rooks Heath High School
Weald College
Whitton School

Norfolk
Norfolk College of Agriculture &
 Horticulture

North Humberside
Bishop Burton College of
 Agriculture

North Yorkshire
Northern Horticultural Society
Scarborough Technical College

Northamptonshire
Moulton College
See also Cambridgeshire

Northumberland
Kirkley Hall College

Nottinghamshire
Brackenhurst College

Shropshire
Walford College Shropshire

Somerset
Cannington College
Yeovil College

South Yorkshire
Barnsley College of Technology
Parsons Cross College
Rother Valley College of Further
 Education

Suffolk
Otley College

Warwickshire
North Warwickshire College of
    Technology & Art
Warwickshire College
See also West Midlands

West Midlands
Solihull College of Technology
Stourbridge College
Tile Hill College of Further
    Education
See also Warwickshire

West Sussex
Brinsbury College of Agriculture &
    Horticulture

West Yorkshire
Dewsbury College (Cleckheaton
    Centre)
Leeds Metropolitan University
Ralph Thoresby High School (Adult
    Education)
Shipley College
Wakefield District College
(Hemsworth Centre)

Wiltshire
Lackham College

Wales

Afan College
Pencoed College

Scotland

Langside College
Threave School of Horticulture

Channel Islands

Highlands College

Eire

Kildalton Agricultural &
    Horticultural College
National Botanic Gardens
Scoil Stiofain

National Vocational Qualification

Centres offering courses leading to
NVQ Phases I and II in Horticulture
(these replaced City and Guilds
phases I and II in September 1992.
City & Guilds phases III and IV
remain the same).

Entry requirements: A general
interest in gardening

England

Avon
Blaise Training Centre
Norton Radstock College of Further
    Education
Bristol Adult Education Area

Bedfordshire
Silsoe College
Shuttleworth College

Berkshire
Berkshire College of Agriculture

Cambridgeshire
Cambridgeshire College of
    Agriculture & Horticulture

Cheshire
Cheshire College of Agriculture

Cornwall
Cornwall College of Further &
    Higher Education

Cumbria
Cumbria College of Agriculture &
  Forestry

Derbyshire
Derbyshire College of Agriculture &
  Horticulture

Devon
Bicton College of Agriculture
Dartington Hall Trust
St Loye's College

Dorset
Dorset College of Agriculture &
  Horticulture

Durham
Durham College of Agriculture &
  Horticulture
Finchale Training College

East Sussex
Brighton College of Technology
Plumpton Agricultural College

Essex
Barking College of Technology
Writtle College

Gloucestershire
Gloucestershire College of
  Agriculture & Horticulture
The National Star Centre College of
  Further Education

Greater Manchester
City College Manchester

Hampshire
Highbury College of Technology
Sparsholt College

Hereford & Worcester
Hereford College of Agriculture
Pershore College of Horticulture

Hertfordshire
Capel Manor Horticultural &
  Environmental Centre

Hertfordshire College of Agriculture
  & Horticulture

Humberside
Bishop Burton College of
  Agriculture

Isle of Wight
Isle of Wight College of Arts &
  Technology

Kent
Canterbury College of Technology
Hadlow College of Agriculture &
  Horticulture
Mid-Kent College of Higher &
  Further Education

Lancashire
Blackpool and Fylde College of
  Further & Higher Education
Bolton Metropolitan College
Burnley College
Myerscough College
Tameside College of Technology
Wigan College of Technology
See also Greater Manchester

Leicestershire
Brooksby College
Coalville Technical College

Lincolnshire
Boston College of Further
  Education
De Montfort University Lincoln

London
South London College
Southwark College
See also Middlesex and Surrey

Merseyside
Knowsley Central Tertiary College
Merseyside Parks Training Centre
St Helens College
St Helens College of Technology

South Mersey College
Southport College of Art &
    Technology
The Hugh Baird College of
    Technology
Wirral Metropolitan College

Middlesex
Norwood Hall School of
    Horticulture & Floristry
Richmond-Upon-Thames College

Norfolk
Norfolk College of Agriculture &
    Horticulture

North Yorkshire
Askham Bryan College
Craven College of Adult Education
Northern Horticultural Society

Northamptonshire
Northamptonshire College of
    Agriculture & Horticulture

Northumberland
Northumberland College of
    Agriculture

Nottinghamshire
Nottinghamshire College of
    Agriculture
Portland Training College

Shropshire
Walford College Shropshire

Somerset
Cannington College
Yeovil College

South Yorkshire
Barnsley College of Technology
Doncaster Metropolitan Insitute of
    Higher Education
Granville College of Further
    Education
Rockingham College of Further
    Education

Rother Valley College of Further
    Education

Staffordshire
Staffordshire College of Agriculture
Staffordshire Technical College

Suffolk
Otley College

Surrey
Merrist Wood College
North East Surrey College of
    Technology

Tyne & Wear
Monkwearmouth College of Further
    Education

Warwickshire
South Warwickshire College of
    Further Education
Warwickshire College
See also West Midlands

West Midlands
Bournville College of Further
    Education
Matthew Boulton Technical College
Solihull College of Technology
South Birmingham College
Tile Hill College of Further
    Education
Wulfrun College
See also Warwickshire

West Sussex
West Sussex College of Agriculture

West Yorkshire
Airdale and Wharfdale College of
    Further Education
Huddersfield Technical College
The Percival Whitley College of
    Further Education
Wakefield District College

Wiltshire
Lackham College

Worcestershire
See Hereford & Worcester

Wales

Clwyd
Welsh College of Horticulture

Dyfed
Ceredigion College of Further
   Education

Gwent
College of Agriculture

Gwynedd
Coleg Pencraig

Mid Glamorgan
Mid Glamorgan College of
   Agriculture & Horticulture

Powys
Coleg Howell Harris

South Glamorgan
South Glamorgan Institute of
   Higher Education

West Glamorgan
Port Talbot College of Further
   Education
Swansea College

Northern Ireland

Belfast Institute of Further & Higher
   Education

Eire

National Botanic Gardens

Channel Islands

Guernsey College of Further
   Education
Highlands College

National Certificate Courses

Duration generally one year, full
time. Entrance requirements:
Minimum age 17, candidates with
GCSEs, City & Guilds or NVQs may
be given preference.

NC in Horticulture

England

Berkshire
Berkshire College of Agriculture

Cambridge
Cambridgeshire College of
   Agriculture & Horticulture

Cheshire
Reaseheath College

Cornwall
Duchy College of Agriculture &
   Horticulture

Derbyshire
Broomfield College

Devon
Bicton College of Agriculture

Dorset
Kingston Maurwood College

Durham
Houghall College

Gloucestershire
Hartpury College

Hampshire
Sparsholt College

Hertfordshire
Oaklands College

Humberside
Bishop Burton College of
   Agriculture

Kent
Hadlow College of Agriculture &
   Horticulture

Lancashire
Myerscough College

Leicestershire
Brooksby College

Lincolnshire
De Montfort University Lincoln

Middlesex
Norwood Hall School of
   Horticulture & Floristry

Norfolk
Norfolk College of Agriculture &
   Horticulture

Northamptonshire
Moulton College

Nottinghamshire
Brackenhurst College

Somerset
Cannington College

Staffordshire
Staffordshire College of Agriculture

Suffolk
Otley College

Surrey
Merrist Wood College

Warwickshire
Warwickshire College

West Sussex
Brinsbury College

Wiltshire
Lackham College

Worcestershire
Pershore College of Horticulture

Yorkshire
Askham Bryan College

Wales

Welsh College of Horticulture

Scotland

Dumfries & Galloway
Threave School of Horticulture

Fife
Elmwood College

Grampian
Aberdeen College of Further
   Education

Lothian
Oatridge Agricultural College

Strathclyde
Langside College

Tayside
Angus College of Further Education
Dundee College

Northern Ireland

Greenmount College of Agriculture
   & Horticulture

National Certificate Courses in Related Subjects

NC in Amenity Horticulture/ Landscape Construction
Oaklands College
Oatridge Agricultural College
  (SCOTVEC course)

NC in Arboriculture
Aberdeen College
  (SCOTVEC course)
Cannington College
Myerscough College

NC in Commercial Horticulture
Brinsbury College
Oaklands College
Welsh College of Horticulture

NC in Garden Centre Operation
Myerscough College

NC in Golf Course Management
Oatridge Agricultural College
  (SCOTVEC course)

NC in Greenkeeping & Sportsturf Management
Oatridge Agricultural College
  (SCOTVEC course)

NC in Groundsmanship & Greenkeeping
Myerscough College

NC in Horticultural Engineering
Oatridge Agricultural College
  (SCOTVEC course)

NC in Interior Landscaping
Oaklands College

NC in Landscape Practice
Myerscough College

NC in Nursery Practice
Myerscough College

Countryside and Leisure Management

NC in Countryside & Related Skills
Broomfield College
Hartpury College
Otley College

NC in Land Use & Countryside Skills
Walford College Shropshire

NC in Practical Habitat Management
Merrist Wood College

Forestry

NC in Forestry
Inverness College

Advanced National Certificate Courses

Duration generally one year, full time or 'thin' sandwich. Entrance requirements: minimum age 18, candidates should hold a NCH or Phase II City and Guilds (replaced by NVQ).

Horticulture and Related Subjects

ANC in Commercial Fruit Production & Marketing
Hadlow College of Agriculture & Horticulture

ANC Greenkeeping
Warwickshire College

ANC in Horticulture
Brooksby College

Cannington College
Hartpury College
Pershore College of Horticulture
Warwickshire College

HNC in Horticulture (SCOTVEC)
Scottish Agricultural College

HNC Landscape Management (SCOTVEC)
Oatridge Agricultural College

HNC Sportsturf Management (SCOTVEC)
Oatridge Agricultural College

First Diploma Courses

Duration generally one year, full time. A BTEC First National Diploma is a vocational course which enables students to progress onto a National Diploma and therefore replaces the four GCSE minimum entrance requirement of many colleges.

Countryside and Leisure Management

1st Diploma in Conservation & Wildlife Habitat Management
Hartpury College

1st Diploma in Leisure & Recreation
Walford College Shropshire

1st Diploma in Outdoor Recreation & Leisure
Hartpury College

1st Diploma in Rural Business Administration
Staffordshire College

1st Diploma in Rural Leisure
Hartpury College

1st Diploma in Rural Studies
Stourbridge College

1st Diploma in Rural/Countryside Skills
Bloomfield College
Cambridgeshire College
Cannington College
Capel Manor Centre
Staffordshire College

Forestry

1st Diploma in Forestry
De Montfort University Lincoln

Horticulture and Related Subjects

1st Diploma in Arboriculture
Holme Lacy College

1st Diploma in Commercial Horticulture
Warwickshire College

1st Diploma in Garden Centre Retailing
Berkshire College

1st Diploma in Golf Studies
Reaseheath College

1st Diploma in Greenkeeping
Oaklands College

1st Diploma in Horticulture
Askham Bryan College
Aylesbury College
Berkshire College
Bicton College

Bishop Burton College
Brinsbury College
Broomfield College
Cambridgeshire College
Cannington College
Capel Manor Centre
De Montfort University Lincoln
Hadlow College
Hartpury College
Houghall College
Moulton College
Norton Radstock College
Oaklands College
Pencoed College
Reaseheath College
South Birmingham College
South London College
Sparsholt College
Staffordshire College
Stoke-on-Trent College
Walford College Shropshire
Writtle College

1st Diploma in Horticulture & Landscaping
Newton Rigg College

1st Diploma in Horticultural Mechanisation
Cannington College
Oaklands College

National Diploma Courses

Duration: generally three years, sandwich courses. Entrance requirements: minimum age 18, candidates should hold 4 GCSEs or a First National Diploma. Twelve months pre-entry work in horticulture is normally required.

Business

ND in Business Studies & Finance
Norfolk College
Oaklands College
Welsh College

Countryside and Leisure Management

ND in Conservation & Wildlife Habitat Management
Hartpury College

ND in Countryside Management
Cambridgeshire College
Cannington College
National Trust
Norfolk College

ND in Countryside Recreation
Merrist Wood College

ND in Environmental Landscape Management
De Montfort University Lincoln

ND in Land Use & Recreation
Houghall College
Walford College Shropshire

ND in Leisure Attraction Management
Lackham College

ND in Rural Business Management
Cannington College

ND in Rural Studies
Stourbridge College

ND in Tourism & Countryside Management
Lackham College

Horticulture and Related Subjects

ND in Amenity Horticultural
Askham College
Cambridgeshire College
Cannington College
Elmwood College
Hartpury College
Kingston Maurwood College
National Trust
Writtle College

ND in Amenity/Landscape Studies
Brinsbury College
Hadlow College

ND in Arboriculture
Merrist Wood College

ND in Commercial Horticulture
Hadlow College
Oaklands College
Writtle College

ND in Engineering & European Studies
Cannington College

ND in Garden Centre Retailing
Hadlow College

ND in Horticulture
Berkshire College
Bicton College
Hadlow College
Houghall College
Lackham College
Myerscough College
Pencoed College
Pershore College
Scottish Agricultural College
Sparsholt College
Staffordshire College

ND in Horticulture Engineering & Mechanisation
Askham Bryan College

ND in Landscape & Amenity Horticulture
Reaseheath College

ND in Landscape Construction
Merrist Wood College
Oatridge College

ND in Pleant Production & Garden Centre Management
Merrist Wood College

ND in Turf Science & Sportsground Maintenance
Myerscough College

ND in Urban Forestry
Askham Bryan College

Higher National Diploma Courses

Duration: generally three years, sandwich course. Entrance requirements: minimum age 18. Candidates should hold a BTEC National Diploma, NCH, Phase II City and Guilds or approved SCOTVEC qualification or hold 1 A Level (and have studied for another), 4 GCSEs, and have 12 months pre-entry horticultural work experience.

Countryside and Leisure Management

HND in Countryside and Leisure Recreation
Merrist Wood College

HND in Leisure Management
Scottish Agricultural College

HND in Recreational Land Management
Myerscough College

HND in Rural Resource Management
Writtle College

Forestry

HND in Forestry
Inverness College

Horticulture and Related Subjects

HND in Golf Course Management
Elmwood College (SCOTVEC course)
Merrist Wood College
Reaseheath College

HND in Golf Greenkeeping With European Studies
Cannington College

HND in Horticulture
Askham College
University of Central England in Birmingham
in conjunction with Pershore College
De Montfort University Lincoln
University of Greenwich
in conjunction with Hadlow College
Hadlow College
in conjunction with University of Greenwich
Pershore College
in conjunction with University of Central England in Birmingham
Scottish Agricultural College
Welsh College

HND in Horticulture With European Studies
Cannington College

HND in Landscape & Amenity Managemet
Writtle College

HND in Landscape Contract Management
Merrist Wood College

Degree Courses

First Degrees

Duration of courses varies: the number of years and the course structure (FT = full time courses/ SW = sandwich courses) of each degree is on the right. Entrance requirements: generally three 'A' Levels, although some universities accept National Diplomas in suitable subjects.

BSc Agriculture
Writtle College with University of
   Essex   3FT

BSc Agricultural Engineering
Writtle College with Anglia
Polytechnic University   3FT

BSc (Hons) Agricultural and Environmental Science
University of Newcastle   3FT
Wye College   3FT

BSc (Hons) Applied Biology (Agricultural Biology)
University of Hertfordshire   4SW

BSc (Hons) Applied and Environmental Biology
University of York   3FT

BSc (Hons) Applied Biology and Crop Protection
University College (Bangor)   3FT

BSc (Hons) Applied Plant Sciences
University of Manchester   4SW
Wye College   3FT

BSc Arboriculture & Environmental Forestry
University of Aberdeen   4FT

BSc (Hons) Combined Studies (Environmental Studies Option)
Manchester Metropolitan
    University   3FT/4SW/5PT

BSc (Hons) Countryside Management
University of Newcastle   3FT
Wye College   3FT

BSc Crop and Soil Science
University College (Bangor)   3FT

BSc (Hons) Crop Technology and Resource Management
University of Bath   4SW

BSc (Hons) Ecology
University of Lancaster   3FT
University of Stirling   4FT
University of York   3FT

BSc Ecological Studies
University of Edinburgh   4FT

BSc (Hons) Environmental Biology
Royal Holloway and New Bedford
    College   3FT

BSc (Hons) Environmental Management
Manchester Metropolitan
    University   3FT/4SW/5PT

BSc Environmental Science
Manchester Metropolitan
    University   3FT/4SW/5PT
University of Stirling   4FT

BSc Environment Studies
Crewe and Alsager College   3FT

University of Hertfordshire   4SW
Wye College (Hons)   3FT

BSc Estate Management
University of Greenwich   3FT/4SW/5PT

BSc Forestry
University of Aberdeen   4FT

BSc Horticulture
University of Hertfordshire   4SW
University of Nottingham   3FT
University of Reading   3FT/4SW
University of Strathclyde   3FT/4SW
Wye College   3FT/4SW

BSc (Hons) Horticulture
Hadlow College with University of
    Greenwich   4SW
University of Hertfordshire   4SW
University of Nottingham   3FT
University of Reading   3FT/4SW
University of Strathclyde   3FT/4SW
Writtle College with University of
    Hertfordshire   4SW
Wye College   3FT/4SW

BSc Horticultural Business Management
Wye College   3FT

BSc Horticulture with European Studies
University of Nottingham   4FT

BSc Horticulture with Horticultural Management
University of Strathclyde   3FT/4SW
University of Strathclyde
    (Hons)   4FT/5SW

BSc (Hons) Horticultural Technology and Management
Myerscough College   4FT

BA (Hons) Landscape and Archaeology
University of Sheffield   3FT

BA (Hons) Landscape Management
Gloucestershire College of
  Agriculture and Horticulture   4FT
Greenwich University   3FT/5PT
Heriot-Watt University   3FT
Leeds Metropolitan
  University   3FT/5PT

BA (Hons) Landscape Design
Manchester Metropolitan
  University   3FT

BSc (Hons) Landscape Management
University of Reading   4SW

BSc (Hons) Landscape Design and Plant Science
University of Sheffield   3FT

BSc (Hons) Landscape Management
University of Reading   4SW

BSc Landscape Studies with Plant Science
Sheffield University   3FT

BSc (Hons) Plant Biochemistry
Royal Holloway and New Bedford
  College   3FT

BSc Plant Biology
Royal Holloway and New Bedford
  College (Hons)   3FT
University of Manchester   3FT

BA Recreation and Environment
North Cheshire College   3FT

B Eng (Hons) Rural Environmental Engineering
Silsoe College   3FT

BSc (Hons) Rural Environmental Studies
University of Aberdeen   4FT
University of Edinburgh   4FT
University of Wales (Bangor)   3FT

BSc and BSc (Hons) Rural Resource Development
Writtle College with Anglia
  Polytechnic University   3FT

BSc Rural Resources Management
Silsoe College (Hons)   4SW
University of Wales (Bangor)   3FT

Post Graduate Studies

Duration: generally 1 year, full time.

GCERT Landscape Studies
University of Sheffield

GD Landscape Architecture
University of Greenwich
Leeds Metropolitan University
Manchester Metropolitan University
University of Sheffield

M.Arch Studies in Landscape
University of Sheffield

MA Landscape Design
University of Sheffield   2FT

MA Landscape Design
University of Sheffield

MA Landscape Management
Manchester University

MLA Landscape Architecture
Edinburgh University   2FT

MLD Landscape Design
Manchester University   2FT

MPhil Landscape Design
Newcastle University   2FT

MSc Agriculture and Amenity Grassland
Aberystwyth University

MSc Agricultural Botany
Aberystwyth University   2FT

MSc Agricultural Engineering
Silsoe College

MSc Applied Entomology and Crop Protection
University of Newcastle

MSc Applied Plant Science
Wye College

MSc Conservation
University College (London)

MSc Conservation and Soil Fertility
Wye College

MSc Countryside Management
Manchester Metropolitan
    University   2/3PT

MSc Ecology
University of Aberdeen
Crewe and Alsager College

MSc Environmental Management
Stirling University

MSc Environmental Resources
University of Salford

MSc Environmental Science
University of Aberdeen

MSc Forestry
University of Aberdeen

MSc Fruit Production
Wye College

MSc/Dip Horticulture
University of Reading

MSc Integrated Pest & Disease Management
Wye College

MSc/Dip Land Resource Management and Panning
Silsoe College

MSc Landscape Ecology, Design & Management
Wye College

MSc Plant Biotechnology
Wye College

MSc Plant Breeding
Aberystwyth   2FT

MSc Plant Disease Management
Aberystwyth

MSc Rural Resources and Environmental Policy
Wye College

MSc Rural Resources Management
Bangor
Edinburgh

MSc Soil Conservation
Silsoe College

MSc Tropical Crop Storage and Progressing
Silsoe College

MSc Tropical & Sub-Tropical Horticultural & Crop Science
Wye College

Addresses

Note: * indicates those colleges also running a wide range of part-time courses on a day release, block release or evening basis – including City and Guilds, NVQs, SCOTVECs and other courses in horticulture, floristry and related subjects.

COLLEGES

England

Airdale & Wharfdale College of Further Education
Calverley Lane, Horsforth, Leeds
LS18 4RQ
Tel: (0113) 258 1723

Askham Bryan College *
Askham Bryan, York YO2 3PR
Tel: (01904) 702121

Aylesbury College *
Hampden Hall, Wendover Road,
Stoke Mandeville,
Buckinghamshire HP22 5TB
Tel: (01296) 434111

Barking College of Technology
Dagenham Road, Romford, Essex
RM7 0XU
Tel: (01708) 766841

Barnsley College of Technology
Church Street, Barnsley, Yorkshire
S70 2AX
Tel: (01226) 730191

Berkshire College of Agriculture *
Hall Place, Burchetts Green,
Maidenhead,
Berkshire SL6 6QR
Tel: (01628) 824444

Bicton College of Agriculture*
East Budleigh, Devon EX9 7BY
Tel: (01395) 568353

Bishop Burton College of Agriculture *
Bishop Burton, Beverley,
North Humberside HU17 8QG
Tel: (01964) 550481

Blackpool & Fylde College of Further & Higher Education
Ashfield Road, Bispham, Blackpool
FY2 0HB
Tel: (0125) 352352

Blaise Training Centre *
Kingsweston Road, Lawrence
Weston, Bristol, Avon BS11 0XF
Tel: (0117) 982 4830

Bolton Metropolitan College
Manchester Road, Bolton,
Lancashire BL2 1ER
Tel: (01204) 31411

Boston College of Further Education
Rowley Road, Boston, Lincolnshire
PE21 6JF
Tel: (01205) 365701

Bournville College of Further Education
Bristol Road South, Birmingham
B31 2AJ
Tel: (0121) 411 1414

Brackenhurst College
Brackenhurst, Southwell,
Nottinghamshire NG25 0QF
Tel: (01636) 812252

Brighton College of Technology *
Centre of Horticulture, Stanmer
Park, Brighton,
Sussex BN1 9PZ
Tel: (01273) 601678

Brinsbury College *
(West Sussex College of Agriculture
& Horticulture), North Heath,
Pulborough, West Sussex RH20 1DL
Tel: (01798) 873832

Bristol Adult Education Area
Stoke Lodge, Shirehampton Road,
Stoke Bishop, Bristol BS9 1BN
Tel: (0117) 968 3112

Bristol University Botanic Gardens
Brackenhill, North Road, Leigh
Woods, Bristol BS8 3PF
Tel: (0117) 973 3682

Brooksby College *
Brooksby, Melton Mowbray,
Leicestershire LE14 2LJ
Tel: (01664) 434 291

Broomfield College *
Morley, Derby DE7 6DN
Tel: (01332) 831345

Burnley College
Shorey Bank, off Ormerod Road,
Burnley,
Lancashire BB11 2RX
Tel: (01282) 36111

**Cambridgeshire College of Agriculture
& Horticulture** *
Cambridge Centre: Landbeach Road,
Milton, Cambridge CB4 6DB
Tel: (01223) 860701

Wisbech Centre:
Newcommon Bridge, Wisbech,
Cambridgeshire PE13 2SJ
Tel: (01945) 581024

Cannington College *
Cannington, Bridgwater, Somerset
TA5 2LS
Tel: (01278) 652226

Canterbury College of Technology
New Dover Road, Canterbury, Kent
CT1 3AJ
Tel: (01227) 66081

**Capel Manor Horticultural &
Environmental Centre** *
Bullsmoor Lane, Enfield, Middlesex
EN1 4RQ
Tel: (01992) 763849

**Cassio College, Dept of Adult and
Social Education**
Lanley Road, Watford, Hertfordshire
WD1 3RH
Tel: (01923) 40311

**Cheltenham & Gloucester College of
Higher Education**
Department of Countryside &
Landscape, Francis Close, Hall
Campus, Swindon Road,
Cheltenham, Gloucestershire
GL50 4AZ
Tel: (01242) 532900

Cheshire College of Agriculture
Reaseheath, Nantwich, Cheshire
CW5 6DF
Tel: (01270) 625131

City College Manchester *
(Wythenshawe Centre), Moor Road,
Wythenshawe, Manchester M23 9BQ
Tel: (0161) 902 0131

Coalville Technical College
Bridge Road, Coalville, Leicestershire
LE67 3PW
Tel: (0153) 836136

**Cornwall College of Further & Higher
Education**
(see Duchy College)

Cranfield Institute of Technology
Silsoe College, Silsoe, Bedfordshire
MK45 4DT
Tel: (01525) 60428

Craven College of Adult Education
High Street, Skipton, North
Yorkshire BD23 1JY
Tel: (01756) 61411

**Cumbria College of Agriculture and
Forestry**
(see Newton Rigg College)

Dartington Hall Trust
The Training & Development Unit,
The Old Postern, Dartington, Devon
TQ9 6EL
Tel: (01803) 866051

Derbyshire College of Agriculture and Horticulture
(see Broomfield College)

Dewsbury College (Cleckheaton Centre)
Town Hall, Church Street,
Cleckheaton, West Yorkshire
BD19 3RH
Tel: (01274) 870125

Doncaster Metropolitan Institute of Higher Education
Waterdale, Doncaster DN1 3EX
Tel: (01302) 22122

Dorset College of Agriculture & Horticulture
(see Kingston Maurward College)

Duchy College of Agriculture & Horticulture *
West Cornwall Centre, Pool,
Redruth, Cornwall TR15 3RD
Tel: (01209) 712911

Durham College of Agriculture and Horticulture
(see Houghall College)

Evesham College of Further Education
Cheltenham Road, Evesham,
Worcestershire WR11 4LX
Tel: (01386) 41091

Farnborough College of Technology
Boundary Road, Farnborough,
Hampshire GU14 6SB
Tel: (01252) 515511

Finchale Training College *
Durham DH1 5RX
Tel: (0191) 386 2634

Frays Adult Education Centre
65 Harefield Road, Uxbridge,
Middlesex UB8 1PJ
Tel: (01895) 254766

Garden Design, College of
Admin Office:
Cothelstone, Taunton, Somerset
TA4 3DP
Tel: (01823) 433215

Gloucestershire College of Agriculture and Horticulture
(see Hartpury College)

Granville College of Further Education
Granville Road, Sheffield S2 2RL
Tel: (0114) 276 0271

Guisborough Agricultural Centre
Avenue Place, off Redcar Road,
Guisborough, Cleveland TS14 6AX
Tel: (01287) 33870

Hadlow College of Agriculture & Horticulture *
Hadlow, Tonbridge, Kent
TN11 0AL
Tel: (01732) 850551

Hampstead Garden Suburb Adult Education Centre
The Institute, Central Square,
London NW11 7BN
Tel: (0181) 455 9951/2

Hartpury College *
Hartpury House, Hartpury,
Gloucestershire GL19 3BE
Tel: (01452) 70283

Hereford College of Agriculture
(see Holme Lacey College)

Hertfordshire College of Agriculture and Horticulture
(see Oaklands College)

Highbury College of Technology
Cosham, Portsmouth, Hampshire
PO6 2SA
Tel: (01705) 383131

Holme Lacy College *
Holme Lacy, Hereford HR2 6LL
Tel: (01432) 870316

Horticultural Correspondence College
Little Notton Farmhouse,
16 Notton, Lacock,
Chippenham, Wiltshire SN15 2NF
Tel: (01249) 730326

Horticultural Therapy
Goulds Ground, Vallis Way, Frome,
Somerset BA11 3DW
Tel: (01373) 464782

Horticultural Unit
Spring Lane, Canterbury, Kent
CT1 1TB
Tel: (01227) 450965

Houghall College *
(Durham College of Agriculture &
Horticulture), Houghall, Durham
DH1 3SG
Tel: (0191) 386 1351

Huddersfield Technical College *
New North Road, Huddersfield,
West Yorkshire HD1 5NN
Tel: (01484) 36521

Hugh Baird College of Technology
Balliol Road, Bootle, Merseyside
L20 7EW
Tel: (0151) 922 6704

Hughbard College
Church Road, Litherland, Liverpool
L21 5HA
Tel: (0151) 489 6704

**Isle of Wight College of Arts &
Technology** *
Medina Way, Newport, Isle of Wight
PO30 5TA
Tel: (01983) 526631

The Kennels Horticultural Centre
Knowsley Park, Prescot, Merseyside
L34 4AQ
Tel: (0151) 489 4437

Kingston Maurward College *
(The Dorset College of Agriculture &
Horticulture),
Dorchester, Dorset DT2 8PY
Tel: (01305) 264738

Kirkley Hall College *
Kirkley Hall, Ponteland, Newcastle
upon Tyne NE20 0AQ
Tel: (01661) 860808

Knowsley Central Tertiary College
Rupert Road, Roby, Merseyside
L36 9TD
Tel: (0151) 489 2002

Knowsley Community College *
Horticulture Centre, Knowsley Park,
Prescot, Merseyside L34 4AQ
Tel: (0151) 426 4437

Lackham College *
Lacock, Chippenham, Wiltshire
SN15 2NY
Tel: (01249) 443111

Loughborough College
Radmoor, Loughborough,
Leicestershire LE11 3BT
Tel: (01509) 215831

Matthew Boulton Technical College
Sherlock Street, Birmingham B5 7DB
Tel: (0121) 440 2681

Merrist Wood College *
Worplesdon, Guildford, Surrey
GU3 3PE
Tel: (01483) 232424

Merton Institute of Adult Education
Whatley Avenue, Wimbledon,
London SW20 9NS
Tel: (0181) 543 9292

**Mid-Kent College of Higher &
Further Education ***
Oakwood Park, Tonbridge Road,
Maidstone, Kent ME16 8AQ
Tel: (01622) 56531

**Monkwearmouth College of Further
Education**
Swan Street, Sunderland SR5 1EB
Tel: (01783) 487119

Moulton College *
West Street, Moulton, Northampton
NN3 1RR
Tel: (01604) 491131

Myerscough College *
Myerscough Hall, Bilsborrow,
Preston, Lancashire PR3 0RY
Tel: (01995) 640611

**National Star Centre College of
Further Education**
Ullenwood Manor, Cheltenham,
Gloucestershire GL52 9QU
Tel: (01242) 527631

Newton Rigg College *
Penrith, Cumbria CA11 0AH
Tel: (01768) 63791

Newton Training
The Old Estate Yard, Newton St
Loe, Bath, Avon BA2 9BR
Tel: (01225) 873805

**Norfolk College of Agriculture &
Horticulture ***
Easton, Norwich, Norfolk NR9 5DX
Tel: (01603) 742105

Northern Horticultural Society
Harlow Carr Gardens, Harrogate,
North Yokshire HG3 1QB
Tel: (01423) 65418

**North East Surrey College of
Technology ***
Reigate Road, Ewell, Epsom, Surrey
KT17 3DS
Tel: (0181) 394 1731

**Northamptonshire College of
Agriculture and Horticulture**
(see Moulton College)

Northumberland College of Agriculture
(see Kirkley Hall College)

**North Warwickshire College of
Technology and Art**
Hinckley Road, Nuneaton,
Warwickshire CV11 6BH
Tel: (01203) 349321

**Norton Radstock College of Further
Education ***
South Hill Park, Radstock, Bath,
Avon BA3 3RW
Tel: (01761) 33161

**Norwood Hall School of Horticulture
& Floristry ***
(Ealing Tertiary College), Norwood
Green, Southall, Middlesex UB2 4LA
Tel: (0181) 231 6265

**Nottinghamshire College of
Agriculture**
(see Brackenhurst College)

Oaklands College *
Hatfield Road, St Albans,
Hertfordshire AL4 0JA
Tel: (01727) 850651

Oldham College of Technology
Rochdale Road, Oldham, Lancashire
OL9 6AA
Tel: (0161) 624 5214

Otley College *
Otley, Ipswich, Suffolk IP6 9EY
Tel: (01473) 785543

The Oundle Area Adult Education Centre
Prince William School, Herne Road,
Oundle, Peterborough,
Cambridgeshire PE6 4BS
Tel: (01832) 73550

Parsons Cross College
Remington Road, Sheffield S5 9PB
Tel: (0114) 232 2841

Percival Whitley College of Further Education
Francis Street, Halifax, Yorkshire
HX1 3VZ
Tel: (01422) 58221

Pershore College of Horticulture *
Pershore, Worcestershire WR10 3JP
Tel: (01386) 552443

Plumpton Agricultural College *
Lewes, East Sussex BN7 3AE
Tel: (01273) 890454

Portland Training College
Harlow Wood, Mansfield,
Nottinghamshire NG18 4TJ
Tel: (01623) 792141

Ralph Thoresby High School (Adult Education)
Farrar Lane, Leeds LS16 7NQ
Tel: (0113) 267 0338

Reaseheath College *
(Cheshire College of Agriculture),
Reaseheath, Nantwich, Cheshire
CW5 6DF
Tel: (01270) 625131

Richmond Adult and Community College
Clifton Road, Twickenham,
Middlesex TW1 4LT
Tel: (0181) 891 5907

Richmond-upon-Thames College
Egerton Road, Twickenham,
Middlesex TW2 7SJ
Tel: (0181) 892 6656

Riseholme Hall
(see Lincolnshire College of
Agriculture and Horticulture)

Rockingham College of Further Education
Wath upon Dearne, Rotherham,
Yorkshire S63 6PX
Tel: (01709) 874310

Rooks Heath High School
Eastcote Lane, South Harrow, West
Middlesex HA2 9AG
Tel: (0181) 422 4675

Rother Valley College of Further Education
Doe Quarry Lane, Dinnington,
Sheffield S31 7NH
Tel: (01909) 550550

Royal Botanic Gardens
School of Horticulture, Kew,
Richmond, Surrey TW9 3AB
Tel: (0181) 332 5545

St Helens College *
Newton Campus, Crow Lane East,
Newton-le-Willows,
Merseyside WA12 9TT
Tel: (01925) 24656

St Helens College of Technology
Water Street, St Helens, Merseyside
WA10 1PZ
Tel: (01744) 33766

St Loye's College
Fairfield House, Topsham Road,
Exeter, Devon EX2 6EP
Tel: (01392) 55428

Scarborough Technical College
Lady Edith's Drive, Scarborough,
Yorkshire YO12 5RN
Tel: (01723) 372105

Shipley College
Exhibition Road, Shipley, West
Yorkshire BD18 3JW
Tel: (01274) 595731

Shuttleworth College
Old Warden Park, Biggleswade,
Bedfordshire SG18 9DX
Tel: (01767) 27441

Silsoe College
(see Cranfield Institute of
Technology)

Solihull College of Technology *
Blossomfield Road, Solihull, West
Midlands B91 1SB
Tel: (0121) 711 2111

South Birmingham College *
Cole Bank Road, Birmingham
B28 8ES
Tel: (0121) 694 5000

Southend Adult Education Centre
Ambleside Drive, Southend-on-Sea,
Essex SS1 2UP
Tel: (01702) 610196

South London College *
Knights Hill, West Norwood,
London SE27 0TX
Tel: (0181) 670 4488

South Mersey College
Childwall Abbey Road, Childwall,
Liverpool L16 0JP
Tel: (0151) 722 5705

**Southport College of Art and
Technology**
Mornington Road, Southport,
Merseyside PR9 0TT
Tel: (01704) 424111

Southwark College
The Cut, London SE1 8LE
Tel: (0171) 928 9561

Sparsholt College *
Sparsholt, Winchester, Hampshire
SO21 2NF
Tel: (01962) 72441

Staffordshire College of Agriculture *
Rodbaston, Penkridge, Stafford
ST19 5PH
Tel: (01785) 712209

Staffordshire Technical College
Moorland Road, Burslem,
Stoke-on-Trent ST6 1JJ
Tel: (01782) 85258

**Stockton and Billingham College of
Further Education**
The Causeway, Billingham,
Cleveland TS23 2DB
Tel: (01642) 360205

Stoke-on-Trent College *
Burslem Campus, Moorland Road,
Burslem, Stoke-on-Trent,
Staffordshire ST6 1JJ
Tel: (01782) 208208

Stourbridge College *
Stourbridge College Horticulture and
Conservation Unit, Leasowes Park
Nursery, Leasowes Lane, Halesowen,
West Midlands B62 8QF
Tel: (0121) 550 0007

Tameside College of Technology
Beaufort Road, Ashton-under-Lyme,
Tameside, Greater Manchester
OL6 6NX
Tel: (0161) 330 6911

Tile Hill College of Further Education
Tile Hill Lane, Tile Hill, Coventry
CV4 9DX
Tel: (01203) 461444

Wakefield District College
Margaret Street, Wakefield
WS1 2DH
Tel: (01924) 370501

Wakefield District College
(Hemsworth Centre) Science Sector
Station Road, Hemsworth,
Pontefract, West Yorkshire WF9 4JP
Tel: (01977) 611169

Walford College Shropshire *
Department of Horticulture,
Radbrook Centre, Radbrook Road,
Shrewsbury, Shropshire SY3 9BL
Tel: (01743) 360266

Warwickshire College *
Moreton Morrell, Warwick CV35 9BL
Tel: (01926) 651367

Weald College
Harrow Weald, Middlesex HA3 6RR
Tel: (0181) 954 9571

West Sussex College of Agriculture
North Heath, Pulborough, Sussex
RH20 1DL
Tel: (01798) 873832

Whitton School
Percy Road, Whitton, Middlesex
TW2 6JW
Tel: (0181) 894 4503

Wigan College of Technology
Parsons Walk, Wigan, Lancashire
WN1 1RR
Tel: (01942) 494911

Wirral Metropolitan College
Lithans Lane, Wallasey, Merseyside
L45 7LT
Tel: (0151) 639 8371

Worcestershire College of Agriculture *
Hindlip, Worcester WR3 8SS
Tel: (01905) 451310

Writtle College *
Chelmsford, Essex CM1 3RR
Tel: (01245) 420705

Wulfrun College *
Department of Applied Science,
Paget Road, Wolverhampton, West
Midlands WV6 0DU
Tel: (01902) 317700

Yeovil College
School of Agriculture and
Horticulture,
Ilchester Road, Yeovil, Somerset
BA21 3BA
Tel: (01935) 23921

Channel Islands

**Guernsey College of Further
Education**
Route des Coutanchez, St Peter Port,
Guernsey GY1 2PZ
Tel: (01481) 727121

**Guernsey College of Further
Education**
St John's Street, St Peter Port,
Guernsey GY1 2PZ
Tel: (01481) 727121

Highlands College
PO Box 1000, Jersey JE4 9QA
Tel: (01534) 608608

Highlands College
Trinity, St Saviour, Jersey JE4 9QA
Tel: (01534) 861252

Scotland

Aberdeen College *
School of Rural Studies, Clinterty,
Kinellar, Aberdeen AB2 0TN
Tel: (01224) 640366

Angus College of Further Education *
Keptie Road, Arbroath, Tayside
DD11 3EA
Tel: (01241) 432600

Dundee College *
Old Glamis Road, Dundee, Tayside
DD3 8LE
Tel: (01382) 834834

Elmwood College *
Carslogie Road, Cupar, Fife
KY15 4JB
Tel: (01334) 652781

Inverness College *
3 Longman Road, Longman South,
Inverness IV1 1SA
Tel: (01463) 236681

Langside College
Woodburn House, Department of
Horticulture, 27 Buchanan Drive,
Rutherglen, Glasgow G73 3PF
Tel: (0141) 647 6300

Oatridge Agricultural College
Ecclesmachan, Broxburn, West
Lothian EH52 6NH
Tel: (01506) 854387

Perth College of Further Education
Crieff Road, Perth, Tayside
PH1 2NX
Tel: (01738) 621171

Royal Botanic Garden
20A Inverleith Row, Edinburgh
EH3 5LR
Tel: (0131) 5527171

Scottish Agricultural College
Auchincruive, Ayr, Strathclyde
KA6 5HW
Tel: (01292) 520331

Threave School of Horticulture
Castle Douglas, Dumfries &
Galloway DG7 1RX
Tel: (01556) 502575

Wales

Afan College
Margam, Port Talbot, West
Glamorgan SA13 2AL
Tel: (01639) 882107

**Ceredigion College of Further
Education**
Llanbadarn, Aberystwyth, Dyfed
SY23 3BP
Tel: (01970) 4511

Coleg Howell Harris
Penlan, Brecon, Powys LD3 9SR
Tel: (01874) 5252

Coleg Pencraig
Llangefni, Gwynedd LL77 7HY
Tel: (01248) 722101

Gwent College of Agriculture
Usk, Gwent NP5 1XJ
Tel: (0129) 132311

**Mid Glamorgan College of
Agriculture and Horticulture**
(see Pencoed College)

Pencoed College
Pencoed, Bridgend, Mid Glamorgan
CF35 5LG
Tel: (01656) 860202

Port Talbot College of Further Education
Port Talbot, West Glamorgan
SA13 2AL
Tel: (01639) 882109

South Glamorgan Institute of Higher Education
Western Avenue, Llandaff, Cardiff,
South Glamorgan CF4 2RD
Tel: (01222) 551111

Swansea College
Tycoch Road, Swansea, West
Glamorgan SA2 9EB
Tel: (01792) 206871

Welsh College of Horticulture *
Northop, Mold, Clwyd CH7 6AA
Tel: (01352) 840861

Northern Ireland

Belfast Institute of Further & Higher Education
College Square East Building,
Belfast, Northern Ireland BT1 6DJ
Tel: (01232) 265000

Greenmount College of Agriculture and Horticulture
Antrim, Northern Ireland BT41 4PU
Tel: (01849) 262114

Eire

Colaiste Stiofain Naofa
Tramore Road, Cork, Eire
Tel: (00353) 21 961020

Kildalton Agricultural and Horticultural College
Piltown, County Kilkenny, Eire
Tel: (00353) 51 643105

National Botanic Gardens
Glasnevin, Dublin 9, Eire
Tel: (00353) 1 8374388

Salesian College of Horticulture
Warrentown, Drumree, County
Neath, Eire
Tel: (00353) 6 1393034

UNIVERSITIES AND DEGREE COURSE COLLEGES

England

Anglia Polytechnic University
(see Writtle College)

University of Bath
School of Biological Science,
Claverton Down, Bath, Avon
BA2 7AY
Tel: (01225) 824695

Crewe and Alsager College
Crewe Road, Crewe, Cheshire
CW1 1DU
Tel: (01270) 500661

De Montfort University Lincoln *
School of Agriculture & Horticulture,
Caythorpe Court, Caythorpe,
Grantham, Lincolnshire NG32 3EP
Tel: (01400) 272521

University of Durham
Department of Biological Sciences,
South Road, Durham DH1 3LE
Tel: (0191) 374 2000

University of Essex
(see Writtle College)

Gloucestershire College of Agriculture and Horticulture
Hartpury House, Gloucester
CL19 3BE
Tel: (01452) 70283

University of Greenwich
School of Landscape Architecture,
Oakfield Lane, Dartford, Kent
DA1 2SZ
Tel: (0181) 316 8000

University of Hertfordshire
School of Natural Sciences, College
Lane, Hatfield, Hertfordshire
AL10 9AB
Tel: (01707) 79000

University of Lancaster
Department of Ecology and
Biological Science, Bailrigg,
Lancaster, Lancashire LA1 4Y
Tel: (01524) 65201

Leeds Metropolitan University
Calverley Street, Leeds, West
Yorkshire LS1 3HE
Tel: (0113) 246 2903
also Department of Architecture and
Landscape
Tel: (0113) 246 2222

Manchester Metropolitan University
Faculty of Community Studies, John
Dalton Building, Chester Street,
Manchester M1 5GD
Tel: (0161) 247 2000
also Department of Architecture and
Landscape,
Faculty of Art and Design, Loxford
Tower, Lower Chatham Street,
Manchester M15 6HA
Tel: (0161) 247 1334

University of Manchester
Faculty of Science, Manchester
M13 9PL
Tel: (0161) 275 6890

University of Newcastle
Faculty of Agriculture, Newcastle
upon Tyne NE1 7RU
Tel: (0191) 232 8511

North Cheshire College
Padgate Campus, Fearnhead,
Warrington, Cheshire WA3 4BS
Tel: (01925) 81434

University of Nottingham
School of Agriculture, Sutton
Bonington, Loughborough,
Leicestershire LE12 5RD
Tel: (0115) 951 6061

University of Reading
Department of Horticulture, Plant
Science Labs, Whiteknights, PO Box
221, Reading, Berkshire RG6 2AS
Tel: (01734) 318071
also Faculty of Urban and Regional
Studies,
Whiteknights, PO Box 219, Reading,
Berkshire RG6 2BU
Tel: (01734) 318187

Royal Holloway and New Bedford College
Egham, Surrey TW20 0EX
Tel: (01784) 34455

Salford University
Department of Biology, Salford,
Manchester M5 4WT
Tel: (0161) 736 5843

University of Sheffield
Department of Landscape
Architecture, Sheffield,
South Yorkshire S10 2TN
Tel: (01142) 768555

Silsoe College
Silsoe, Bedford MK45 4DT
Tel: (01525) 60428

University College London
Department of Biology, (Darwin)
Gower Street, London WC1E 6BT
Tel: (0171) 387 7050

Wye College (University of London)
Ashford, Kent TN25 5BH
Tel: (01233) 812401

University of York
Ecology Department, Heslington,
York YO1 5DD
Tel: (01904) 430000

Writtle College
Chelmsford, Essex CM1 3RR
Tel: (01245) 420705

also
Department of Landscape
Architecture, 20 Chambers Street,
Edinburgh EH1 1JZ
Tel: (0131) 667 1011

Heriot-Watt University
Department of Landscape
Architecture, Lauriston Place,
Edinburgh EH3 9DF
Tel: (0131) 229 9311

University of Stirling
The Ecology Department, Stirling
FK9 4LN
Tel: (01768) 73171

University of Strathclyde
McCance Building, 16 Richmond
Street, Glasgow G1 1XQ
Tel: (0141) 552 4400

Scotland

University of Aberdeen
Department of Forestry, St Machar
Drive, Aberdeen, Grampian
AB9 2UD
Tel: (01224) 272677
also
Department of Agriculture, 581 King
Street, Aberdeen, Grampian
AB9 1UD
Tel: (01224) 480291

University of Edinburgh
Department of Forestry and Natural
Resources, Kings Buildings, Mayfield
Road, Edinburgh EH9 3JU
Tel: (0131) 650 1000

Wales

**Aberystwyth University (University
College of Wales)**
Department of Agricultural Sciences,
Penglais, Aberystwyth, Dyfed
SY23 3DD
Tel: (01970) 623111

University of Wales
School of Biological Science, Deiniol
Road, Bangor, Gwynedd LL57 2UW
Tel: (01248) 351151

Gardening for the Disabled and Elderly

T hough there is always room for improvement, the needs of elderly and disabled gardeners have been realistically addressed over the past decade. Consequently there is much available in the way of special tools and equipment and many gardens open to the public cater for special needs.

There are also, of course, many specialist organizations which cater for particular areas of disabled gardening. If you are disabled yourself or care for a disabled person, they'll be able to help with guidance on how to get the best out of your gardening.

For further details write for a brochure to the National Trust (see address on page 22).

National Trust Gardens Accessible to the Disabled

Key:

W – Wheelchairs are provided, there is special parking for wheelchair users, and also access for them to Lavatories, Refreshments and Shop. All these facilities are available unless indicated by a ✗, ✗ or ✗.

✳ – Beware.

SHS – special hearing scheme – guides have been trained to understand special requirements of hearing impaired people

ENGLAND

Berkshire

Basildon Park, Lower Basildon, Reading RG8 9NR *Tel*: (01734) 843040	W	Volunteer-driven 5 seater buggy Braille guide

Buckinghamshire

Claydon House, Nr Buckingham MK18 2EY *Tel*: (01296) 730349	W	Guided tours Braille guide

Cliveden, Maidenhead, Taplow SL6 0JA *Tel*: (01628) 605069	W	Self-drive buggies Scented rose garden
Stowe Landscape Gardens, Buckingham MK18 5EH *Tel*: (01280) 822850		Battery-powered self-drive cars

Cambridgeshire

Anglesey Abbey, Lode, Cambridge CB5 9EJ *Tel*: (01223) 811200	W	Self-drive buggies Scented plants, Hyacinth garden Busy weekends, bank holidays and August
Wimpole Hall, Arrington, Royston SG8 0BW *Tel*: (01223) 207257	W	2 self-drive buggies and scooter; please book Braille guide

Cheshire

Dunham Massey Hall, Altrincham WA14 4SJ *Tel*: (0161) 941 1025	W	Self-drive buggy; please book Electric wheelchair Large print and Braille guides ✳ Cobbled area, ✳ Canal trips SHS
Little Moreton Hall, Congleton CW12 4SD *Tel*: (01260) 272018	W	SHS Self-drive buggy; please book Large print and Braille guides
Tatton Park, Knutsford WA16 6QN *Tel*: (01565) 750780	W	Self-drive duet cycle

Cornwall

Cotehele House, St Dominick, Saltash PL12 6TA *Tel*: (01579) 50434	W	Roses and other scented plants Busy afternoons Braille guide
Lanhydrock, Bodmin PL30 5AD *Tel*: (01208) 73320	W	Aromatic plants Busy Sundays, bank holidays, school holidays Self-drive buggy; please book Braille guide

Trelissick Garden, Nr Truro TR3 6QL *Tel*: (01872) 862090	W	Aromatic garden 1 Self-drive buggy; please book Braille guide
Trengwainton Garden, Nr Penzance TR20 8RZ *Tel*: (01736) 63148	W	Rhododendrons, streams Braille guide
Trerice, Nr Newquay TR8 5JJ *Tel*: (01637) 875404	W	Braille guide

Cumbria

Acorn Bank Garden, Temple Sowerby, Penrith CA10 1SP *Tel*: (017683) 61893		Herb garden, beck
Sizergh Castle Garden, Nr Kendal LA8 8AE *Tel*: (01539) 60070	W	Rock garden Self-drive buggy Braille guide

Derbyshire

Calke Abbey, Ticknall DE73 1LE *Tel*: (01332) 863822	W	Volunteer-driven buggy Braille guide Crowded at holiday times SHS
Hardwick Hall, Doe Lea, Chesterfield S44 5QJ *Tel*: (01246) 850430		Walled flower garden, orchard, herb garden Braille guide SHS Busy at weekends, bank holidays and August
Kedleston Hall, Derby DE6 4JN *Tel*: (01332) 842191	W	Braille guide SHS Make prior arrangements before visit

Devon

Arlington Court, Nr Barnstaple EX31 4LP *Tel*: (01271) 850296	W	Make prior arrangements before visit
Buckland Abbey, Yelverton PL20 6EY *Tel*: (01647) 433306	W	Braille guide and tapes, * herb garden on steep slope

Castle Drogo, Drewsteignton EX6 6PB *Tel*: (01647) 433306	W	Scented plants
Killerton House & Garden, Exeter EX5 3LE *Tel*: (01392) 881345	W	Motorized buggy Scented plants
Knightshayes Court & Garden, Tiverton EX16 7RQ *Tel*: (01884) 254665	W	Scented plants
Saltram House, Plympton PL7 3UH *Tel*: (01752) 336546	W	Braille guide Scented plants

Dorset

Kingston Lacy, Wimborne BH21 4EA *Tel*: (01202) 883402	W	Self-drive vehicle

Gloucestershire

Hidcote Manor Garden, Chipping Campden GL55 6LR *Tel*: (01386) 438333	W	Scented plants
Westbury Court Garden, Westbury-on-Severn GL14 1PD *Tel*: (0145 276) 461	W	Scented plants

Hampshire

Hinton Ampner, Alresford SO24 0LA *Tel*: (01372) 53401	W	Scented plants Braille guide
Mottisfont Abbey Garden, Nr Romsey SO51 0LP *Tel*: (01794) 341220	W	Rose garden Volunteer-driven buggy Braille guide
The Vyne, Sherborne St John, Basingstoke RG26 5DX *Tel*: (01256) 881337	W	Braille guide

Hereford & Worcester

Berrington Hall, Leominster HR6 0DW *Tel*: (01568) 5721	W	Self-drive vehicle Braille guide
Croft Castle, Leominster HR6 9PW *Tel*: (01526 885) 246	W	Braille guide
Hanbury Hall, Droitwich WR6 9BX *Tel*: (01527) 84214	W	Braille guide

Hertfordshire

Shaw's Corner, Ayot St Lawrence, Welwyn AL6 9BX *Tel*: (01438) 820307	W	

Kent

Chartwell, Westerham TN16 1PS *Tel*: (01732) 866368	W	Rose garden and scented plants * Difficult for wheelchairs
Emmetts Garden, Ide Hill, Sevenoaks TN14 6AY *Tel*: (01732) 367	W	Motorized buggy, fountain and waterfall
Ightham Mote, Ivy Hatch, Sevenoaks TN15 0NT *Tel*: (01732) 810378	W	
Scotney Castle Garden, Lamberhurst TN3 8JN *Tel*: (01892) 890651	W	Herb garden
Sissington Castle Garden, Nr Cranbrook TN17 2AB *Tel*: (01580) 712850	W	Special plan Herb garden and scented plants

Lancashire

Gawthorpe Hall, Padiham BB12 8UA *Tel*: (01282) 78511	W	Make prior arrangements before visit

Rufford Old Hall, Ormskirk LA40 1SG *Tel*: (01704) 821254	W	Braille guide

Lincolnshire

Belton House, Grantham NG32 2LS *Tel*: (01476) 66116	W	Braille guide SHS
Gunby Hall, Spilsby PE23 5SS *Tel*: NT on (01909) 486411	W	Rose and herb garden

London

Ham House, Richmond, Surrey TW10 7RS *Tel*: (0181) 940 1950	W	Braille guide SHS
Morden Hall Park, Morden, Surrey *Tel*: (0181) 687 0881		Rose garden River walk

Merseyside

Speke Hall, Liverpool L24 1XD *Tel*: (0151) 427 7231	W	Large print and Braille guides

Norfolk

Blickling Hall, Aylesham, Norwich NR11 6NF *Tel*: (01263) 733084	W	Plant centre Scooter Braille guide
Felbrigg Hall, Norwich NR11 8PR *Tel*: (0126 375) 444	W	Braille guide
Oxburgh Hall, King's Lynn PE 33 9PS *Tel*: (0136 621) 258	W	Route map for W

Northamptonshire

Canons Ashby House, Daventry NN11 6SD *Tel*: (01327) 860044	W	SHS

Northumberland

Wallington, Cambo, Morpeth NE61 4AR *Tel*: (0167 074) 283	W	Powered scooters Braille guide Rose garden and scented plants

Shropshire

Attingham Park, Shrewsbury SY4 4TP SY4 4TP *Tel*: (0174 377) 203	W	Self-drive buggy; please book Braille guide
Dudmaston, Quatt, Bridgnorth WV15 6QN *Tel*: (01746) 780866	W	* Steep slopes Large print and Braille guides Scented plants

Somerset

Barrington Court Garden, Nr Ilminster *Tel*: NT on (01985) 847777		Self-drive buggy Braille guide Scented plants
Dunster Castle, Nr Minehead TA24 6SL *Tel*: (01643) 821314		Self-drive car Multi-seat buggy Braille guide SHS
Lytes Cary Manor, Nr Somerton TA11 7HU *Tel*: (01985) 847777		Scented plants Braille guide
Montacute House & Garden, Nr Yeovil TA15 6XP *Tel*: (01935) 823289	W	Scented plants Braille guide SHS
Tintinhull Garden, Nr Yeovil BA22 8PZ *Tel*: (01985) 847777		Scented plants Braille guide

Staffordshire

Moseley Old Hall, Fordhouses, Wolverhampton WV10 7HY *Tel*: (01902) 782808	Large print and Braille guides
Shugborough, Milford, Stafford ST17 0XB *Tel*: (01889) 881388	Self-drive buggies Large print, Braille and taped guides Rose garden

Suffolk

Ickworth, Bury St Edmunds IP29 5QE *Tel*: (0128 488) 270		Braille guide
Melford Hall, Sudbury CO10 9AA *Tel*: (01787) 880286	W	✳ Steps

Surrey

Clandon Park, Nr Guildford GU4 7RQ *Tel*: (01483) 222482	W	Braille guide
Claremont Landscape Garden, Esher KT10 9JG *Tel*: (01372) 467806	W	Braille guide
Hatchlands Park, East Clandon, Nr Guildford GU4 7RT *Tel*: (01483) 222787	W	Lawns and grassy walks
Polesden Lacy, Nr Dorking RH5 6BD *Tel*: (01372) 458203	W	Avoid bank holidays Rose and lavender gardens
Winkworth Arboretum, Nr Godalming GU8 4AD *Tel*: (01483) 208477		Enquiries to Head Gardener

East Sussex

Bateman's, Burwash, Etchingham TN19 7DS *Tel*: (01435) 882302	W	Route avoiding steps Scented plants
Sheffield Park Garden, Uckfield TN22 3QR *Tel*: (01825) 790655	W	Self-drive buggy Signed route Bluebells and water

West Sussex

Nymans Garden, Handcross, Nr Haywards Heath RH17 6EB *Tel*: (01444) 400321	W	Self-drive buggy Route plan for W Old roses, scented plants

Petworth House & Pleasure Grounds, Nr Midhurst GU28 0AE *Tel*: (01798) 42207	W	Self-drive Scooter Braille guide
Standen, East Grinstead RH19 4NE *Tel*: (01342) 323029	W	* Hillside garden Scented plants
Wakehurst Place Garden, Ardingly, Haywards Heath RH17 6TN *Tel*: (0181) 332 5066	W	Route plan for W

Tyne & Wear

Washington Old Hall, Washington NE38 7LE *Tel*: (0191) 4166879		Scented plants

Warwickshire

Baddesley Clinton, Knowle, Solihull B93 0DQ *Tel*: (01564) 783294	W	Braille guide
Charlecote Park, Wellsbourne, Stratford-upon-Avon CV35 9ER *Tel*: (01789) 470277	W	Braille guide SHS Video
Coughton Court, Alcester B49 5JA *Tel*: (01789) 762435	W	Braille and taped guides
Packwood House, Lapworth, Solihull B94 6AT *Tel*: (01564) 782024	W	
Upton House, Nr Banbury OX15 6HT *Tel*: (0129) 587266	W	Volunteer-driven buggy

Wiltshire

Stourhead, Stourton, Warminster BA12 6QH *Tel*: (01747) 840348	W	Self-drive buggy; please book SHS Rhododendrons and azaleas * Steep lakeside path

North Yorkshire

Beningborough Hall, Shipton-by-Beningborough, York YO6 1DD *Tel*: (01904) 470666	W	Self-drive buggy Braille guide ✳ Cobbled yards
Fountains Abbey, Ripon HG4 3DZ *Tel*: (01765) 86333	W	Powered buggies – please book Braille guide
Nunnington Hall, York YO6 5UY *Tel*: (014395) 283		River, peacocks Braille guide

West Yorkshire

East Riddlesden Hall, Keighley BD20 5EL *Tel*: (01535) 607075	✳ Access through house Braille guide SHS

Wales

Clwyd

Erddig, Nr Wrexham LL13 OYT *Tel*: (01978) 355314	W	Make prior arrangements before visit Braille guide

Gwynedd

Penrhyn Castle, Nr Bangor LL57 4AN *Tel*: (01248) 353084	W	Volunteer-drive buggy; please book Braille guide SHS
Plas Newydd, Llanfairpwll, Anglesey LL61 6EQ *Tel*: (01248) 714795	W	Braille guide Rose garden

Powys

Powis Castle, Welshpool SY21 8RF *Tel*: (01938) 554336	Scented plants Braille guide

Northern Ireland

Armagh

Ardress House, Portadown BT62 1SQ *Tel*: (01762) 851236		✳ Gravel paths SHS
The Argory, Dungannon BT71 6NA *Tel*: (0186 87) 84753		SHS

Down

Castle Ward, Strangford, Downpatrick BT30 7LS *Tel*: (0139 686) 204	W	Scented plants in rock gardens Woodland and lake walks SHS
Mount Stewart, Newtownards BT22 2AD *Tel*: (0124 774) 387	W	Lake, scented plants Self-drive buggy; please book
Rowallane, Saintfield, Ballynahinch, Co. Down BT24 7LH *Tel*: (01238) 510131	W	Scented plants Make prior arrangements before visit Special tours SHS

Fermanagh

Florence Court, Enniskillen BT92 1AA *Tel*: (0136 582) 249		Self-drive buggy W SHS

Londonderry

Springhill, Moneymore, Magherafelt BT45 7NQ *Tel*: (0164 87) 48210		Herb garden

Scotland

Central and Tayside Region

House of Dun, A935 Brechin – Montrose *Tel*: (0167 481) 264	W	✳ Gravel paths Braille guides

Highland Region

Brodie Castle, Nr Forres, off A96 *Tel*: (0130 94) 371	W	**X** Taped and Braille guides Audio guide
Inverewe Garden, Poolewe, Wester Ross *Tel*: (0144 586) 229	W	Route plan for W Access to greenhouse

Lothian, Fife and Border Regions

Falkland Palace, on A912, 11miles north of Kirkcaldy *Tel*: (01337) 857397	W	Scented garden **X X X**

West Region

Brodick Castle, Isle of Arran *Tel*: (01770) 2202	W	
Culzean Castle, Nr Maybole, Ayrshire *Tel*: (0165 56) 274	W	Child's W Motorized buggies; please book Carrychairs
Greenbank Garden, Clarkston, Glasgow G76 8RB *Tel*: (0141) 639 3281	W	Raised beds Access to greenhouse
Threave Garden, Castle Douglas *Tel*: (01556) 502575	W	Electric W; please book

Grampian Region

Crathes Castle, A93, 3 miles east of Banchory *Tel*: (0133 044) 525	W	Taped guide
Haddo House, off B999, 19 miles north of Aberdeen *Tel*: (01651) 851440	W	* Gravel paths Braille guide
Pitmedden Garden, on A920, 14 miles north of Aberdeen *Tel*: (01651) 842352		* Grass paths in wet weather

Suppliers of Tools for Easier Gardening

Better Methods-Europe
Brantwood House, Kimberley Road,
Parkstone, Poole, Dorset BH14 8SQ
Tel: (01202) 740142. Some mail order

Black and Decker
Westpoint, The Grove, Slough,
Berkshire SL1 1QQ
Tel: (01753) 79311

Blackwell Products
Unit 4, Riverside Industrial Estate,
Riverway, London SE10 0BH
Tel: (0181) 305 1431. Mail order

Bob Andrews Ltd
Unit 1, Bilton Industrial Estate,
Lovelace Road, Bracknell, Berkshire
RG12 4YT
Tel: (01344) 862111

Bosmere Products Ltd
Northumberland Works,
Northumberland Road, Portsmouth,
Hampshire PO5 1DP
Tel: (01705) 863541. Mail order

Felco
Burton McCall Ltd, 163 Parker
Drive, Leicester LE4 0JP
Tel: (0116) 234 0800. Mail order

CeKa Works Ltd
Pwllheli, Gwynedd LL53 5LH
Tel: (01758) 701070

Chase Organics (GB) Ltd
Coombelands House, Coombelands
Lane, Addlestone, Surrey KT15 1HY
Tel: (01932) 820958. Mail order

Cookson Plantpak
Mundon, Maldon, Essex CM9 8NT
Tel: (01621) 740140

JB Corrie and Co Ltd
Frenchmans Road, Petersfield,
Hampshire GU32 3AP
Tel: (01730) 262552/6

Croydex
North Way, Walworth Industrial
Estate, Andover, Hampshire
SP10 5AW
Tel: (01264) 65881

Dixon Farming and Garden Aids
168 Springdale Road, Corfe Mullen,
Wimborne, Dorset BH21 3QN
Tel: (01202) 692194. Mail order

Easyreach
1 Innisfree Close, Harrogate, North
Yorkshire HG2 8PL
Tel: (01423) 883811. Mail order

Fiskars Ltd (Wilkinson Sword)
Brocastle Avenue, Waterton
Industrial Estate, Bridgend, South
Glamorgan CF31 3YN
Tel: (01656) 655595

Forest Fencing Ltd
Stanford Ct, Stanford Bridge,
Worcester WR6 6SR
Tel: (018865) 451. Mail order

Frank Odell Ltd
70 High Street, Teddington,
Middlesex TW11 8JE
Tel: (0181) 8158/1007. Mail order

Flymo Ltd
Aycliffe Industrial Estate, Newtown,
Aycliffe, Co. Durham DL5 6HD
Tel: (01325) 300303

Gardena (Distributed by Markt (UK) Ltd)
7 Dunhams Ct, Dunhams Lane,
Letchworth, Hertfordshire
CM23 4BU
Tel: (01462) 686688

Geebo
Hailsham, East Sussex BN27 3DT
Tel: (01323) 840771

Geeco Ltd
Gore Road Industrial Estate, New
Milton, Hampshire BH25 6SE
Tel: (01425) 614600

Glenside Organics Ltd
Glenside Farm, Plean, Stirlingshire
FK7 8BA
Tel: (01876) 816655. Mail order

TH Grace Esq
Redford House, Wiggonholt,
Pulborough, West Sussex RH20 2EP
Tel: (01903) 742945. Mail order

Griffin Tools
Level Street, Brierley Hill, West
Midlands DY5 1UA
Tel: (01384) 77789

Hallgate Selection
Ash Priors, Taunton, Somerset
TA4 3NF
Tel: (01823) 257939. Mail order

Haws Elliot Ltd
Rawlings Road, Smethwick, Warley,
West Midlands B67 5AB
Tel: (0121) 420 2494. Mail order

Helping Hand Co Ledbury Ltd
Unit L9, Bromyard Road Trading
Estate, Ledbury, Herefordshire
HR8 1NS
Tel: (01531) 5678. Mail order

Hills Industries Ltd
Pontygwindy Industrial Estate,
Caerphilly, Mid Glamorgan
CF8 3HO
Tel: (01222) 883951

Homecraft Supplies Ltd
Low Moor Estate, Kirkby-in-
Ashfield, Nottinghamshire NG17 7JZ
Tel: (01623) 754047. Mail order

Howells of Sheffield
PO Box 383, Sheffield, Yorkshire
S8 0AT
Tel: (0114) 255 1072

Hozelock Ltd
Haddenham, Aylesbury,
Buckinghamshire HP17 8JD
Tel: (01844) 291881

ICI Garden Products
Woolmead House, East Woolmead
Walk, Farnham, Surrey GU9 7UB
Tel: (01252) 733919

Jenks and Cattell Ltd
Neachells Lane, Wednesfield,
Wolverhampton, West Midlands
WV11 3PU
Tel: (01902) 731271

Langdon (London) Ltd
5 Worminghall Road, Ickford,
Buckinghamshire HP18 9JJ
Tel: (018447) 337. Mail order

Michael Banks Marketing
Ruxley Ridge, Claygate, Esher,
Surrey KT10 0JE
Tel: (01372) 67922/3. Mail order

Metpost Ltd
Mardy Road, Cardiff CF3 8EQ
Tel: (01222) 777877

Multi-Purpose Garden Tools
Unit 1X, Dolphin Square, Bovey
Tracey, Devon TQ1 3AS
Tel: (01626) 833213

Organiser Belt Co
90 Orbel Street, London SW11 3NY
Tel: (0181) 228 0668

QV Garden Products
Maidstone Road, Nettlestead,
Maidstone, Kent ME18 5HP
Tel: (01622) 871666. Mail order

Qualcast (Home and Garden Equipment) Ltd
Coleridge Street, Sunnyhill, Derby
DE3 7JT
Tel: (01332) 760202

Rainbow Tools (Sheffield) Ltd
Meadow Way, Swinton Meadows
Industrial Estate, Swinton,
Rotherham, South Yorkshire
S64 8AB
Tel: (01709) 585817

Redashe
Unit 11, Hewitts Industrial Estate,
Elmbridge Road, Cranleigh, Surrey
GU6 8CW
Tel: (01483) 275774

RY, Robinson Young Ltd
Ibson House, Eastern Way, Bury St
Edmunds, Suffolk IP32 7AB
Tel: (01284) 766261

Rolcut Ltd
Blatchford Road, Horsham, West
Sussex RH13 5QU
Tel: (01403) 65997

Sow Easy Sales & Marketing Ltd
Celandine House, Templewood Lane,
Farnham Common, Buckinghamshire
SL2 3HF
Tel (01753) 644588

Spear and Jackson
Handsworth Road, Sheffield, South
Yorkshire S13 9BR
Tel: (0114) 244 9911

Standard Manufacturing Co
55 Woods Lane, Derby DE3 8UD
Tel: (01332) 43369

Tandown Products
Victoria House, Victoria Street,
Millbrook, Stalybridge, Tameside
SK15 3HX
Tel: (0161) 303 1883. Mail order

Tollgate Tool Sales
Tollgate House, Tollgate Lane, Bury
St Edmunds, Suffolk IP32 6DG
Tel: (01284) 763636. Mail order

Tool-Mate Ltd
PO Box 58, Ipswich, Suffolk
IP9 1PD
Tel: (0147334) 749. Mail order

The Trailerbarrow Co
Elson House, Buxted, Sussex
TN22 4LW
Tel: (01825) 813291

A E Vince Patents
6 Penaber, Criccieth, Gwynedd
LL52 OES
Tel: (01766) 522454. Mail order

Weeder Ltd
Brick Heath Road, Wolverhampton,
West Midlands WV1 2ST
Tel: (01902) 352982

Wilkinson Sword
– *see* Fiskars

Wolf Tools Ltd
Alton Road, Ross-on-Wye,
Herefordshire HR9 5NE
Tel: (01989) 767600. Mail order

A Wright & Son Ltd
Midland Works, 16–18 Sidney Street,
Sheffield, South Yorkshire S1 4RH
Tel: (0114) 272 2677. Mail order

Resources for the Disabled

Advisory Committee For Blind Gardeners
c/o Mr Reg Cove, 55 Eton Avenue, London NW3 3ET
Tel: (0171) 722 9703

The Arthritis and Rheumatism Council for Research
41 Eagle Street, London WC1R 4AR
Tel: (0171) 405 8572

Buckinghamshire Association for Gardening with Disabled People
c/o Bob Millard, 47 Station Road, Winslow, Buckinghamshire MK18 3DZ
Tel: (01296) 712627

Cassette Library for Blind Gardeners
c/o Miss Kathleen Fleet, 48 Tolcarne Drive, Pinner, Middlesex HA5 2DQ
Tel: (0181) 868 4026

The Country Landowners Association (CLA)
Publishes *A Guide to Countryside Recreation for Disabled People*
CLA Publications Dept, 16 Belgrave Square, London SW1X 8PQ
Tel: (0181) 235 0511

Disabled Living Foundation
380–4 Harrow Road, London W9 2HU
Tel: (0171) 289 6111

Federation to Promote Horticulture for the Disabled
Thorngrove, Common Mead Lane, Gillingham, Dorset SP8 4RE
Tel: (01747) 822242

Gardening for the Disabled Trust
Hayes Farm House, Hayes Lane, Peasmarsh, East Sussex TN31 6XR
Write for information

Herefordshire Growing Point
c/o Holme Lacy College, Holme Lacy, Hereford HR2 6LL
Tel: (01432) 870316

Horticultural Therapy
Goulds Ground, Vallis Way, Frome, Somerset BA11 3DW
Tel: (01373) 464782

Joint Disabled Living Centres Council
c/o TRAIDS, 76 Clarendon Park Road, Leicester LE2 3AD
Tel: (0116) 270 0747/8

Mary Marlborough Lodge
Nuffield Orthopaedic Centre NHS Trust, Windmill Road, Headington, Oxford OX3 7LD
Tel: (01865) 227593

MENCAP
123 Golden Lane, London
EC1Y 0RT
Tel: (0181) 253 9433

National Library for the Blind
48 Tolcarne Drive, Pinner, Middlesex
HA5 2DQ
Tel: (0181) 868 4026

National Trust Gardens for the Disabled
The National Trust, 36 Queen Anne's Gate, London SW1H 9AS
Tel: (0171) 222 9251

National Trust for Scotland
Friends of Greenbank Garden, c/o Mrs Kathy Price, 23 Langtree Avenue, Glasgow G46 7LJ
Tel: (0141) 638 7361

North Regional Association for the Blind
Headingley Castle, Headingley Lane, Leeds LS6 2DQ
Tel: (0113) 275 2666

The Royal Association for Disability and Rehabilitation
(RADAR)
25 Mortimer St, London W1N 8AB
Tel: (0171) 637 5400

The Royal National Institute for the Blind
224 Great Portland Street, London W1N 6AA
Tel: (0171) 388 1266

Scottish Braille Press
Craigmillar Park, Edinburgh
EH16 5NB
Tel: (0131) 667 0628

Scottish Council on Disability
Princes House, 5 Shandwick Place, Edinburgh EH2 4RG
Tel: (0131) 229 8632

Scottish National Federation for the Welfare of the Blind
8 St Leonards Bank, Perth, Perthshire PH2 8EB
Tel: (01738) 26969

Society for Promotion of Rehabilitation in Gardening (SPRIG)
c/o John Catlin, OT Dept, Dept of Psychiatry, Chase Farm Hospital, The Ridgeway, Enfield EN2 8JL
Tel: (0181) 366 6600

Southern & Western Regional Association for the Blind
55 Eton Avenue, London NW3 3ET
Tel: (0171) 722 9703

Spastics Society
12 Park Crescent, London N1N 4EQ
Tel: (0171) 636 5020

Talking Newspapers for the Blind
Browning Road, Heathfield
TN21 8DB
Tel: (01435) 866102

Wales Council for the Blind
Oak House, 12 The Bulwark, Brecon, Powys LD3 7AD
Tel: (01874) 4576

Wales Council for the Disabled
Caerbragdy Industrial Estate, Bedwas Rd, Caerphilly, Mid Glamorgan CF8 3SL
Tel: (01222) 869224

Plant Collections

The National Council for the Conservation of Plants and Gardens is an organization committed to conserving stocks of precious plants, especially those that may be at risk. To this end, their members have helped to establish an extraordinary number of collections.

The National Collections are held by organizations and individuals and are purely a labour of love. The collection holders often have a unique and detailed knowledge of their particular speciality which they're pleased to share with others and sometimes you can even buy the plants.

Some of the collections are in gardens open to the public and can be viewed whenever the gardens are open, but many are in private establishments. So, if you wish to visit, you may well need to write for an appointment. All are well worth the trouble.

The details of the collections are available in the *National Plant Collections Directory* which can be obtained from the following address.

National Council for the Conservation of Plants and Gardens
The Pines, Wisley Garden, Woking, Surrey GU23 6QB
Tel: (01483) 211465

Gardens Open to the Public

There's no better way to get inspiration for your own garden than to visit other people's. Even the largest stately home gardens can inspire ideas for the tiniest plot. All you need to do is to scale them down. A garden visit is also a wonderful day out and a certain way to improve your gardening knowledge.

Fortunately, there's no country in the world better endowed with fine gardens open to the public than Britain. To list them all here would be impossible but any one of the following books and leaflets will provide the necessary information.

Blue Guide – Gardens of England
Written by: Frances Gapper, Patience Gapper and Sally Drury
Published by: A & C Black
Price £14.99

British Car Rental Guide to British Gardens
A free leaflet containing information of over 60 gardens obtainable from:
The British Travel Centre
12 Regent St, Piccadilly Circus, London SW1Y 4PQ

Gardens Handbook
Published by: The National Trust
36 Queen Anne's Gate, London SW1H 9AS
Price £3.95

Gardens of England & Wales (The Yellow Book)
Published by: The National Gardens Scheme
Hatchlands Park, East Clandon, Guildford, Surrey GU4 7RT
Price £3.00

The Gardeners' Guide to Britain
Written by: Patrick Taylor
Published by: Pavilion
Price £10.99

Good Gardens Guide
Edited by: Graham Rose and Peter King
Published by: Vermillion
Price £12.99

The Guide to over 100 Properties
Published by: The National Trust for Scotland
5 Charlotte Square, Edinburgh
EH2 4DU
Price £1.00 (35p p&p)

The Shell Guide to the Gardens of England & Wales
Written by: Sarah Hollis and Derry Moore
Published by: André Deutsch
Price £17.95

Scotland's Garden
Published by: The Scotland Gardens Scheme
31 Castle Terrace, Edinburgh EH1 2EL
Price £2.00 (50p p&p)

Arboreta and Botanic Gardens

B ritain is blessed with almost certainly the best living plant directories in the world. If you need to check out a tree or shrub before planting, visit one of the many arboreta listed below. There's one within driving distance of you. They're perfect places, too, for a family or a group day out, packed with interest for the keen plantsman or woman and magical places if you just fancy a wander amongst the plants. Special times to visit are spring and autumn when the colours are nothing short of magnificent.

Botanic gardens are much more than gardens open to the public. They do important work in the fields of conservation and research and are an absolute mine of information about plants. Most will also be pleased to answer questions. Many run 'Friends' organizations which help support their work and provide many benefits for members.

Make sure you check opening times before visiting.

England

Bath
The Botanical Gardens, Royal Victoria Park, Bath, Avon BA1 2NR
Tel: (01225) 477000
Monday–Friday, 8 a.m.–1 hour before sunset
Saturday & Sunday, 10 a.m.–1 hour before sunset

Birmingham
Birmingham Botanical Gardens, Westbourne Road, Edgbaston, Birmingham B15 3TR
Tel: (0121) 454 1860
Daily, 9 a.m.–dusk (8p.m. in summer)

The University Botanic Gardens, Winterbourne, Edgbaston Park Road, Birmingham B15 2TT
Tel: (0121) 414 5613
Permission of director required

Bradford
Bradford Botanic Garden, Lister Road, Bradford 9, Yorkshire BD9 4NR
Tel: (01274) 544822
Daily

Bristol
University Botanic Gardens, Department of Botany, Bracken Hill, North Road, Leigh Woods, Bristol BS8 3PF
Tel: (0117) 973 3682
During working hours.
Saturday & Sunday by arrangement.

Cambridge
University Botanic Garden, Bateman Street, Cambridge CB2 1JF
Tel: (01223) 336265
Monday–Saturday, garden: 8 a.m.–dusk; greenhouses: 2 p.m.– 5 p.m.

Durham
Botanical Garden, Botany Department, Hollingride Lane, Durham DH1 3TN
Tel: (0191) 3742670
Daily, 10 a.m.–4 p.m.

Egham
London University Botanic Gardens, Egham Hill, Egham, Surrey TW20 0EX
Tel: (01784) 433303
By appointment all year, 9 a.m.–4 p.m.

Exeter
The Grounds and Gardens of the University, Northcote House, The Queen's Drive, Exeter, EX4 4QQ
Tel: (01392) 263263
Daily, throughout the year

Godalming
Winkworth Arboretum, Hascombe Road, Godalming, Surrey GU8 4AD
Tel: (01483) 208477
Daily, sunrise to sunset

Goudhurst
Bedgebury National Pinetum Goudhurst, Kent TN17 2SL
Tel: (01580) 211044
Daily, 10 a.m.–8 p.m., or sunset

Harrogate
Northern Horticultural Society Harlow Carr Botanical Gardens, Crag Lane, Harrogate, North Yorkshire HG3 1QB
Tel: (01423) 565418
Daily, 9.30 a.m.–sunset

Hull
University Botanic Garden and Experimental Garden, Thwaite Street, Cottingham, North Humberside HU16 4QX
Tel: (01482) 849620
1 April–30 September: Thursday, 1 p.m.–4.30 p.m.
Other times by appointment

Kew
Royal Botanic Gardens, Kew, Richmond, Surrey TW9 3AE
Tel: (0181) 940 1171
Gardens and Houses: Daily, 9.30 a.m.–4.30 p.m. (excluding Christmas Day, New Year's Day and May Day)

Leeds
Plant Sciences Experimental Gardens, The University, Leeds LS2 9JT
Tel: (0113) 243 1751
With permission of Director

Leicester
Botanic Garden, Beaumont Hall, Stoughton Drive South, Leicester LE2 2NA
Tel: (0116) 271 7725
Monday–Thursday, 10 a.m.–5 p.m.
Friday, 10 a.m.–3.30 p.m.

Liverpool
City of Liverpool Botanic Gardens, Calderstones and Harthill, Liverpool L18 3JD
Tel: (0151) 225 5910
Garden: 8.30 a.m.–4 p.m. in winter. 8 a.m.–9 p.m. in summer
Greenhouses: 1 p.m.–4 p.m. in winter. 1 p.m.–5 p.m. in summer
University of Liverpool Botanic Garden. See *Ness*

London
Chelsea Physic Garden, 66 Royal
Hospital Road, Chelsea, London
SW3 4HS
Tel: (0171) 352 5646
Open to students and teachers with
permission of Director
Also April–October, Sunday &
Wednesday, 2 p.m.–5 p.m.
University of London Botanic
Garden. See *Egham*

Manchester
Fletcher Moss Botanical Gardens,
Mill Gate Lane, Manchester
M20 2SW
Tel: (0161) 434 1877
Daily, dawn–dusk

Ness
The University of Liverpool Botanic
Garden, Ness, Neston, S. Wirral,
Merseyside L64 4AY
Tel: (0151) 336 2135
March–October: Daily, 9.30 a.m.–
sunset. November–February: Daily,
9.30 a.m.–4 p.m.

Oxford
University Botanic Garden, High
Street, Oxford OX1 4AX
Tel: (01865) 276920
Weekdays, 8.30 a.m.–5 p.m. Sunday
10 a.m.–12 noon, 2 p.m.–5 p.m.

Reading
The Plant Science Botanic Garden,
The University, Whiteknights,
Reading, Berkshire RG6 2AS
Tel: (01734) 318092
Permission of the Director required

Sheffield
Botanic Gardens, Clarkehouse Road,
Sheffield, South Yorkshire S10 2LN
Tel: (0114) 267 1115
Daily, during daylight hours

Southampton
University Botanic Garden, Biology
Department, Building 44,
Southampton, Hampshire SO9 5NH
Tel: (01703) 595000
Daily, 9 a.m.–4.30 p.m.

Tresco
Tresco Abbey Gardens, Isles of
Scilly, Cornwall TR24 0QJ
Tel: (01720) 22849
Weekdays, 10 a.m.–4 p.m.

Ventnor
Botanic Garden, The Undercliffe
Drive, Ventnor, Isle of Wight
PO38 1UL
Tel: (01983) 855397
Temperate House: Daily,
10 a.m.–5 p.m.

Wakehurst Place
Ardingly, Haywards Heath, Sussex
RH17 6TN
Tel: (01444) 892701
Opening times as Kew

Westonbirt
Westonbirt Arboretum, Nr Tetbury,
Gloucestershire GL8 8QS
Tel: (01666) 880220
Daily, 10 a.m.–8 p.m. or dusk

Wisley
The RHS Garden, Wisley, Ripley,
Woking, Surrey GU23 6QA
Tel: (01483) 224234
Weekdays, 10a.m.–sunset or 7p.m.,
whichever is earlier.
Sunday (10 a.m.–2 p.m members
only), 2 p.m.–sunset, whichever is
earlier

York
Museum Gardens, York YO1 2DR
Tel: (01904) 629745
Daily, 8 a.m.–6 p.m.

Scotland

Aberdeen
Cruickshank Botanic Garden, St
Machar Drive, Old Aberdeen
AB9 2UD
Tel: (01224) 272704
Daily

Benmore
Younger Botanic Garden, Benmore,
Nr Dunoon PA23 8QU
Tel: (01369) 706261
Mid-March–end October: Daily,
10 a.m.–6 p.m.

Dundee
University Botanic Garden, 516
Perth Road, Dundee DD2 1LW
Tel: (01382) 66939
Monday–Saturday, 9 a.m.–4.30 p.m.

Edinburgh
Royal Botanic Garden, Edinburgh
EH3 5LR
Tel: (0131) 5527171
Garden: February–October: Daily,
9 a.m. (Sunday 11 a.m.)–1 hour
before sunset
November–January: 9 a.m. (Sunday
11 a.m.)–sunset
Planthouses: Daily, 11 a.m. (Sunday
11 a.m.)–5 p.m.

Glasgow
Botanic Gardens, Great Western
Road, Glasgow G12 0UE
Tel: (0141) 334 2422
Garden: Daily, 7 a.m.–sunset
Glasshouses: Monday–Saturday,
1 p.m.–4.45 p.m. Sunday,
12 noon–4.45 p.m.

Logan
Botanic Garden, Port Logan, by
Stranraer, Dumfries and Galloway
D99 9ND
Tel: (017768) 6231
March–October: Daily,
10 a.m.–6 p.m.

St Andrews
Botanic Garden, The University of St
Andrews, The Canongate, St
Andrews, Fife KY16 8RT
Tel: (01334) 462866
Monday–Friday, 10 a.m.–4 p.m.

Wales

Aberystwyth
University College of Wales, Botany
Garden, Aberystwyth SY23 3DA
Tel: (01970) 615514
With permission of Director

Cardiff
Dyffryn Gardens, St Nicholas,
Cardiff CF5 6SU
Tel: (01222) 593328
Summer months: 10 a.m.–7 p.m.

Swansea
Botanic Garden, University College,
Singleton Park, Swansea, Glamorgan
SA2 8PX
Tel: (01792) 205678
Daily, 9 a.m.–5 p.m.

Northern Ireland

Belfast
The Botanic Garden Park,
Stranmillis, Belfast, Co. Antrim
BT9 5AU
Tel: (01232) 324902
Daily, 7.30 a.m.–dusk

Coleraine
University of Ulster, Coleraine, Co.
Londonderry BT52 1SA
Tel: (01265) 44141
Daylight hours

Eire

Dublin
Trinity College Botanic Garden,
Palmerston Park, Dublin 6, Republic
of Ireland
Tel: (00353) 1 497 2070
Monday–Friday, 9 a.m.–5 p.m.

National Botanic Gardens,
Glasnevin, Dublin 9, Republic of
Ireland
Tel: (00353) 1 837 4388
Summer: Daily, 9 a.m.–6 p.m.
Winter: Daily, 9 a.m.–4.30 p.m.

Malahide
Talbot Botanic Gardens, Malahide
Castle, Co. Dublin, Republic of
Ireland
Tel: (00353) 1 846 2456
May–September: Daily,
2 p.m.–4.30 p.m.

Horticultural Shows

E very year there are dozens, if not hundreds of horticultural shows around the country, from the tiny village flower show to the extravagant Chelsea Flower Show in London.

At all of them you can enjoy a wonderful gardening day out, surrounded by the sights and smells of thousands of flowers all in peak condition. And above all, you'll have the chance to pick the best gardening brains in the country. They're all gathered there in one place at one time and they're always willing to help and answer questions.

You'll find exiting new plants and products and at most you'll be able to buy what takes your fancy there and then. There are also good design ideas laid out before you in specially made show gardens. You should make sure you visit at least one of them during the season to see what's new and to keep abreast of developments. Naturally we hope we'll have the opportunity of meeting you at the BBC's own Gardeners' World Live Show.

Don't forget too that, apart from those listed here, there are many smaller shows during the season so check your local paper. And for the best in seasonal plants, treat yourself to a visit to one of the RHS monthly shows at the Horticultural Halls at Vincent Square and Greycoat Street, Westminster, London.

The list below runs chronologically.

Horticultural Shows

International Spring Gardening Fair
Olympia, London
Easter weekend
Organizers:
News International Exhibitions Ltd,
P O Box 495, Virginia Street,
London E1 9XY
Tel: (0171) 782 6000

Harrogate Spring Flower Show
Valley Gardens, Harrogate, North Yorkshire
Late April
Organizers:
Show Secretary
North of England Horticultural Society,
4a South Park Road,
Harrogate, North Yorkshire
HG1 5QU
Tel: (01423) 561049

Malvern Spring Gardening Show
Three Counties Showground,
Malvern, Worcestershire
Early May
Organizers:
Show Secrectary
Three Counties Horticultural Society,
The Showground, Malvern,
Worcestershire WR13 6NW
Tel: (01684) 892751

Chelsea Flower Show
Royal Hospital, Chelsea, London
End May
Organizers:
Shows Department, RHS,
80 Vincent Square, London
SW1P 2PE
Tel: (0171) 828 1744

The Great Garden and Countryside Festival
Holker Hall, Cumbria
Beginning June
Organizers:
Show Director, Holker Hall,
Cark in Cartmel, Grange-over-Sands,
Cumbria LA11 7PL
Tel: (0153) 955 8328

BBC Gardeners' World Live
National Exhibition Centre,
Birmingham
Middle June
Organizers:
BBC Haymarket Exhibitions,
60 Waldegrave Road, Teddington,
Middlesex TW11 8LG
Tel: (0181) 943 5000

Hampton Court Palace Flower Show
Hampton Court Palace, East
Molesey, Surrey
Early July
Organizers:
RHS (see above)

Gateshead Summer Flower Show
Gateshead Central Nursery,
Whickham Highway, Gateshead,
Tyne & Wear
End July
Organizers:
Gateshead Metropolitan Borough
Council, Prince Consort Road,
Gateshead, Tyne & Wear NE8 4HJ
Tel: (0191) 490 1616 ext. 272

Ayr Flower Show
Rozelle Park, Ayr.
Early August
Organizers:
Mr P M Gibbs, Leisure Services,
Kyle & Carrick District Council,
30 Miller Road,
Ayr KA7 2AY
Tel: (01292) 282842

Shrewsbury Flower Show
The Quarry, Shrewsbury, Shropshire
Middle August
Organizers:
Show Secretary, Quarry Lodge,
Shrewsbury, Shropshire SY1 1RN
Tel: (01743) 364051

Wisley Flower Festival
RHS Garden, Wisley, Surrey
Middle August
Organizers:
RHS, Wisley, Woking,
Surrey GU23 6QB
Tel: (01483) 224234

Southport Flower Show
Victoria Park, Southport, Merseyside
Middle August
Organizers:
Show Administrator,
42 Hoghton Street, Southport,
Merseyside PR9 0PQ
Tel: (01704) 547147

Harrogate Great Autumn Flower Show
Exhibition Halls, Harrogate
Middle September
Organizers:
Show Organizer, North of England
Horticulture Society (see above)

Malvern Autumn Show
Three Counties Showground,
Malvern, Worcestershire
End September
Organizers:
RHS, Malvern Autumn Show,
Three Counties Showground,
Malvern,
Worcestershire WR13 6NW
Tel: (01684) 892751

Specialist Nurseries

T his country abounds with small and not-so-small specialist nurseries who are the aristocrats of the industry. If you're interested in a particular genus or a certain type of plant, it's at such places that you'll find the widest range. It's important that we patronize the smaller specialists in particular, since their loss would make the gardening trade immeasurably poorer.

For further information and a huge range of nurseries, the Hardy Plant Society's *Plantfinder* is invaluable. You'll find it in most good bookshops.

Acacia
Celyn Vale Nurseries
Carrog, Corwen, Clwyd LL21 9LD
Tel: (01490) 83671

Acer
Hippopottering Nursery
Orchard House, Brackenhill Road,
Haxey, Nr Doncaster, South
Yorkshire DN9 2LR
Tel: (01427) 752185

P M A Plant Specialities
Lower Mead, West Hatch, Taunton,
Somerset TA3 5RN
Tel: (01823) 480774

Achimenes
Stanley Mossop
Boonwood Garden Centre, Gosforth,
Seascale, Cumbria CA20 1BP
Tel: (01946) 821817

Alpines
Anglia Alpines
Needingworth Road, Bluntisham,
Huntingdon, Cambridgeshire
PE17 3RJ
Tel: (01487) 840103

Ardfearn Nursery
Bunchrew, Inverness Highland
IV3 6RH
Tel: (01463) 243250

Beechcroft Nursery
127 Reigate Road, Ewell, Surrey
KT17 3DE
Tel: (0181) 393 4265
No mail order

Blairhoyle Nursery
Port of Menteith, Stirling, Central
FK8 3LF
Tel: (018775) 669
No mail order

Brambling House Alpines
119 Sheffield Road, Warmsworth,
Doncaster, South Yorkshire DN4
9QX
Tel: (01302) 850730

Broadstone Alpines
13 The Nursery, High Street, Sutton
Courtenay, Abingdon, Oxfordshire
OX14 4UA
Tel: (01235) 847557

J M Burgess
Alpine Nursery, Sisland, Norwich,
Norfolk NR14 6EF
Tel: (01508) 520724
No mail order

Castle Alpines
Castle Road, Wootton, Woodstock,
Oxfordshire OX20 1EG
Tel: (01993) 812162

John Clayfield
Llanbrook Alpine Nursery, Hopton
Castle, Clunton, Shropshire
SY7 0QG
Tel: (015474) 298

County Park Nursery
Essex Gardens, Hornchurch, Essex
RM11 3BU
Tel: (01708) 445205
No mail order

Jack Drake
Inshriach Alpine Nursery, Aviemore,
Invernesshire PH22 1QS
Tel: (01540) 651287

Field House Nurseries
Leake Road, Gotham, Nottingham
NG11 0JN
Tel: (0115) 983 0278

Hartside Nursery Garden
Nr Alston, Cumbria CA9 3BL
Tel: (01434) 381372

Highgates Nursery
166a Crich Lane, Belper, Derbyshire
DE5 1EP
Tel: (01773) 822153
No mail order

Lewdon Farm Alpine Nursery
Medland Lane, Cheriton Bishop, Nr
Exeter, Devon EX6 6HF
Tel: (01647) 24283

Martin Nest Nurseries
Grange Cottage, Harpswell Lane,
Hemswell, Gainsborough,
Lincolnshire DN21 5UP
Tel: (01427) 668369

Newton Hill Alpines
335 Leeds Road, Newton Hill,
Wakefield, Yorkshire WF1 2JH
Tel: (01924) 377056

Nicky's Rock Garden Nursery
Broadhayes, Stockland, Honiton,
Devon EX14 9EH
Tel: (01404) 881213
No mail order

Norden Alpines
Hirst Road, Carlton, Nr Goole,
Humberside DN14 9PX
Tel: (01405) 861348
No mail order

The Old Manor Nursery
Twyning, Gloucester GL20 6DB
Tel: (01684) 293516

Pitts Farm Nursery
Shrewley, Warwick, Warwickshire
CV35 7BB
Tel: (0192684) 2737

Potterton & Martin
The Cottage Nursery, Moortown
Road, Nettleton, Caistor,
Lincolnshire LN7 6HX
Tel: (01472) 851792

Rivendell Alpines
Horton Heath, Wimborne, Dorset
BH21 7JN
Tel: (01202) 824013

Ryal Nursery
East Farm Cottage, Ryal,
Northumberland NE20 0SA
Tel: (01661) 886562

Siskin Plants
April House, Davey Lane,
Charsfield, Woodbridge, Suffolk
IP13 7QG
Tel: (01473 37) 567

39 Steps
Grove Cottage, Forge Hill,
Lydbrook, Gloucestershire
GL17 9QS
Tel: (01594) 860544
No mail order

Thuya Alpine Nursery
Glebelands, Hartpury,
Gloucestershire GL19 3BW
Tel: (01452) 700548

West Kington Nurseries Ltd
Pound Hill, West Kington, Nr
Chippenham, Wiltshire SN14 7JG
Tel: (01249) 782822
No mail order

White Cottage Alpines
Eastgate, Rudston, Driffield, East
Yorkshire YO25 0UX
Tel: (01262) 420668

Alstroemeria
Steven Bailey
Silver Street, Sway, Lymington,
Hampshire SO41 6ZA
Tel: (01797) 270607

Aquatics
Bennett's Water Gardens, Putton
Lane, Chickerell, Weymouth, Dorset
DT3 4AF
Tel: (01305) 785150

Blagdon Water Garden Centre Ltd
Bath Road, Upper Langford, Avon
BS18 7DN
Tel: (01934) 852973

Deanswood Plants
Potteries Lane, Littlethorpe, Ripon,
North Yorkshire HG4 3LF
Tel: (01765) 603441

Gardeners' World & English Water
Garden
Rock Lane, Washington, West
Sussex RH20 3BL
Tel: (01903) 892006

Higher End Nursery
Hale, Fordingbridge, Hampshire SP6
2RA
Tel: (01725) 22243

Honeysome Aquatic Nursery
The Row, Sutton, Nr Ely,
Cambridgeshire CB6 2PF
Tel: (01353) 778889

Maydencroft Aquatic Nurseries
Maydencroft Lane, Gosmore,
Hitchin, Hertfordshire SG4 7QD
Tel: (01462) 456020

Reedley Nursery
Robinson Lane, Reedley, Brierfield,
Nr Nelson, Lancashire BB9 5QS
Tel: (01282) 693376

Rowden Gardens
Brentor, Nr Tavistock, Devon
PL19 0NG
Tel: (01822) 810275

Stapeley Water Gardens Ltd
London Road, Stapeley, Nantwich,
Cheshire CW5 7LH
Tel: (01270) 623868

The Water Garden Nursery
Highcroft, Moorend, Wembworthy,
Chulmleigh, Devon EX18 7SG
Tel: (01837) 83566

Wildwoods Water Gardens Ltd
Theobalds Park Road, Crews Hill,
Enfield, Middlesex EN2 9BP
Tel: (0181) 366 0243

Aquilegia
John Drake
Hardwicke House, Fen Ditton,
Cambridgeshire CB5 8TF
Tel: (01223) 292246
Mail order only

Architectural Plants
Architectural Plants
Cooks Farm, Nuthurst, Horsham,
West Sussex RH13 6LH
Tel: (01403) 891772

Aster
Misses I Allen & J Huish
Quarry Farm, Wraxall, Bristol, Avon
BS19 1LE
Tel: (01275) 810435

Old Court Nurseries Ltd
Colwall, Nr Malvern, Worcestershire
WR13 6QE
Tel: (01684) 40416

Astilbe
Park Green Nurseries
Wetheringsett, Stowmarket, Suffolk
IP14 5QH
Tel: (01728) 860139

Auricula
Field House Nurseries
Leake Road, Gotham, Nottingham
NG11 0JN
Tel: (0115) 983 0278

Brenda Hyatt
1 Toddington Crescent, Bluebell Hill,
Chatham, Kent ME5 9QT
Tel: (01634) 863251

Azalea
Coghurst Nursery
Ivy House Lane, Near Three Oaks,
Hastings, East Sussex TN35 4NP
Tel: (01424) 425371

Exbury Enterprises Ltd
Exbury, Nr Southampton,
Hampshire SO4 1AZ
Tel: (01703) 898625

Glendoick Gardens Ltd, Glencarse,
Perth PH2 7NS
Tel: (01738) 860205

Knaphill & Slocock Nurseries
Barrs Lane, Knaphill, Woking,
Surrey GU21 2JW
Tel: (01483) 481212

Lea Rhododendron Gardens Ltd
Lea, Matlock, Derbyshire DE4 5GH
Tel: (01629 534) 380

Leonardslee Gardens
1 Mill Lane, Lower Beeding, West
Sussex RH13 6PX
Tel: (01403) 891412

Millais Nurseries
Crosswater Lane, Churt, Farnham,
Surrey GU10 2JN
Tel: (01252) 792698

F Morrey & Sons
Forest Nursery, Kelsall, Tarporley,
Cheshire CW6 0SW
Tel: (01829) 751342
No mail order

Pound Lane Nurseries
Ampfield, Nr Romsey, Hampshire
SO51 9BL
Tel: (01703) 739685

Wall Cottage Nursery
Lockengate, Bugle, St Austell,
Cornwall PL26 8RU
Tel: (01208) 831259

Whitehills Nurseries
Newton Stewart, Wigtownshire
DG8 6SL
Tel: (01671) 402049

Bamboo
Bamboo Nursery
Kingsgate Cottage, Wittersham,
Tenterden, Kent TN30 7NS
Tel: (01797) 270607

Drysdale Nursery
Bowerwood Road, Fordingbridge,
Hampshire SP6 1BN
Tel: (01425) 653010

Fulbrooke Nursery
43 Fulbrooke Road, Cambridgeshire
CB3 9EE
Tel: (01223) 311102

Jungle Giants
Plough Farm, Wigmore,
Herefordshire HR6 9UW
Tel: (01568) 86708

Begonias
Blackmore & Langdon Ltd
Pensford, Bristol, Avon BS18 4JL
Tel: (01275) 332300

Halsway Nursery
Halsway, Nr Crowcombe, Taunton,
Somerset TA4 4BB
Tel: (019848) 243

Bonsai
Bromage & Young
St Mary's Gardens, Worplesdon,
Surrey GU3 3RS
Tel: (01483) 232893

Herons Bonsai Nursery
Wire Mill Lane, Newchapel, Nr
Lingfield, Surrey RH7 6HJ
Tel: (01342) 832657

Samlesbury Bonsai Nursery
The Boat House, Potters Lane,
Samlesbury, Preston, Lancashire
PR5 0UE
Tel: (01772) 877213

Peter Trenear
Chantreyland, Chequers Lane,
Eversley Cross, Basingstoke,
Hampshire RG27 0NX
Tel: (01734) 732300

Bromeliads
Vesutor Ltd
The Bromeliad Nursery,
Marringdean Road, Billingshurst,
West Sussex RH14 9EH
Tel: (01403) 784028

Bulbs

Jacques Amand Ltd
The Nurseries, 145 Clamp Hill,
Stanmore, Middlesex HA7 3JS
Tel: (0181) 954 8138

Avon Bulbs
Burnt House Farm, Mid-Lambrook,
South Petherton, Somerset
TA13 5HE
Tel: (01460) 242177

Bloms Bulbs Ltd
Primrose Nursery, Park Lane,
Sharnbrook, Bedford MK44 1LW
Tel: (01234) 782424
see Liliaceae

Rupert Bowlby
Gatton, Reigate, Surrey RH2 0TA
Tel: (01737) 642221

Broadleigh Gardens
Bishops Hull, Taunton, Somerset
TA4 1AE
Tel: (01823) 286231

Paul Christian – Rare Plants
PO Box 468, Wrexham, Clwyd
LL13 9XR
Tel: (01978) 366399
Mail order only

Copford Bulbs
Dorsetts, Birch Road, Copford,
Colchester, Essex CO6 1DR
Tel: (01206) 330008

De Jagers of Marden, Kent
TN12 9BP
Tel: (01622) 831235

Knightshayes Garden Trust
The Garden Office, Knightshayes,
Tiverton, Devon EX16 7RG
Tel: (01884) 259010
No mail order

John Shipton (Bulbs)
Y Felin, Henllan Amgoed, Whitland,
Dyfed SA34 0SL
Tel: (01994) 240125

Van Tubergen UK Ltd
Bressingham, Diss, Norfolk
IP22 2AB
Tel: (01379) 688282
Mail order only

J Walkers Bulbs
Washway House Farm, Holbeach,
Spalding, Lincolnshire PE12 7PP
Tel: (01406) 426216
Mail order only

Buxus

Langley Boxwood Nursery
Langley Court, Rake, Liss,
Hampshire GU33 7JL
Tel: (01730) 894467

Cacti and Succulents

Bradley Batch Nursery
64 Bath Road, Bridgwater, Somerset
TA7 9QJ
Tel: (01458) 210256

Bridgemere Nurseries
Bridgemere, Cheshire CW5 7QB
Tel: (019365) 381/239

Croston Cactus
43 Southport Road, Chorley,
Lancashire PR7 6ET
Tel: (01257) 452555

Cruck Cottage Cacti
Cruck Cottage, Pickering, North
Yorkshire YO18 8PJ
Tel: (01751) 472042

East Midlands Cactus Nursery
Manor Close, Milton Keynes,
Buckinghamshire MK10 9AA
Tel: (01908) 665584

Eau Brink Cactus Nursery,
Tilney All Saints, Norfolk
PE34 4SQ
Tel: (01553) 617635

Felspar Cacti
20 Reawla Lane, Hayle, Cornwall
TR27 5HQ
Tel: (01736) 850321

W G Geissler
Winsford, Slimbridge,
Gloucestershire GL2 7BW
Tel: (01453) 890340

Glenhirst Cactus Nursery
Station Road, Nr Boston,
Lincolnshire PE20 3NX
Tel: (01205) 820314

Greenslacks Nurseries
Ocot Lane, Scammonden,
Huddersfield, Yorkshire HD3 3FR
Tel: (01484) 842584

Harvest Nurseries
Harvest Cottage, Iden, Nr Rye,
Sussex TH31 7QA
Tel: (01797) 280493

Holly Gate Cactus Nursery
Billingshurst Road, Ashington, West
Sussex RH20 3BA
Tel: (01903) 892930

Jumanery Cacti
St Catherine's Lodge, Whaplode St
Catherine, Lincolnshire PE12 6SR
Tel: (01406 34) 373

K & C Cacti
Fern Cottage, Barnstaple, Devon
EX32 0SF
Tel: (01598) 760393

Kent Cacti
(Office) 35 Rutland Way, Orpington,
Kent BR5 4DY
Tel: (01689) 836249

Long Man Gardens
Lewes Road, Polgate, East Sussex
BN26 5RS
Tel: (01323) 870816

Oakleigh Nurseries
Monkwood, Alresford, Hampshire
SO24 0HB
Tel: (01962) 773344

Pete & Ken Cactus Nursery
Saunders Lane, Nr Canterbury, Kent
CT3 2BX
Tel: (01304) 812170

A & A Phipps
62 Samuel White Road, Bristol
BS15 3LX
Tel: (0117) 960 7591

The Plant Lovers
Candesby House, Spilsby,
Lincolnshire PE23 5RU
Tel: (01754) 85256

Preston-Mafham Collection
2 Willoughby Close, Alcester,
Warwickshire B49 5QJ
Tel: (01789) 762938

Chris Rodgerson
35 Lydgate Hall Crescent, Sheffield,
South Yorkshire S10 5NE
Tel: (0114) 268 5533

Robert Scott
78 Bousley Rise, Surrey KT16 0LB
Tel: (01932) 872667

Toobees Nursery
20 Inglewood, Woking, Surrey
GU21 3HX
Tel: (01483) 722600

Westfield Cacti
Kennford, Devon EX6 7XD
Tel: (01392) 832921

Whitestone Gardens Ltd
The Cactus House, Thirsk, Yorkshire
YO7 2PZ
Tel: (01845) 597467

K M & R J R Willoughby
Willows Mead, Whittle-le-Woods,
Lancashire PR6 7DJ
Tel: (01257) 262107

H & S Wills
2 St Brannocks Park Road,
Ilfracombe, Devon EX34 8HU
Tel: (01271) 863949

Roy Young Seeds
23 Westland Chase, King's Lynn,
Norfolk PE33 0QH
Tel: (01553) 840867

Camellias
Ard Daraich Shrub Nursery
Ardgour, by Fort William,
Invernesshire PH33 7AB
Tel: (018555) 248
No mail order

Bodnant Gardens
Tal-y-Cafn, Colwyn Bay, North
Wales LL28 5RE
Tel: (01492) 650460

Coghurst Nursery
Ivy House Lane, Near Three Oaks,
Hastings, East Sussex TN35 4NP
Tel: (01424) 425371

Exbury Enterprises Ltd
Exbury, Nr Southampton,
Hampshire SO4 1AZ
Tel: (01703) 898625

Porthpean House Gardens
Porthpean, St Austell, Cornwall
PL26 6AX
Tel: (01726) 72888

Trehane Camellia Nursery
Stapehill Road, Hampreston,
Wimborne, Dorset BH21 7NE
Tel: (01202) 873490

Trewidden Estate Nursery
Trewidden Gardens, Penzance,
Cornwall TR20 8TT
Tel: (01736) 62087

Trewithen Nurseries
Grampound Road, Truro, Cornwall
TR2 4DD
Tel: (01726) 882764

Campanula
K W Davis
Lingen Nursery, Lingen, Bucknell,
Shropshire SY7 0DY
Tel: (01544) 267720

Padlock Croft
Peter & Susan Lewis
19 Padlock Road, West Wratting,
Cambridgeshire
CB1 5LS
Tel: (01223) 290383

Carnations *see also* **Pinks**
Steven Bailey
Silver Street, Sway, Lymington,
Hampshire SO41 6ZA
Tel: (01590) 682227

Haywards Carnations
The Chace Gardens, Stakes Road,
Purbrook, Waterlooville, Hampshire
PO7 5PL
Tel: (01705) 263047

Woodfield Bros
Wood End, Clifford Chambers,
Stratford-on-Avon, Warwickshire
CV37 8HR
Tel: (01789) 205618

Carnivorous Plants
Marston Exotics
Brampton Lane, Madley,
Herefordshire HR2 9LX
Tel: (01981) 251140

Plantcraft
(Office) 35 Rutland Way, Orpington,
Kent BR5 4DY
Tel: (01689) 830157

Potterton & Martin
The Cottage Nursery, Moortown
Road, Nettleton, Caistor,
Lincolnshire
LN7 6HX
Tel: (01472) 851792

Chamomile
Morehavens
28 Denham Lane, Gerrards Cross,
Buckinghamshire SL9 0EX
Tel: (01494) 873601

Chrysanthemum
Collinwood Nurseries
Mottram St Andrew, Macclesfield,
Cheshire SK10 4QR
Tel: (01625) 582272

Halls of Heddon
(Office) West Heddon Nurseries,
Heddon-on-the-Wall, Newcastle-
upon-Tyne NE15 0JS
Tel: (01661) 852445

Rileys' Chrysanthemums
Alfreton Nurseries, Woolley Moor,
Alfreton, Derbyshire DE5 6FF
Tel: (01246) 590320

H Woolman Ltd
Grange Road, Dorridge, Solihull,
West Midlands B93 8QB
Tel: (01564) 776283

Clematis
John Beach (Nursery) Ltd
(Office) 9 Grange Road,
Wellesbourne, Warwickshire
CV35 9RL
Tel: (01926) 624173

Caddick's Clematis Nurseries
Lymm Road, Thelwall, Warrington,
Cheshire WA13 0UF
Tel: (01925) 757196

Fisk's Clematis Nursery
Westleton, Saxmundham, Suffolk
IP17 3AJ
Tel: (01728) 648263

Glyndley Nurseries
Hailsham Road, Pevensey, East
Sussex BN24 5BS
Tel: (01323) 766165
Mail order only

M Oviatt-Ham
(Office) Ely House, 15 Green Street,
Willingham, Cambridgeshire
CB4 5JA
Tel: (01954) 260481

Peveril Clematis Nursery
Christow, Exeter, Devon EX6 7NG
Tel: (01647) 52937
No mail order

Priorswood Clematis
Priorswood, Widbury Hill, Ware,
Hertfordshire SG12 7QH
Tel: (01920) 461543

Sherston Parva Nursery
21 Court Street, Sherston, Wiltshire
SN16 0LL
Tel: (01666) 840623
No mail order

Treasures of Tenbury Ltd
Burford House Gardens, Tenbury
Wells, Worcestershire WR15 8HQ
Tel: (01584) 810777

The Valley Clematis Nursery
Willingham Road, Hainton,
Lincolnshire LN3 6LN
Tel: (01507) 313398

Coleus
Halsway Nursery
Halsway, Nr Crowcombe, Taunton,
Somerset TA4 4BB
Tel: (019848) 243

Conifers
Barncroft Nurseries
Dunwood Lane, Longsdon, Nr Leek,
Stoke-on-Trent, Staffordshire
ST9 9QW
Tel: (01538) 384310
No mail order

Beechcroft Nursery
127 Reigate Road, Ewell, Surrey
KT17 3DE
Tel: (0181) 393 4265
No mail order

The Conifer Garden
1 Churchfield Road, Chalfont St
Peter, Buckinghamshire SL9 9EN
Tel: (01850) 786310
No mail order

Kenwith Nursery (Gordon Haddow)
The Old Rectory, Littleham,
Bideford, North Devon EX39 5HW
Tel: (01237) 473752

Lime Cross Nursery
Herstmonceux, Hailsman, East
Sussex BN27 4RS
Tel: (01323) 833229
No mail order

Lincluden Nursery
Bisley Green, Bisley, Woking, Surrey
GU24 9EN
Tel: (01483) 797005
No mail order

Norwich Heather & Conifer Centre
54a Yarmouth Road, Thorpe,
Norwich, Norfolk NR7 0HE
Tel: (01603) 39434

Conservatory Plants
Abbot's House Garden
10 High Street, Abbots Langley,
Hertfordshire WD5 0AR
Tel: (01923) 264946

B & H M Baker
Bourne Brook Nurseries, Greenstead
Green, Halstead, Essex CO9 1RJ
Tel: (01787) 472900
No mail order

Chessington Nurseries Ltd
Leatherhead Road, Chessington,
Surrey KT9 2NF
Tel: (01372) 725638

Deelish Garden Centre
Skibbereen, Co. Cork, Eire
Tel: (010353) (0) 2821374

Hardy Exotics
Gilly Lane, Whitecross, Penzance,
Cornwall TR20 8BZ
Tel: (01736) 740660

Long Man Gardens
Lewes Road, Wilmington, Polegate,
East Sussex BN26 5RS
Tel: (01323) 870816

Lower Severalls Herb Nursery
Crewkerne, Somerset TA18 7NX
Tel: (01460) 73234

Newington Nurseries
Bathway Farm, Chewton Mendip,
Somerset BA3 4LN
Tel: (01761) 241283

Pleasant View Nursery
Two Mile Oak, Nr Denbury, Newton
Abbot, Devon TQ12 6DG
Tel: (01803) 813388

Reads Nursery
Hales Hall, Loddon, Norfolk
NR14 6QW
Tel: (01508) 548395

Clive Simms
Woodhurst, Essendine, Stamford,
Lincolnshire PE9 4LQ
Tel: (01780) 55615

Sunbeam Nurseries
Bristol Road, Frampton Cotterell,
Avon BS17 2AU
Tel: (01454) 776926

Westdale Nurseries
Holt Road, Bradford-on-Avon,
Wiltshire BA15 1TS
Tel: (01225) 863258

Convallaria
Special Plants
Laurels Farm, Upper Wraxall,
Chippenham, Wiltshire SN14 7AG
Tel: (01225) 891686

Cordyline
The Torbay Palm Farm
St Marychurch Road, Coffinswell,
Nr Newton Abbot, Devon TQ12 4SE
Tel: (01803) 872800

Cornus
Royal Horticultural Society's Garden
Rosemoor, Great Torrington, Devon
EX38 8PH
Tel: (01805) 24067
No mail order

Cyclamen
Little Creek Nursery
39 Moor Road, Banwell, Weston-
super-Mare, Avon BS24 6EF
Tel: (01934) 823739

Tile Barn Nursery
Standen Street, Iden Green,
Benenden, Kent TN17 4LB
Tel: (01580) 240221

Daffodils
Ballydorn Bulb Farm
Killinchy, Newtownards, Co Down,
N Ireland BT23 6QB
Tel: (01238) 541250
Mail order only

Brian Duncan
Novelty & Exhibition Daffodils, 15
Ballynahatty Road, Omagh, Co.
Tyrone, Northern Ireland BT78 1PN
Tel: (01662) 242931

J Walkers Bulbs
Washway House Farm, Holbeach,
Spalding, Lincolnshire PE12 7PP
Tel: (01406) 426216
Mail order only

Dahlias
Tom Bebbington Dahlias
Lady Gate Nursery, 47 The Green,
Diseworth, Derbyshire DE7 2QN
Tel: (01332) 811565

Ian Butterfield
Butterfields Nursery, Harvest Hill,
Bourne End, Buckinghamshire
SL8 5JJ
Tel: (016285) 25455

Halls of Heddon
(Office) West Heddon Nurseries,
Heddon-on-the-Wall, Newcastle-
upon-Tyne NE15 0JS
Tel: (01661) 852445

Oscroft's Dahlias
'Woodside', Warwick Road,
Chadwick End, Nr Solihull, West
Midlands B93 0BP
Tel: (01564) 782450
and
Sprotbrough Road, Doncaster, South
Yorkshire DN5 8BE
Tel: (01302) 785026

Philip Tivey & Son
28 Wanlip Road, Syston,
Leicestershire LE7 8PA
Tel: (0116) 269 2968

Delphinium
Blackmore & Langdon
Pensford, Bristol, Avon BS18 4JL
Tel: (01275) 332300

Harrisons Delphiniums
Newbury Cottage, Play Hatch,
Reading, Berkshire RG4 9QN
Tel: (01734) 470810

Stuart Ogg
Hopton, Fletching Street, Mayfield,
East Sussex TN20 6TL
Tel: (01435) 873322

Woodfield Bros
Wood End, Clifford Chambers,
Stratford-upon-Avon, Warwickshire
CV37 8HR
Tel: (01789) 205618

Erodium
Charter House Nursery
2 Nunwood, Stepford Road,
Dumfries & Galloway DG2 0HX
Tel: (01387) 720363

Eucalyptus
Celyn Vale Nurseries
Carrog, Corwen, Clwyd LL21 9LD
Tel: (01490) 83671

Liscahane Nursery
Ardfert, Tralee, Co. Kerry, Eire
Tel: (010353) (0) 66 34222

Euphorbia
Farmhouse Plants
Royal Farm House, Elstead,
Godalming, Surrey GU8 6LA
Tel: (01252) 702460
No mail order. Phone for appt

Ferns
Fibrex Nurseries Ltd
Honeybourne Road, Pebworth, Nr
Stratford-upon-Avon, Warwickshire
CV37 8XT
Tel: (01789) 720788

J & D Marston
Culag, Green Lane, Nafferton,
Driffield, East Yorkshire YO25 0LF
Tel: (01377) 254487

Foliage
Dingle Plants and Gardens
Stamford Road, Pilsgate, Stamford,
Lincolnshire PE9 3HW
Tel: (01780) 740775

Stillingfleet Lodge Nurseries
Stillingfleet, York YO4 6HW
Tel: (01904) 728506

Fuchsia
B & H M Baker
Bourne Brook Nurseries, Greenstead
Green, Halstead, Essex CO9 1RJ
Tel: (01787) 472900
No mail order

R J Blythe
Potash Nursery, Cow Green,
Bacton, Stowmarket, Suffolk
IP14 4HJ
Tel: (01449) 781671

Goulding's Fuchsias
West View, Link Lane, Bentley,
Nr Ipswich, Suffolk
IP9 2DP
Tel: (01473) 310058

Jackson's Nurseries
Clifton Campville, Nr Tamworth,
Staffordshire B79 0AP
Tel: (01827) 373307

Laburnum Nurseries
c/o 6 Manor House Gardens, Main
Street, Humberstone Village,
Leicestershire
LE5 1AE
Tel: (0116) 276 6522

Little Brook Fuchsias
Ash Green Lane West, Ash Green,
Nr Aldershot, Hampshire
GU12 6HL
Tel: (01252) 29731
No mail order

C S Lockyer
Lansbury, 70 Henfield Road, Coalpit
Heath, Bristol, Avon
BS17 2UZ
Tel: (01454) 772219

Markham Grange Nurseries
Long Lands Lane, Brodsworth, Nr
Doncaster, South Yorkshire
DN5 7XB
Tel: (01302) 330430

Kathleen Muncaster Fuchsias
18 Field Lane, Morton,
Gainsborough, Lincolnshire
DN21 3BY
Tel: (01427) 612329

Oakleigh Nurseries
Monkwood, Alresford, Hampshire
SO24 0HB
Tel: (01962) 773344

Oldbury Nurseries
Brissenden Green, Bethersden, Kent
TN26 3BJ
Tel: (01233) 820416
No mail order

J V Porter
12 Hazel Grove, Southport,
Merseyside PR8 6AX
Tel: (01704) 533902

John Smith & Son
Hilltop Nurseries, Thornton,
Leicestershire LE67 1AN
Tel: (01530) 230331

Ward Fuchsias
5 Pollen Close, Sale, Cheshire
M33 3LP
Tel: (0161973) 6467

Galanthus
Broadleigh Gardens
Bishops Hull, Taunton, Somerset
TA4 1AE
Tel: (01823) 286231

Gentians
Angus Heathers
10 Guthrie Street, Letham, Forfar,
Tayside DD8 2PS
Tel: (01307) 818504
No mail order

Geraniums
Catforth Gardens
Roots Lane, Catforth, Preston,
Lancashire PR4 0JB
Tel: (01772) 690561
No mail order

Frances Mount Perennial Plants
1 Steps Farm, Polstead, Colchester,
Essex CO6 5AE
Tel: (01206) 262811

Hosford's Geraniums & Garden
Centre
Cappa, Enniskeane, Co. Cork, Eire
Tel: (00353) (1) 2339159

Brian Sulman
54 Kingsway, Mildenhall, Bury St
Edmunds, Suffolk IP28 7HR
Tel: (01638) 712297
Mail order only

The Vernon Geranium Nursery
Cuddington Way, Cheam, Sutton,
Surrey SM2 7JB
Tel: (0181) 393 7616

Grasses
Farmhouse Plants
Royal Farm House, Elstead,
Godalming, Surrey GU8 6LA
Tel: (01252) 702460
No mail order. Phone for appt

Hoecroft Plants
Severals Grange, Wood Norton,
Dereham, Norfolk NR20 5BL
Tel: (01362) 844206

Lesley Marshall
Islington Lodge Cottage, Tilney All
Saints, King's Lynn, Norfolk
PE34 4SF
Tel: (01553) 765103

Trevor Scott
Thorpe Park Cottage, Thorpe-le-
Soken, Essex CO16 0HN
Tel: (01255) 861308

Simply Plants
17 Dunhoe Brook, Eaton Socon,
Cambridgeshire PE19 3DW
Tel: (01480) 475312
No mail order

Heathers
Angus Heathers
10 Guthrie Street, Letham, Forfar,
Tayside DD8 2PS
Tel: (0130781) 504
No mail order

Barncroft Nurseries
Dunwood Lane, Longsdon, Nr Leek,
Stoke-on-Trent, Staffordshire
ST9 9QW
Tel: (01538) 384310
No mail order

Blairhoyle Nursery
Port of Menteith, Stirling, Central
FK8 3LF
Tel: (018775) 669
No mail order

Denbeigh Heather Nurseries
All Saints Road, Creeting St Mary,
Ipswich, Suffolk IP6 8PJ
Tel: (01449) 711220

Greenacres Nursery
Bringsty, Worcestershire WR6 5TA
Tel: (01885) 482206
No mail order

The Heather Garden
139 Swinston Hill Road, Dinnington,
Sheffield, South Yorkshire S31 7RY
Tel: (01909) 565510

Herb & Heather Centre
West Haddlesey, Nr Selby, North
Yorkshire YO8 8QA
Tel: (01757) 228279

Naked Cross Nurseries
Waterloo Road, Corfe Mullen,
Wimborne, Dorset
BH21 3SR
Tel: (01202) 693256
No mail order

Norwich Heather & Conifer Centre
54a Yarmouth Road, Thorpe,
Norwich, Norfolk NR7 0HE
Tel: (01603) 39434

Okell's Nurseries
Duddon Heath, Nr Tarporley,
Cheshire CW6 0EP
Tel: (01829) 741512

Otters' Court Heathers
Otters' Court, West Camel, Yeovil,
Somerset BA22 7QF
Tel: (01935) 850285

Pennyacre Nurseries
Station Road, Springfield, Fife
KY15 5RU
Tel: (01334) 55852

Ridgeway Heather Nursery
Park House, Plaish, Church Stretton,
Salop SY6 7HY
Tel: (01694) 771574
No mail order

Speyside Heather Garden Centre
Dulnain Bridge, Highland
PH26 3PA
Tel: (01479) 851359

Wingates
62A Chorley Road, Westhoughton,
Bolton, Lancashire BL5 3PL
Tel: (01942) 813357
No mail order

Hedera
Fibrex Nurseries Ltd
Honeybourne Road, Pebworth, Nr
Stratford-upon-Avon, Warwickshire
CV37 8XT
Tel: (01789) 720788
No mail order

Whitehouse Ivies
Brookhill, Halstead Road, Fordham,
Colchester, Essex CO6 3LW
Tel: (01206) 240077

Hellebores
Helen Ballard
Old Country, Mathon, Malvern,
Hereford & Worcester WR13 5PS
Tel: (01886 880) 215

Fibrex Nurseries Ltd
Honeybourne Road, Pebworth, Nr
Stratford-on-Avon, Warwickshire
CV37 8XT
Tel: (01789) 720788
No mail order

Little Creek Nursery
39 Moor Road, Banwell, Weston-
super-Mare, Avon BS24 6EF
Tel: (01934) 823739

Phedar Nursery
Bunkers Hill, Romiley, Stockport,
Cheshire SK6 3DS
Tel: (0161 430) 3772

Washfield Nursery
Horn's Road, Hawkhurst, Kent
TN18 4QU
Tel: (01580) 752522

Herbs
Arne Herbs
Limeburn Nurseries, Limeburn Hill,
Chew Magna, Avon BS18 8QW
Tel: (01275) 333399

Cherry Close Herbs
Meldreth Road, Whaddon, Nr
Royston, Hertfordshire SG8 5RN
Tel: (01223) 207418

Cheshire Herbs
Fourfields, Forest Road, Nr
Tarporley, Cheshire CW6 9ES
Tel: (01829) 760578

The Cottage Herbery
Mill House, Boraston Ford,
Boraston, Nr Tenbury Wells,
Hereford & Worcester WR15 8LZ
Tel: (01584) 781575

Daphne ffiske Herbs
Rosemary Cottage, Bramerton,
Norwich, Norfolk N14 7DW
Tel: (01508) 538187

Eden Plants
Eden, Rossinver, Co. Leitrim, Eire
Tel: (00353) (0) 7254122

Elly Hill Herbs
Elly Hill House, Barmpton,
Darlington, Co. Durham DL1 3JF
Tel: (01325) 464682

Elsworth Herbs
Avenue Farm Cottage, 31 Smith
Street, Elsworth, Cambridgeshire
CB3 8HY
Tel: (01954) 267414

Herb & Heather Centre
West Haddlesey, Nr Selby, North
Yorkshire YO8 8QA
Tel: (01757) 228279

The Herbary Plant Centre
89 Station Road, Herne Bay, Kent
CT6 5QQ
Tel: (01227) 362409
No mail order

The Herb Farm
Lea Meadow
Peppard Road, Sonning Common,
Reading, Berkshire RG4 9NJ
Tel: (01734) 724220

The Herb Garden
Plant Hunter's Nursery, Capel Ulo,
Pentre Berw, Gaerwen, Anglesey,
Gwynedd LL60 6LF
Tel: (01248) 421064

The Herb Nursery
Grange Farm, Main Street,
Thistleton, Rutland LE15 7RE
Tel: (01572) 767658

Hexham Herbs
Chesters Walled Garden, Chollerford,
Hexham, Northumberland NE46 4BQ
Tel: (01434) 681483
No mail order

Iden Croft Herbs
Frittenden Road, Staplehurst, Kent
TN12 0DH
Tel: (01580) 891432

Lisdoonan Herbs
98 Belfast Road, Saintfield, Co.
Down, Northern Ireland BT24 7HF
Tel: (01232) 813624
No mail order

Lower Severalls Herb Nursery
Crewkerne, Somerset TA18 7NX
Tel: (01460) 73234

Marle Place Plants and Gardens
Marle Place, Brenchley, Nr
Tonbridge, Kent TN12 7HS
Tel: (01892) 722304

Oak Cottage Herb Garden
Nesscliffe, Nr Shrewsbury, Salop
SY4 1DB
Tel: (0174381) 262

The Old Mill Herbary
Helland Bridge, Bodmin, Cornwall
PL30 4QR
Tel: (01208) 841206

Parkinson Herbs
Barras Moor Farm, Perran-ar-
Worthal, Truro, Cornwall TR3 7PE
Tel: (01872) 864380

Planthunters Nursery
Whittington, via Carnforth,
Lancashire LA6 2QF
Tel: (015395) 61126

Poyntzfield Herb Nursery
Nr Balblair, Black Isle, Dingwall,
Ross & Cromarty, Highland IV7 8LX
Tel: (01381) 610352 evs

Scotland Farmhouse Herbs
12 Hares Green, South Molton,
North Devon EX36 4SF
Tel: (01769) 573274

Wye Valley Herbs
The Nurtons, Tintern, Chepstow,
Gwent NP6 7NX
Tel: (01291) 689253

Hosta
Ann & Roger Bowden
Cleave House, Sticklepath,
Okehampton, Devon EX20 2NN
Tel: (01837) 840481

Goldbrook Plants
Hoxne, Eye, Suffolk IP21 5AN
Tel: (01379) 668770

Kittoch Plants
Kittoch Mill, Busby Road,
Carmunnock, Glasgow, Strathclyde
G76 9BJ
Tel: (0141) 644 4712

Mickfield Market Garden
The Poplars, Mickfield, Stowmarket,
Suffolk IP14 5LH
Tel: (01449) 711576

Iris
Croftway Nursery
Yapton Road, Barnham, Bognor
Regis, West Sussex PO22 0BH
Tel: (01243) 552121

Zephyrwude Irises
48 Blacker Lane, Crigglestone,
Wakefield, West Yorkshire
WF4 3EW
Tel: (01924) 252101
Mail order only

Ivy – *see* **Hedera**

Lavandula
Jersey Lavender Ltd
Rue du Pont Marquet, St Brelade,
Jersey, Channel Islands JE3 8DS
Tel: (01534) 42933
No mail order

Norfolk Lavender
Caley Mill, Heacham, King's Lynn,
Norfolk PE31 7JE
Tel: (01485) 570384

Lewisia
Ashwood Nurseries
Greensforge, Kingswinford, West
Midlands DY6 0AE
Tel: (01384) 401996

Liliaceae
Bloms Bulbs Ltd
Primrose Nursery, Park Lane,
Sharnbrook, Bedford MK44 1LW
Tel: (01234) 782424

Bullwood Nursery
54 Woodlands Road, Hockley, Essex
SS5 4PY
Tel: (01702) 203761

J Walkers Bulbs
Washway House Farm, Holbeach,
Spalding, Lincolnshire PE12 7PP
Tel: (01406) 426216
Mail order only

Lupins
Woodfield Bros
Wood End, Clifford Chambers,
Stratford-on-Avon, Warwickshire
CV37 8HR
Tel: (01789) 205618

Magnolia
Bodnant Garden Nursery Ltd
Tal-y-Cafn, Colwyn Bay, North
Wales LL28 5RE
Tel: (01492) 650460

Meconopsis
Craigieburn Classic Plants
Craigieburn House, by Moffat,
Dumfriesshire DG10 9LF
Tel: (01683) 21250

Lingholm Gardens
Lingholm, Keswick, Cumbria
CA12 5UA
Tel: (017687) 72003
No mail order

Michaelmas Daisy – *see* **Aster**

Narcissus
Bloms Bulbs Ltd
Primrose Nursery, Park Lane,
Sharnbrook, Bedford MK44 1LW
Tel: (01234) 782424

Carncairn Daffodils
Broughshane, Ballymena, Co.
Antrim, Northern Ireland BT43 7HF
Tel: (01266) 861216

Brian Duncan
Novelty & Exhibition Daffodils
15 Ballynahatty Road, Omagh, Co.
Tyrone, Northern Ireland BT78 1PN
Tel: (01662) 242931

Evelix Daffodils
Aird Asaig, Evelix, Dornoch,
Sutherland IV25 3NG
Tel: (01862) 810715

Orchids
Burnham Nurseries
Forches Cross, Newton Abbot,
Devon TQ12 6PZ
Tel: (01626) 52233

Greenaway Orchids
Rookery Farm, Puxton, Nr Weston-
super-Mare, Avon BS24 6TL
Tel: (01934) 820448

Mansell & Hatcher Ltd
Cragg Wood Nurseries, Woodlands
Drive, Rawdon, Leeds LS19 6LQ
Tel: (0113) 250 2016

McBeans Orchids Ltd
Cooksbridge, Lewes, East Sussex
BN8 4PR
Tel: (01273) 400228

Orchid Sundries and Hardy
Orchids Ltd
New Gate Farm, Scotchey Lane,
Stour Provost, Gillingham, Dorset
SP8 5LT
Tel: (01747) 838368

Westwood Nursery
65 Yorkland Avenue, Welling, Kent
DA16 2LE
Tel: (0181) 301 0886
Mail order only

Woodstock Orchids
Woodstock House, 50 Pound Hill,
Great Brickhill, Buckinghamshire
MK17 9AS
Tel: (01525 261) 352

Palms
The Palm Centre
563 Upper Richmond Road West,
London SW14 7ED
Tel: (0181) 876 3223

The Palm Farm
Thornton Hall Gardens, Station
Road, Thornton Curtis, Nr Ulceby,
Humberside DN39 6XF
Tel: (01469) 531232

Passiflora
Greenholm Nurseries
(Office) Lampley Road, Kingston
Seymour, Clevedon, Avon BS21 6XS
Tel: (01934) 833350

Pelargonium
Denmead Geranium Nurseries
Hambledon Road, Denmead,
Waterlooville, Hampshire PO7 6PS
Tel: (01705) 240081

Fibrex Nurseries Ltd
Honeybourne Road, Pebworth, Nr
Stratford-upon-Avon, Warwickshire
CV37 8XT
Tel: (01789) 720788
No mail order

Jarvis Brook Geranium Nurseries
Tubwell Lane, Jarvis Brook,
Crowborough, Sussex TN6 3RH
Tel: (01892) 662329

Derek Lloyd Dean
8 Lynwood Close, South Harrow,
Middlesex HA2 9PR
Tel: (0181) 864 0899
Mail order only

Oakleigh Nurseries
Monkwood, Alresford, Hampshire
SO24 0HB *Tel*: (01962) 773344

The Vernon Geranium Nursery
Cuddington Way, Cheam, Sutton,
Surrey SM2 7JB
Tel: (0181) 393 7616

A D & N Wheeler
Pye Court, Willoughby, Rugby,
Warwickshire CV23 8BZ
Tel: (01788) 890341

Phlox
Blackmore & Langdon Ltd
Pensford, Bristol, Avon BS18 4JL
Tel: (01275) 332300

Pieris
The High Garden
Court Wood, Newton Ferrers, South
Devon PL8 1BW
Tel: (01752) 872528

Pinks
Allwood Bros
Mill Nursery, Hassocks, West Sussex
BN6 9NB
Tel: (01273) 844229

Hayward's Carnations
The Chace Gardens, Stakes Road,
Purbrook, Waterlooville, Hampshire
PO7 5PL
Tel: (01705) 263047

Kingstone Cottage Plants
Weston-under-Penyard, Ross-on-
Wye, Herefordshire HR9 7NX
Tel: (01989) 565267

Mill Cottage Plants
The Mill, Henley Lane, Wookey,
Somerset BA5 1AP
Tel: (01749) 676966

Mills' Farm Plants & Gardens
Norwich Road, Mendlesham, Suffolk
IP14 5NQ
Tel: (01449) 766425

Pinks & Carnations
22 Chetwyn Avenue, Bromley Cross,
Nr Bolton, Lancashire BL7 9BN
Tel: (01204) 306273

Southview Nurseries
Chequers Lane, Eversley Cross,
Basingstoke, Hampshire RG27 0NT
Tel: (01734) 732206

Three Counties Nurseries
Marshwood, Bridport, Dorset
DT6 5QJ
Tel: (01297) 678257
Mail order only

Pleiones
Ian Butterfield
Butterfields Nursery, Harvest Hill,
Bourne End, Buckinghamshire
SL8 5JJ
Tel: (016285) 25455

Westwood Nursery
65 Yorkland Avenue, Welling, Kent
DA16 2LE
Tel: (0181) 301 0886
Mail order only

Primula
Abriachan Nurseries
Loch Ness Side, Inverness IV3 6LA
Tel: (01463) 861232

Cottage Garden Plants Old & New
Cox Cottage, Lower Street, East
Morden, Wareham, Dorset
BH20 7DL
Tel: (01929) 459496

Craigieburn Classic Plants
Craigieburn House, by Moffat,
Dumfriesshire DG10 9LF
Tel: (01683) 21250

Field House Nurseries
Leake Road, Gotham, Nottingham
NG11 0JN
Tel: (0115) 983 0278

Lingholm Gardens
Lingholm, Keswick, Cumbria
CA12 5UA
Tel: (017687) 72003
No mail order

Mrs Ann Lunn
The Fens, Old Mill Road, Langham,
Colchester, Essex CO4 5NU
Tel: (01206) 272259

Pulmonaria
Stillingfleet Lodge Nurseries
Stillingfleet, Yorkshire YO4 6HW
Tel: (01904) 728506

Rhododendrons
Ballalheannagh Gardens
Glen Roy, Lonan, Isle of Man
Tel: (01624) 861875

Bodnant Garden Nursery Ltd
Tal-y-Cafn, Colwyn Bay, Clwyd
LL28 5RE
Tel: (01492) 650460

Coghurst Nursery
Ivy House Lane, Near Three Oaks,
Hastings, East Sussex TN35 4NP
Tel: (01424) 425371

Exbury Enterprises Ltd
Exbury, Near Southampton,
Hampshire SO4 1AZ
Tel: (01703) 898625

Glendoick Gardens Ltd
Glencarse, Perth PH2 7NS
Tel: (01738) 860205

The High Garden
Court Wood, Newton Ferrers, South
Devon PL8 1BW
Tel: (01752) 872528

Hydon Nurseries Ltd
Clock Barn Lane, Hydon Heath,
Godalming, Surrey GU8 4AZ
Tel: (01483) 860252

Knaphill & Slocock Nurseries
Barrs Lane, Knaphill, Woking,
Surrey GU21 2JW
Tel: (01483) 481212

Lea Rhodondendron Gardens Ltd
Lea, Matlock, Derbyshire DE4 5GH
Tel: (01629 534) 380

Leonardslee Gardens
1 Mill Lane, Lower Beeding, West
Sussex RH13 6PX
Tel: (01403) 891412

Millais Nurseries
Crosswater Lane, Churt, Farnham,
Surrey GU10 2JN
Tel: (01252) 792698

F Morrey & Sons
Forest Nursery, Kelsall, Tarporley,
Cheshire CW6 0SW
Tel: (01829) 751342
No mail order

Pound Lane Nurseries
Ampfield, Nr Romsey, Hampshire
SO51 9BL
Tel: (01703) 739685

G Reuthe Ltd
Crown Point Nursery, Sevenoaks
Road, Ightham, Nr Sevenoaks, Kent
TN15 0HB
Tel: (01732) 810694

Trewithen Nurseries
Grampound Road, Truro, Cornwall
TR2 4DD
Tel: (01726) 882764

Wall Cottage Nursery
Lockengate, Bugle, St Austell,
Cornwall PL26 8RU
Tel: (01208) 831259

Whitehills Nurseries
Newton Stewart, Wigtownshire,
Scotland DG8 6SL
Tel: (01671) 402049

Roses
Abbey Rose Gardens
Burnham, Buckinghamshire SL1 8NJ
Tel: (01628) 603000

Acton Beauchamp Roses
Nr Worcester WR6 5AE
Tel: (01531) 640433

Anderson's Rose Nurseries
Friarsfield Road, Cults, Aberdeen
AB1 9QT
Tel: (01224) 868881

Apuldram Roses
Apuldram Lane, Dell Quay,
Chichester, West Sussex PO20 7EF
Tel: (01243) 785769

David Austin Roses
Bowling Green Lane, Albrighton,
Wolverhampton, West Midlands
WV7 3HB
Tel: (01902) 373931

Battersby Roses
Pear Tree Cottage, Old Battersby,
Great Ayton, Cleveland TS9 6LU
Tel: (01642) 723402

Peter Beales Roses
London Road, Attleborough,
Norfolk NR17 1AY
Tel: (01953) 454707

Walter Bentley & Sons Ltd
The Nurseries, Loughborough Road,
Wanlip, Leicester LE7 8PN
Tel: (0116) 267 3702

Bowood Garden Centre
Bowood Estate, Calne, Wiltshire
SN11 0LZ
Tel: (01249) 816828
No mail order

Brannel Farm Roses
Brannel Farm, St Stephens, Coombe,
St Austell, Cornwall PL25 7LG
Tel: (01726) 882468

Brokenbacks Roses
Broxhill Road, Havering-atte-Bower,
Romford, Essex RM4 1QH
Tel: (01708) 377744

Burrows Roses
Meadow Croft, Spondon Road, Dale
Abbey, Derbyshire DE7 4PQ
Tel: (01332) 668289
Mail order only

Cants of Colchester Ltd
Nayland Road, Mile End, Colchester
CO4 5EB
Tel: (01206) 844008

John Charles Nurseries Ltd
64 Derby Road, Risley, Derbyshire
DE7 3SU
Tel: (01159) 396024

Paul Chessum
21 High Street, Great Barford,
Bedford MK44 3JH
Tel: (0176 727) 559

Chichester Roses Ltd
Chalder Farm, Sidlesham,
Chichester, West Sussex PO20 7RN
Tel: (01243) 641219

Cley Nurseries
Holt Road, Cley-Next-The-Sea, Holt,
Norfolk NR25 7TX
Tel: (01263) 740892

James Cocker & Sons
Whitemyres, Lang Stracht, Aberdeen
AB9 2XH
Tel: (01224) 313261

W H Collin & Sons (Roses) Ltd
The Manor House, Knossington,
Oakham, Leicestershire LE15 8LX
Tel: (01664) 454323

Cottage Garden Roses
Woodlands House, Stretton, Nr
Stafford ST19 9LG
Tel: (01785) 840217

D & W Croll Ltd
Dalhousie Nurseries, Broughty Ferry,
Dundee DD5 2PP
Tel: (01382) 78921

Peter Delves Rose Grower
Woolhouse Nursery, Redford,
Midhurst, Sussex GU29 0QH
Tel: (01428) 76257

Dickson Nurseries Ltd
Milecross Road, Newtownards, Co.
Down, Northern Ireland BT23 4SS
Tel: (01247) 812206

Doubleday & Co
Walnut Hill, Surlingham, Norwich,
Norfolk NR14 7DQ
Tel: (015088) 8097

English Cottage Roses Ltd
The Nurseries, Stapleford Lane,
Toton, Beeston, Nottingham
NG9 5FD
Tel: (0115) 949 1100

Leo Esser & Son
Grange Farm Nursery, Barton Road
(B1441), Wisbech, Cambridgeshire
PE13 4TH
Tel: (01945) 582262

Fryer's Nurseries Ltd
Manchester Road, Knutsford,
Cheshire WA16 0SX
Tel: (01565) 755455

Gandy's Roses Ltd
North Kilworth, Nr Lutterworth,
Leicestershire LE17 6HZ
Tel: (01858) 880398

Godly's Roses
Dunstable Road, Redbourn, St
Albans, Hertfordshire AL3 7PS
Tel: (01582) 792255

Greenhead Roses
Greenhead Nursery, Old Greenock
Road, Inchinnan, Renfrew,
Strathclyde PA4 9PH
Tel: (0141 812) 0121

Hadspen Garden & Nursery
Hadspen House, Castle Cary,
Somerset BA7 7NG
Tel: (01749) 813707
No mail order

Handley Rose Nurseries
Lightwood Road, Marsh Lane, Nr
Sheffield S31 9RG
Tel: (01246) 432921

R Harkness & Co Ltd
Cambridge Road, Hitchin,
Hertfordshire SG4 0JT
Tel: (01462) 420402

F Haynes & Partners Ltd
(Office) 56 Gordon Street, Kettering,
Northamptonshire NN16 0RX
Tel: (01536) 519836

Highfield Nurseries
Whitminster, Gloucestershire
GL2 7PL
Tel: (01452) 740266

Hill Park Nurseries
Kingston bypass, Surbiton, Surrey
KT6 5HN
Tel: (0181) 398 0022

Hockenhull Roses
28 Hallfields Road, Tarvin, Chester
CH3 8LL
Tel: (01829) 40045

Hunts Court Garden & Nursery
North Nibley, Dursley,
Gloucestershire GL11 8DZ
Tel: (01453) 547440

C & K Jones (Rose Specialists)
Golden Fields Nursery, Barrow
Lane, Tarvin, Cheshire CH3 8JF
Tel: (01829) 740663

Just Roses
Beales Lane, Northiam, Nr Rye, East
Sussex TN31 6QY
Tel: (01797) 252355

Layham Nurseries & Garden Centre
Lower Road, Staple, Nr Canterbury,
Kent CT3 1LH
Tel: (01304) 813267

LeGrice Roses
Norwich Road, North Walsham,
Norfolk NR28 0DR
Tel: (01692) 402591

Mattock's Roses
The Rose Nurseries, Nuneham
Courtenay, Oxfordshire OX44 9PY
Tel: (01865) 343265

Nottcutts Nurseries Ltd
Woodbridge, Suffolk IP12 4AF
Tel: (01394) 383344

O K Roses
Ferriby High Road, North Ferriby,
North Humberside HU14 3LA
Tel: (01482) 634237

A J Palmer & Son
Denham Court Nursery, Denham
Court Drive, Denham, Uxbridge,
Middlesex UB9 5BQ
Tel: (01895) 832035

Pennine Nurseries
Shelley, Huddersfield HD8 8LG
Tel: (01484) 605511

J B Philp & Son Ltd
Elm Park Garden Centre, Pamber
End, Basingstoke, Hampshire
RG26 5QW
Tel: (01256) 850587

Pocock's Nurseries
Dandys Ford Lane, Sherfield English,
Romsey, Hampshire SO51 6FT
Tel: (01794) 23514

Rearsby Roses
Melton Road, Rearsby, Leicestershire
LE7 8YP
Tel: (0116) 260 1211

Redhill Roses
Thurlby Farm, Thurlby Lane,
Stanton-on-the-Wolds,
Nottinghamshire NG12 5PL
Tel: (016077) 4359

R V Roger Ltd
The Nurseries, Pickering, North
Yorkshire YO18 7HG
Tel: (02751) 72226

Roses & Shrubs Garden Centre
Newport Road, Albrighton, Nr
Wolverhampton, West Midlands
WV7 3EE
Tel: (01902) 374200/373233

Rosslow Roses
North Street Farm, North Street,
Hellingly, Hailsham, East Sussex
BN27 4DZ
Tel: (01323) 440888

Andrew de Ruiter (Rose Specialist)
9 Ingersley Road, Bollington,
Cheshire SK10 5RE
Tel: (01625) 574389
Mail order only

Rumwood Nurseries
Langley, Maidstone, Kent
ME17 3ND
Tel: (01622) 861477

John Sanday (Roses) Ltd
Over Lane, Almondsbury, Bristol,
Avon BS12 4DA
Tel: (01454) 612195

Shaw Rose Trees
2 Hollowgate Hill, Willoughton,
Gainsborough, Lincolnshire
DN21 5SF
Tel: (01427) 668230

Slacks Roses
White Post Rose Gardens,
Farnsfield, Newark, Nottinghamshire
NG22 8HZ
Tel: (01623) 882773

St Bridget Nurseries Ltd
Old Rydon Lane, Exeter, Devon
EX2 7JY
Tel: (01392) 873672

J A Steele & Sons Ltd
The Market Place, Regent Street,
Newtownards, County Down,
Northern Ireland
Tel: (01247) 818378

Henry Street
Swallowfield Road Nursery,
Arborfield, Reading, Berkshire
RG2 9JY
Tel: (01734) 761223

Stydd Nursery
Stonygate Lane, Ribchester, Nr
Preston, Lancashire PR3 3YN
Tel: (01254) 878797

Timmermans Roses
Lowdham Lane, Woodborough,
Nottinghamshire NG14 6DN
Tel: (0115) 966 3193

John Train & Sons
Benston, Station Road, Tarbolton,
Ayrshire KA5 5NT
Tel: (01292) 541336

L W Van Geest (Farms) Ltd
Wool Hall Farm, Wykeham,
Spalding, Lincolnshire PE12 6HW
Tel: (01775) 725041

Warley Rose Gardens Ltd
Warley Street, Great Warley,
Brentwood, Essex CM13 3JH
Tel: (01277) 221966

F & G F Webb
Orchard Nurseries, 90 Peters Point,
Sutton Bridge, Spalding, Lincolnshire
PE12 9UX
Tel: (01406) 350098

Whartons Nurseries (Harleston) Ltd
Station Road, Harleston, Norfolk
IP20 9EY
Tel: (01379) 852157

Wheatcroft Ltd
Edwalton, Nottinghamshire
NG12 4DE
Tel: (0115) 921 6061

Trevor White Old-Fashioned Roses
Bennetts Brier, The Street, Felthorpe,
Norwich, Norfolk NR10 4AB
Tel: (01603) 755135
Mail order only

Wisbech Plant Co. Ltd
Walton Road, Wisbech,
Cambridgeshire PE13 3EF
Tel: (01945) 582588

Wyevale Nurseries Ltd
Kings Acre, Hereford, Hereford &
Worcester HR4 7AY
Tel: (01432) 352255

Saintpaulia
African Violet Centre
Terrington St Clement, King's Lynn,
Norfolk PE34 4PL
Tel: (01553) 828374

Salvia
Craigieburn Classic Plants
Craigieburn House, by Moffat,
Dumfriesshire DG10 9LF
Tel: (01683) 21250

Saxifraga
Waterperry Gardens Ltd
Waterperry, Nr Wheatley,
Oxfordshire OX33 1JZ
Tel: (01844) 339226
No mail order

Sedum
R Stephenson
55 Beverley Drive, Choppington,
Northumberland NE62 5YA
Tel: (01670) 817901

Sempervivum
Mary & Peter Mitchell
11 Wingle Tye Road, Burgess Hill,
West Sussex RH15 9HR
Tel: (01444) 236848

Alan C Smith
127 Leaves Green Road, Keston,
Kent BR2 6DG
Tel: (01959) 572531

H & S Wills
2 St Brannocks Park Road,
Ilfracombe, Devon EX34 8HU
Tel: (01271) 863949
Mail order only

Streptocarpus
Efenechtyd Nurseries
Llanelidan, Ruthin, Clwyd
LL15 2LG
Tel: (0197 888) 677

Succulents – *see* **Cacti**

Thymus
Hexham Herbs
Chesters Walled Garden,
Chollerford, Hexham,
Northumberland NE46 4BQ
Tel: (01434) 681483

Tillandsia
Plantcraft
(Office) 35 Rutland Way, Orpington,
Kent BR5 4DY
Tel: (01689) 830157

The Tropical Rain Forest
66 Castlegrove Avenue, Leeds, West
Yorkshire LS6 4BS
Tel: (0113) 278 9810

Vesutor Ltd
The Bromeliad Nursery,
Marringdean Road, Billingshurst,
West Sussex RH14 9EH
Tel: (01403) 784028

Topiary
Langley Boxwood Nursery
Langley Court, Rake, Liss,
Hampshire GU33 7JL
Tel: (01730) 894467

Tropaeolum
Plantworld
Burnham Road, South Woodham
Ferrers, Chelmsford, Essex CM3 5QP
Tel: (01245) 320482

Tulips
Bloms Bulbs Ltd
Primrose Nursery, Park Lane,
Sharnbrook, Bedford MK44 1LW
Tel: (01234) 782424

Vines
Greenland Nurseries
11 Long Lane, Clayton West,
Huddersfield, Yorkshire HD8 9PR
Tel: (01484) 865964
Mail order only

St Anne's Vineyard
Wain House, Oxenhall, Newent,
Gloucestershire GL18 1RW
Tel: (01989) 720313

Yearlstone Vineyard
Chilverton, Coldridge, Crediton,
Devon EX17 6BH
Tel: (01363) 83302

Viola
Bouts Cottage Nurseries
Bouts Lane, Inkberrow,
Worcestershire WR7 4HP
Tel: (01386) 792923
Mail order only

R G M Cawthorne
Lower Daltons Nursery, Swanley
Village, Swanley, Kent BR8 7NU
Mail order only. Written appt only

Cottage Garden Plants Old & New
Cox Cottage, Lower Street, East
Morden, Wareham, Dorset
BH20 7DL
Tel: (01929) 459496

C W Groves & Son
West Bay Road, Bridport, Dorset
DT6 4BA
Tel: (01308) 422654

Hazeldene Nursery
Dean Street, East Farleigh,
Maidstone, Kent ME15 0PS
Tel: (01622) 726248

Elizabeth MacGregor
Ellenbank, Tongland Road,
Kirkcudbright, Dumfries & Galloway
DG6 4UU
Tel: (01557) 330620

Elizabeth Smith
Downside, Bowling Green,
Constantine, Falmouth, Cornwall
TR11 5AP
Tel: (01326) 40787
Mail order only

Violet
Cottage Garden Plants Old & New
Cox Cottage, Lower Street, East
Morden, Wareham, Dorset
BH20 7DL
Tel: (01929) 459496

Crankan Nurseries
New Mill, Penzance, Cornwall
TR20 8UT
Tel: (01736) 62897

Hazeldene Nursery
Dean Street, East Farleigh,
Maidstone, Kent ME15 0PS
Tel: (01622) 726248

Elizabeth MacGregor
Ellenbank, Tongland Road,
Kirkcudbright, Dumfries & Galloway
DG6 4UU
Tel: (01557) 330620

Elizabeth Smith
Downside, Bowling Green,
Constantine, Falmouth, Cornwall
TR11 5AP
Tel: (01326) 40787
Mail order only

Robinson's of Whaley Bridge
20 Vaughan Road, Whaley Bridge,
Stockport, Cheshire SK12 7JT
Tel: (01663) 732991
Mail order only

Wildflowers
Arne Herbs
Limeburn Nurseries, Limeburn Hill,
Chew Magna, Avon BS18 8QW
Tel: (01275) 333399

Candlesby Herbs
Cross Keys Cottage, Candlesby,
Spilsby, Lincolnshire PE23 5SF
Tel: (01754) 890211

Hexham Herbs
Chesters Walled Garden,
Chollerford, Hexham,
Northumberland NE46 4BQ
Tel: (01434) 681483

Kingsfield Conservation Nursery
Broadenham Lane, Winsham, Chard,
Somerset TA20 4JF
Tel: (01460) 30070

Landlife Wildflowers Ltd
The Old Police Station, Lark Lane,
Liverpool L17 8UU
Tel: (0161) 794 9314

Marle Place Plants and Gardens
Marle Place, Brenchley, Nr
Tonbridge, Kent TN12 7HS
Tel: (0189272) 2304

Salley Gardens
Flat 3, 3 Millicent Road, West
Bridgford, Nottingham NG2 7LD
Tel: (0115) 982 1366 (evngs)
Open by appt

The Wildflower Centre
Church Farm, Sisland, Loddon,
Norwich, Norfolk NR14 6EF
Tel: (01508) 20235

The Wildlife Gardening Centre
Witney Road, Kingston Bagpuize,
Abingdon, Oxford OX13 5AN
Tel: (01865) 821660

MISCELLANEOUS

Australasian Plants
Tim Ingram
Copton Ash, 105 Ashford Road,
Faversham, Kent ME13 8XW
Tel: (01795) 535919

China & South Korea
Mallet Court Nursery
Curry Mallet, Taunton, Somerset
TA3 6SY
Tel: (01823) 480748

**New Zealand & Falkland Island
Plants**
County Park Nursery
Essex Gardens, Hornchurch, Essex
RM11 3BU
Tel: (01708) 445205
No mail order

South American Plants
Greenway Gardens
Churston Ferrers, Brixham, Devon
TQ5 0ES
Tel: (01803) 842382

FRUIT

Soft Fruit
Chris Bowers & Sons
Whispering Trees Nurseries,
Wimbotsham, Norfolk PE34 8QB
Tel: (01366) 388752

Deacon's Nursery
Moor View, Godshill, Isle of Wight
PO38 3HW
Tel: (01983) 840750

Family Trees
PO Box 3, Botley, Hampshire
SO3 2EA
Tel: (01329) 834812

Greenland Nurseries
11 Long Lane, Clayton West,
Huddersfield, Yorkshire HD8 9PR
Tel: (01484) 865964
Mail order only

Ken Muir
Honeypot Farm, Rectory Road,
Weeley Heath, Clacton on Sea, Essex
CO16 9BJ
Tel: (01255) 830181

Citrus & Figs
Reads Nursery
Hales Hall, Loddon, Norfolk
NR14 6QW
Tel: (01508) 548395

Fruit Trees
Chris Bowers & Sons
Whispering Trees Nurseries,
Wimbotsham, Norfolk PE34 8QB
Tel: (01366) 388752

Deacon's Nursery
Moor View, Godshill, Isle of Wight
PO38 3HW
Tel: (01983) 840750

The Fruit Garden
Mulberry Farm, Woodnesborough,
Sandwich, Kent CT13 0PT
Tel: (01304) 813454

Highfield Nurseries
Whitminster, Gloucestershire
GL2 7PL
Tel: (01452) 740266

Mail Order: Highfield Plant &
Garden Centre, Bristol Road,
Whitminster, Gloucestershire
GL2 7PB
Tel: (01452) 741444

Paul Jasper (Trees & Roses)
The Lighthouse, Bridge Street,
Leominster, Hereford & Worcester
HR6 8DU
Tel: (01568) 611540
Mail order only

Keepers Nursery
446 Wateringbury Road, East
Malling, Kent ME19 6JJ
Tel: (01622) 813008

Ken Muir
Honeypot Farm, Rectory Road,
Weeley Heath, Clacton on Sea, Essex
CO16 9BJ
Tel: (01255) 830181

New Trees Nurseries
2 Nunnery Road, Canterbury, Kent
CT1 3LS
Tel: (01227) 761209

J Tweedie Fruit Trees
Maryfield Road Nursery, Maryfield,
Nr Terregles, Dumfries DG2 9TH
Tel: (01387) 720880

VEGETABLES

Asparagus
Michael Bennett
Long Compton, Shipston-on-Stour,
Warwickshire CV36 5JN
Tel: (0160 884) 676
Mail order only

Trevor Sore
Marward House, Stock Corner
Farm, Bury St Edmunds, Suffolk
IP28 8DW
Tel: (01638) 712779

Globe Artichoke
Michael Bennett
Long Compton, Shipston-on-Stour,
Warwickshire CV36 5JN
Tel: (0160 884) 676
Mail order only

Sea Kale
AR Paske
The South Lodge, Gazeley Road,
Kentford, Newmarket, Suffolk CB8
7QA
Tel: (01638) 750613

Seed Specialists

You'll probably be quite surprised at the number of seedsmen there actually are. The big companies like Suttons and Unwins are the people who advertise so they're known to most of us, and it's from them that we can get most of our requirements. However, if you want something more unusual there are several specialist firms who may be able to help. Do note that some, just like the specialized nurseries, make a small charge for their catalogue.

Allwoods Bros
Hassocks, West Sussex BN6 9NB
Tel: (01273) 844229
Dianthus

Alpine Garden Society
AGS Centre, Avon Bank, Pershore,
Worcestershire WR10 3JP
Tel: (01386) 554790

Ashwood Nurseries
Greensforge, Kingswinford, West
Midlands DY6 0AE
Tel: (01384) 401996
Lewisia, cyclamen, auricula

B & T World Seeds
Whitnell House, Fiddington,
Bridgwater, Somerset TA5 1JE
Tel: (01278) 733209
Ornamentals and exotics

Bakker Holland
PO Box 111, Spalding,
Lincolnshire PE12 6EL
Tel: (01775) 711411
General list

John Barber (Hertford) Ltd
Old Cross Wharf, Hertford
SG14 1RB
Tel: (01992) 582304
General list

J W Boyce
40 Fordham, Ely, Cambridgeshire
CB7 5JU
Tel: (01638) 721158
Vegetables and flowers

S & N Brackley
117 Winslow Road, Wingrave,
Aylesbury, Buckinghamshire
HP22 4QB
Tel: (01296) 681384
Sweet peas and vegetables

D T Brown & Co Ltd
Station Road, Poulton-le-Fylde,
Blackpool FY6 7HX
Tel: (01253) 882371
General list

Bullwood Nursery
54 Woodlands Road, Hockley, Essex
SS5 4PY
Tel: (01702) 203761
Lilies & rare perennials

Carters Seeds Ltd
Hele Road, Torquay, Devon
TQ2 7QJ
Tel: (01803) 616156
General list

John Chambers
15 Westleigh Road, Barton Seagrave,
Kettering, Northamptonshire
NN15 5AJ
Tel: (01933) 652562
Wildflowers

Chase Organics (GB) Ltd
Coombelands House, Coombelands
Lane, Addlestone, Surrey KT15 1HY
Tel: (01932) 820958
General list – organic

Cheshire Herbs
Fourfields, Forest Road, Nr
Tarporley, Cheshire CW6 9ES
Tel: (01829) 760578
Herbs

Chiltern Seeds
Bortree Stile, Ulverston, Cumbria
LA12 7PB
Tel: (01229) 581137
General list

Country Gardens
69–71 Mainstreet, East Leake,
Leicestershire LE12 6PF
Tel: (01509) 852905
*Unusual varieties of vegetables and
flowers*

Cowcombe Farm Herbs
Gipsy Lane, Chalford, Stroud,
Gloucestershire GL6 8HP
Tel: (01285) 760544
Herbs & wildflowers

Craven's Nursery
1 Foulds Terrace, Bingley, West
Yorkshire BD16 4LZ
Tel: (01274) 561412
*Show auriculas, primulas, pinks &
alpines*

B & D Davies
2 Wirral View, Connah's Quay,
Deeside, Clwyd CH5 4TE
Tel: (01244) 818833
Conifers and shrubs

Dig and Delve Organics
Fen Road, Blo' Norton, Diss,
Norfolk IP22 2JH
Tel: (01379) 898377

Samuel Dobie & Sons Ltd
Broomhill Way, Torquay, Devon
TQ2 7QW
Tel: (01803) 616281
General list

Jack Drake
Inshriach Alpine Nursery, Aviemore,
Invernesshire PH22 1QS
Tel: (01540 651) 287
Rare alpines

Emorsgate Seed
Terrington Court, Terrington St
Clement, Kings Lynn, Norfolk
PE34 4NT
Tel: (01553) 829028
Wildflowers & grasses

Equatorial Plants
7 Gray Lane, Barnard Castle,
County Durham DL12 8PD
Tel : (01833) 690519
Orchid seed and seedlings

Field House Nurseries
Leake Road, Gotham,
Nottinghamshire NG11 0JN
Tel: (0115) 983 0278
Primulas & alpines

Mr Fothergill's Seeds Ltd
Gazeley Road, Kentford,
Newmarket, Suffolk CB8 7QB
Tel: (01638) 751161
General list

Glenhirst Cactus Nursery
Station Road, Swineshead, Nr
Boston, Lincolnshire PE20 3NX
Tel: (01205) 820314
Cacti and succulents

Peter Grayson
34 Glenthorne Close, Brampton,
Chesterfield, Derbyshire S40 3AR
Tel: (01246) 278503
Sweet peas

Greenholm Nursery
Lampley Road, Kingston Seymour,
Clevedon, Avon BS21 6XS
Tel: (01934) 833350
Passiflora

Harrisons Delphiniums
Newbury Cottage, Play Hatch,
Reading, Berkshire RG4 9QN
Tel: (01734) 470810
Delphiniums

James Henderson & Sons
Kingholm Quay, Dumfries DG1 4SU
Tel: (01387) 52234
Scottish seed potatoes

Holden Clough Nursery
Holden, Bolton-by-Bowland,
Clitheroe, Lancashire BB7 4PF
Tel: (01200) 447615
Alpines

Holly Gate Cactus Nursery
Billingshurst Road, Ashington, West
Sussex RH20 3BA
Tel: (01903) 892930
Cacti and succulents

W W Johnson & Son Ltd
London Road, Boston, Lincolnshire
PE21 8AD
Tel: (01205) 365051
General list

Kings Crown Quality Seeds
Monks Farm, Pantlings Lane,
Coggeshall Road, Kelvedon,
Colchester, Essex CO5 9PG
Tel: (01376) 570000
General list

Landlife Wildflowers Ltd
The Old Police Station, Lark Lane,
Liverpool L17 8UU
Tel: (0161) 794 9314
Native herbaceous plants

Mackay's Garden Centre
Castlepark Road, Sandycove, Co.
Dublin, Eire
Tel: (00353) 1 2807385
General list

S E Marshall & Co Ltd
Regal Road, Wisbech,
Cambridgeshire PE13 2RF
Tel: (01945) 583407
General List

J E Martin
4 Church Street, Market
Harborough, Leicestershire
LE16 7AA
Tel: (01858) 462751
Scottish & Dutch seed potatoes

S M McArd (Seeds)
39 West Road, Pointon, Sleaford,
Lincolnshire NG34 0NA
Tel: (01529) 240765
Unusual & giant vegetables

Milton Seeds
3 Milton Avenue, Blackpool,
Lancashire FY3 8LY
Tel: (01253) 394377
General list

Monocot Nursery
Jacklands, Jacklands Bridge,
Tickenham, Clevedon, Avon
BS21 6SG
Tel: unavailable
Bulbous and tuberous plants

Natural Selection
1 Station Cottages, Hullavington,
Chippenham, Wiltshire SN14 6ET
Tel: (01666) 837369
Unusual British natives

Andrew Norfield Trees & Seeds
Lower Meend, St Briavels,
Gloucestershire GL15 6RW
Tel: (01594) 530134
Germinated seeds

Stuart Ogg
Hopton, Fletching Street, Mayfield,
East Sussex TN20 6TL
Tel: (01435) 873322
Delphiniums

Phedar Nursery
Bunkers Hill, Romiley, Stockport,
Cheshire SK6 3DS
Tel: (0161) 430 3772
Helleborus

Pinks & Carnations
22 Chetwyn Avenue, Bromley Cross,
Nr Bolton, Lancashire BL7 9BN
Tel: (01204) 306273
Carnations

Plant World Botanic Gardens
Seed Dept, St Marychurch Road,
Newton Abbot, Devon TQ12 4SE
Tel: (01803) 872939
Ornamentals

Potterton & Martin
The Cottage Nursery, Moortown
Road, Nettleton, Caister,
Lincolnshire LN7 6HX
Tel: (01472) 851792
Alpines & dwarf bulbs

Roger Poulett
Nurse's Cottage, North Mundham,
Chichester, Sussex PO20 6JY
Tel: (01243) 785496
*Helleborus, cyclamen, corydalis,
hepatica*

W Robinson & Sons Ltd
Sunny Bank, Forton, Nr Preston,
Lancashire PR3 0BN
Tel: (01524) 791210
Mammouth vegetable seed

R V Roger Ltd
The Nurseries, Pickering, North
Yorkshire YO18 7HG
Tel: (01751) 72226
Bulbs & seed potatoes

Salley Gardens
Flat 3, 3 Millicent Road, West
Bridgford, Nottingham NG2 7LD
Tel: (0115) 982 1366 (evngs)
Dye & medicinal herbs

The Seed House
9a Widley Road, Cosham,
Portsmouth, Hampshire PO6 2DS
Tel: (01705) 325639
Australian seeds

Seeds by Size
45 Croufield, Boxmoor, Hemel
Hempstead, Hertfordshire HP1 1PA
Tel: (01422) 251458
General list

Stewart's (Nottingham) Ltd
3 George Street, Nottingham
NG1 3BH
Tel: (0115) 947 6338
General list

Suffolk Herbs
Monks Farm, Pantlings Lane,
Kelvedon, Essex CO5 9PG
Tel: (01376) 572456
Herbs, wildflowers

Suttons Seeds Ltd
Hele Road, Torquay, Devon
TG2 7QJ
Tel: (01803) 614455
General list

Thompson & Morgan
London Road, Ipswich, Suffolk
IP2 0BA
Tel: (01473) 688821
General list

Thuya Alpine Nursery
Glebelands, Hartpury,
Gloucestershire GL19 3BW
Tel: (01452) 700548
Alpines

Edwin Tucker & Sons Ltd
Brewery Meadow, Stonepark,
Ashburton, Devon TQ13 7DG
Tel: (01364) 652403
Seed potatoes

Unwins Seeds Ltd
Mail Order Dept. Histon,
Cambridgeshire CB4 4ZZ
Tel: (01945) 588522
General list

Uzumara Orchids
9 Port Henderson, Gairloch,
Rosshire IV21 2AS
Tel: (01445) 741228
Streptocarpus and African orchids

Van Hage Seed Specialists
Great Amwell, Ware, Hertfordshire
SG12 9RP
Tel: (01920) 870811

Wildseeds
Branas Llandderfel, Gwynedd
LL23 7RF
Tel: (016783) 427
Wildflowers

Roy Young Seeds
23 Westland Chase, West Winch,
King's Lynn, Norfolk PE33 0QH
Tel: (01553) 840867
Cacti & succulents

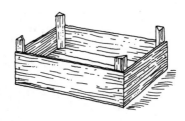

Garden Equipment and Supplies

W e have many enquiries from viewers of *Gardeners' World* about products we have used on the programmes. So, to provide as much information as possible, this list includes tools, equipment and sundries that have been tried and tested at Barnsdale. We do not wish to infer that products not listed here are of inferior quality, but simply that those that are have been used over the years and are considered good value.

GC = available at garden centres.

General

Aquatic sundries
Stapeley Water Gardens Ltd,
London Road, Stapeley, Nantwich,
Cheshire CW5 7LH
Tel: (01270) 623868

Barley straw pads for clearing pond algae
Green Ways, Burley Orchard
Cottage, Herrings Lane, Chertsey,
Surrey KT16 8PS
Tel: (01483) 281391

Boots
Hawkins lightweight walking boots –
shoe shops and sports shops

Bow saw
Sandvik – GC

Brassica collars
Fyba – GC

Capillary matting
ICI – GC

Cloches
Chase glass barn cloche – Power
Garden Products, 3 Daytona Drive,
Allesley, Coventry CV5 9QG
Tel: (01676) 23062

Gardena - GC
Melbourne Frames, (large field
frames), MWHS, PO Box 15,
Crockham Hill, Edenbridge, Kent
TN8 6SG
Tel: (01732) 864967

Specialised Designs Ltd, (lantern
cloche), Unit D7, Taylor Industrial
Estate, Risley, Warrington WA3 6BL
Tel: (01925) 766265

Mylan Products, (tunnel cloche),
Squirrels Wood, Reigate Rd,
Leatherhead, Surrey KT22 8QY
Tel: (01372) 373890

Tunnel cloche – PG Horticulture
Ltd, Street Farm, Thornham Magna,
Eye, Suffolk IP23 8HB
Tel: (01379) 71515

Twinwall cloche – Twinwall Garden Products, 7 Curtain Rd, London EC2A 3LT
Tel: (0171) 377 9277

Cold frames
Access Irrigation Ltd, Crick, Northampton NN6 7XS
Tel: (01788) 823811

Compost
Goldengrow Coir Compost – GC

Compost Bins
Garrotta bin – GC
The Hotterotter Co, PO Box 37, Abergavenny, Gwent
Tel: (01873) 840328

Rotol, Original Organics Ltd, Units 4/5, Farthings Lodge, Business Centre, Plymtree, Devon EX15 2JY
Tel: (01884) 277681

Digging tools
Wilkinson Sword – GC
Bulldog – GC
Spear and Jackson – GC
Terrex spade – Wolf Tools – GC

Disinfectant
Jeyes Fluid – GC

Drainpipe adaptors (to save rainwater)
Rain Save – Raindrain Ltd, Albert Mill, Mill St West, Dewsbury, West Yorkshire WF12 9AE
Tel: (01924) 468564

Floating cloche, (spun polypropylene)
Agryl P17 – Agralan
The Old Brickyard, Ashton Keynes, Swindon, Wiltshire SN6 6QR
Tel: (01285) 860015

Fruit cage and fruit arch
Agriframes, Charlwoods Rd, East Grinstead, West Sussex RH19 2HG
Tel: (01342) 318181

Fruit crusher (for making juice and wine)
Vigo Vineyards Supplies, Bolhayes, Clayhidon, Cullompton, Devon EX15 3PN
Tel: (01823) 680844

Galvanised flower buckets
Terrace and Garden Ltd, Orchard House, Patmore End, Ugley, Bishop's Stortford, Hertfordshire CM22 6JA
Tel: (01799) 543289

Grit, Horticultural
Croxden Horticultural Products – GC

Hormone rooting liquid
PBI Roota – GC

Hormone rooting powder
Doff Hormone Rooting Powder – GC
Seradix – GC

Knives
Victorinox – Burton McCall Ltd, 163 Parker Drive, Leicester LE4 0JP
Tel: (0116) 234 0800

Knife (pocket)
Victorinox – GC

Labels (aluminium)
Andrew Crace Designs, 49 Bourne Lane, Much Hadham, Hertfordhire SG10 6ER
Tel: (01279) 842685

Labels (scraperboard)
MacPennys Products, Burley Rd, Bransgore, Nr Christchurch, Dorset BH23 8DB
Tel: (01425) 672348 or GC

Lawn Edger, motorised
Homelite – Faxon Industries, Lower Everlands Rd, Hungerford, Berkshire RG17 0D
Tel: (01488) 684545

Lawn fertilizer distributor
Scotts – GC

Lawn rake (hand)
Spear and Jackson – GC

Lawn raker (electric)
Black and Decker – GC

Leaf Sweeper
Ginge – J T Lowe Ltd, Consort
House, Princes Rd, Ferndown,
Dorset BH22 9JG
Tel: (01202) 871717 or – GC or
garden machinery specialists

Bob Andrews, 11 Bilton Industrial
Estate, Lovelace Rd, Bracknell,
Berks RG12 8YT
Tel: (01344) 862111

Lighting
Hozelock-ASL – GC

Liquid fertilizer
Fisons Liquinure (general), Fisons
Tomorite, Phostrogen (high potash) –
GC

Log saw
Sandvik – GC

Loppers
Burton McCall Ltd, 163 Parker
Drive, Leicester LE4 0JP
Tel: (0116) 234 0800

Modules (for sowing in greenhouse)
PG Horticulture, Street Farm,
Thornham Magna, Eye, Suffolk
IP23 8HB
Tel: (01379) 678515
AP Propapacks – GC

Mowers
Honda, Flymo, Victa, Hayter,
Yamaha – GC or garden machinery
specialists

Mowers, mulching
Alko – GC or garden machinery
specialists.
Homelite – Faxon Industries, Lower
Everlands Rd, Hungerford, Berkshire
RG17 0DX
Tel: (01488) 684545

Netting
Nortene – GC
Netlon – GC

Ornamental containers
Plastic – Proteus Planters, Yanworth
House, Yanworth, Cheltenham,
Gloucestershire GL54 3LQ
Tel: (01285) 720007

Wood – Andrew Crace Designs,
49 Bourne Lane, Much Hadham,
Hertfordshire SG10 6ER
Tel: (01279) 842685

Glazed pottery: Oriel International,
The Priory, Newport, Essex
CB11 3TH
Tel: (0171) 734 8859

Terracotta – Whichford Pottery,
Whichford, Nr Shipston-on-Stour,
Warwickshire CV36 5PG
Tel: (01608) 684416

The Potting Shed, Lee Valley Forge,
Wharf Rd, Wormley, Hertfordshire
EN10 6HF
Tel: (01992) 470905

Robus Pottery and Tiles, Evington
Park, Hastingleigh, Ashford, Kent
TN25 5JH
Tel: (01233) 750330

pH meter
Sudbury – GC

Plant supports
Gro-Thru, Valley Wirework Co. Ltd,
792/792A Weston Rd Trading Estate,
Slough, Berkshire SL1 4HR
Tel: (01753) 521992

Link Stakes, Upper Boddington,
Daventry, Northamptonshire
NN11 6DL
Tel: (01327) 60329

Power Garden Products, 3 Daytona
Drive, Allesley, Coventry CV5 9QG
Tel: (01676) 23062

Porous pipe for sub-irrigation.
Porous Pipe Ltd, PO Box 2, Colne,
Lancashire
Tel: (01282) 871778
Hozelock – GC

Access Garden Products, Crick,
Northampton NN6 7XS
Tel: (01788) 822301

Pot feet
John Huggins, Courtyard Pottery,
Groundwell Farm, Cricklade Rd,
Swindon, Wiltshire SN2 5AU
Tel: (01793) 727466

Pots – plastic
Ward – GC

Pots – terracotta etc
Whichford Pottery, Whichford, Nr
Shipston-on-Stour, Warwickshire
CV36 5PG
Tel: (01608) 684416

Propagators
Parrafin – Parasene, M H Berlyn
Co., Dudley Rd, Halesowen, West
Midlands B63 3LR
Tel: (0121) 550 1951
Ward – GC

Propagating blanket
Prylorn Ltd, Elmhurst Yard, High
St, Chatteris, Cambridgeshire
PE16 6NP
Tel: (01354) 695779

Pruning saw
Felco – Burton McCall Ltd, 163
Parker Drive, Leicester LE4 0JP
Tel: (0116) 234 0800
Sandvik – GC

Rakes and hoes
Wilkinson Sword – GC
Spear and Jackson – GC
Bulldog – GC

Secateurs
Felco – Burton McCall Ltd, 163
Parker Drive, Leicester LE4 0JP
Tel: (0116) 234 0800
Rolcut – GC

Shears
Sandvik – GC
Wilkinson Sword – GC

Sheep shears
Burgon and Ball, La Plata Works,
Holme Lane, Sheffield S6 4JY
Tel: (0114) 233 8262

Shredders
Alko – Garden machinery stockists.
Allen Power Equipment, The
Broadway, Didcot, Oxon OX11 8ES
Tel: (01235) 813936

Globe Organic Services, Solihull,
West Midlands B92 7BR
Tel: (0121) 707 4120

Soil warming cable
Jemp Engineering Ltd, Canal Estate,
Station Rd, Langley, Berkshire
SL3 6EG
Tel: (01753) 548327

Soil test kits
Sudbury – GC

Sprayers
Hozelock-ASL – GC
Solo Sprayers, Brunel Rd, Leigh-on-Sea, Essex SS9 5JN
Tel: (01702) 525740

Brass pump-sprayer – Haws Watering Cans, 120 Beakes Rd, Smethwick, Warley, West Midlands B67 5AB
Tel: (0121) 420 2494

Statuary, stone urns etc.
Haddonstone Ltd, The Forge House, Church Lane, East Haddon, Northampton NN6 8DB
Tel: (01604) 770771

Antiques: Hollowarys, Lower Court, Suckley, Worcestershire WR6 5DE
Tel: (01886) 884665

Terracotta: Robus Pottery and Tiles, Evington Park, Hastingleigh, Ashford, Kent TN25 5JH
Tel: (01233) 750330

Strawberry mats
Fyba Products – GC

Tools, (spades, forks, rakes, hoes, trowels, shears, etc.)
Wilkinson Sword, Bulldog, Spear and Jackson, Jenks and Cattell – GC

Tree pruner (extending)
Darlac, PO Box 996, Slough, Berkshire SL3 9JF
Tel: (01753) 547790

Tree ties
Rainbow – GC

Trug Baskets
The Truggery, Coopers Croft, Herstmonceux, East Sussex BN27 1QL
Tel: (01323) 832314

Twine
Rainbow – GC

Vacuum leaf-sweeper
Flymo – GC
Black and Decker – GC

Vine eyes
Rainbow – GC

Watering cans
Haws Watering Cans, 120 Beakes Rd, Smethwick, Warley, West Midlands B67 5AB
Tel: (0121) 420 2494

Watering equipment
Hozelock-ASL – GC
Gardena – GC

Waterproof tape, (for repairing glass and clear polythene)
Sellotape – GC

Water Saving
Bowley Bros, 32 Canal St, South Wigston, Leicestershire LE8 2PL
Tel: (0116) 277 0472

Wheelbarrows
Hammerlin – GC, builders' merchants

Wheel Hoe
Jalo Engineering Ltd, Brook Rd, Wimbourne, Dorset BH21 2BH
Tel: (01202) 885079

Windbreak plastic
Netlon – GC

Wood preservative
Cuprinol – GC, builders' merchants
Sadolin – builders' merchants
PBI Woody – GC

Organic

Organic gardeners sometimes experience problems getting hold of the special materials and products they need. Most can be obtained through the Henry Doubleday Research Association, Ryton Gardens, Coventry or Chase Organics, Addlestone, Surrey. The following companies can also supply direct. (See also 'Composts and Soil Conditioners' on p.176.)

Biological control predators
HDRA, Ryton Gardens, Coventry, West Midlands CV8 3LG
Tel: (01203) 303517

English Woodlands Biocontrol, Hoyle Depot, Graffham, Petworth, West Sussex GU28 0LR
Tel: (01798) 867574

Compost containers
see p. 123

Environmesh insect-proof netting
Agralan, The Old Brickyard, Ashton Keynes, Swindon, Wiltshire SN6 6QR
Tel: (01285) 860015

Fertilizers
Chase Organics (GB) Ltd, Coombelands House, Coombelands Place, Addlestone, Surrey KT15 1HY
Tel: (01932) 820958

Humber Fertilizers, PO Box 27, Stoneferry, Hull, Humberside HU8 8DQ
Tel: (01482) 20458
Fisons Origins Range – GC

Greenvale Farm Ltd, Wonastow Rd, Monmouth, Gwent NP5 3XX
Tel: (01677) 422953
Maxicrop – GC

Organic Concentrates Ltd, 3 Broadway Court, Chesham, Buckinghamshire HP5 1EN
Tel: (01494) 792229

Super-Natural Ltd, Bore Place Farm, Chiddingstone, Edenbridge, Kent TN8 7AR
Tel: (01732) 463255

Horticultural Fleece
Agralan, The Old Brickyard, Ashton Keynes, Swindon, Wiltshire SN6 6QR
Tel: (01285) 860015
Nortene – GC

Grease for grease-banding
Agralan, The Old Brickyard, Ashton Keynes, Swindon, Wiltshire SN6 6QR
Tel: (01285) 860015
Corrys grease, Synchemical – GC

Grease bands
Boltac. PBI – GC

Green Manure Seeds
E W King and Co Ltd, Monks Farm, Pantlings Lane, Coggeshall Rd, Kelvedon, Colchester, Essex CO5 9PG
Tel: (01376) 570000

Humming Line
Buzzline, Agralan, The Old Brickyard, Ashton Keynes, Swindon, Wiltshire SN6 6QR
Tel: (01285) 860015

Mulch
Cocoa shell – Sunshine of Africa,
Afton Manor, Freshwater,
Isle of Wight PO40 9TW
Tel: (01983) 755388

Mulch sheet
Nortene – GC

Mulching sheet
(Black polythene) Nortene, GC
(Woven) Small Lots, Higham Rd,
Burton Latimer, Northamptonshire
NN15 5PU
Tel: (01536) 724777

Papronet insect-proof plastic
Direct Wire Ties, Wyke Works,
Heddon Rd, Hull, Humberside
NU9 5NL
Tel: (01482) 712630

Pheromone traps for codling moth and plum sawfly
Agralan, The Old Brickyard, Ashton
Keynes, Swindon, Wiltshire
SN6 6QR
Tel: (01285) 860015

Wormery
Original Organics Ltd, Units 4/5,
Farthings Lodge, Business Centre,
Plymtree, Devon EX15 2JY
Tel: (01884) 277681

Yellow sticky traps for whitefly
Agralan, The Old Brickyard, Ashton
Keynes, Swindon, Wiltshire
SN6 6QR
Tel: (01285) 860015

Garden Chemicals

A t Barnsdale I garden completely organically without the use of man-made chemicals. The price I pay is a little more time controlling some pests physically, though most is done by my natural allies. I also suffer an occasional spell of nail-biting when my roses show the first signs of greenfly and I lose faith. It doesn't last long and nor do the greenfly, and the rewards are great with my garden becoming a haven for wildlife. I also enjoy the comforting knowledge that I'm not harming anything – including me.

However, you may well wish to continue to use chemicals so a list is included here. Above all, please follow to the letter the guidelines for use on the back of the bottle. The list is drawn directly from the leaflet issued by the British Agrochemicals Association – 'Garden Chemicals'. You'll find the address of the Association on p. 160.

Garden chemicals come and go. New ones appear from time to time and older ones are often withdrawn for safety reasons. This list was up to date at the time of going to press but may change during the year.

Lawns and Grassed Areas

L1 Selective Weedkillers only: used to control many common lawn weeds. Refer to product label for specific advice on weeds controlled.

	Name	Supplier	Active Ingredient(s)
1	Bio Lawn Weedkiller	pbi	2,4-D and dicamba
2	Bio Supertox	pbi	2,4-D and mecoprop
3	Bio Supertox Spot Weeder	pbi	2,4-D and mecoprop
4	Bio Weed Pencil	pbi	MCPA, mecoprop and dicamba
5	Bio Spraydex Lawn Spot Weeder	pbi	2,4-D and mecoprop
6	Levington Clover-Kil	Levington	2,4-D and dichlorprop
7	Levington RTU Clover-Kil	Levington	2,4-D and dichlorprop
8	Levington RTU Lawn Weedkiller	Levington	2,4-D and dichlorprop

Name	Supplier	Active Ingredient(s)
9 Levington Water-On Lawn Weedkiller	Levington	2,4-D and dichlorprop
10 Murphy Lawn Weedkiller	Levington	2,4-D and dichlorprop
11 Green Up Spot Lawn Weedkiller	Vitax	2,4-D and mecoprop
12 Green Up Weedfree Lawn Weedkiller	Vitax	2,4-D and dicamba
13 Green Up Weedfree Spot Weedkiller for Lawns	Vitax	2,4-D and dicamba
14 Lawn Weed Gun	ICI	2,4-D and dicamba
15 Verdone 2	ICI	2,4-D and mecoprop

L2 Selective Weedkiller/Fertilizer Mixes: used to control many common lawn weeds and feed grass. Refer to label for specific advice on weeds controlled.

Name	Supplier	Active Ingredient(s)
16 Bio Supergreen and Weed	pbi	2,4-D, mecoprop and fertilizer
17 Bio Toplawn	pbi	2,4-D, dicamba and fertilizer
18 Levington Evergreen Feed and Weed	Levington	MCPA, mecoprop and fertilizer
19 Levington Evergreen Feed and Weed Liquid	Levington	MCPA, mecoprop, dicamba and fertilizer
20 Levington's Lawncare Liquid (Lawn Fertilizer with Weedkiller)	Levington	MCPA, mecoprop, dicamba and fertilizer
21 Gem Lawn Feed & Weed	Gem	Mecoprop, 2,4-D and fertilizer
22 Green Up Lawn Feed & Weed	Vitax	2,4-D, mecoprop, dicamba with fertilizer
23 Lawncare Liquid Weed and Feed	ICI	Dicamba, dichlorprop, MCPA and fertilizer
24 Murphy Lawn Weedkiller and Lawn Tonic	Levington	2,4-D, dichlorprop and urea

L3 Selective Weedkiller/Fertilizer/Mosskiller Mixes: used to control moss, many common lawn weeds and feed grass. Refer to label for specific advice on weeds controlled.

	Name	Supplier	Active Ingredient(s)
25	Bio Supergreen Feed, Weed and Mosskiller	pbi	2,4-D, mecoprop, ferrous sulphate and fertilizer
26	Levington Evergreen Extra	Levington	MCPA, mecoprop, ferrous sulphate and fertilizer
27	Gem Lawn Feed & Weed plus Mosskiller	Gem	Mecoprop, 2,4-D, ferrous sulphate and fertilizer
28	Green Up Feed N' Weed plus Mosskiller	Vitax	2,4-D, mecoprop and ferrous sulphate
29	Green Up Lawn Feed N' Weed plus mosskiller	Vitax	Dichlorophen, mecoprop, dichlorprop, 2,4-D, dicamba, benazolin and fertilizer
30	Triple Action Grasshopper (with refill)	ICI	2,4-D, dicamba, ferrous sulphate and fertilizer

L4 MosskillerFertilizer Mixes: used to control moss and feed grass.

	Name	Supplier	Active Ingredient(s)	Details
31	Bio Velvas	pbi	Ferrous sulphate and fertilizer	
32	Levington Autumn Extra	Levington	Ferrous sulphate and fertilizer	For autumn use
33	Levington Lawn Sand	Levington	Ferrous sulphate and nitrogen fertilizer	
34	Levington Mosskil Extra	Levington	Ferrous sulphate and fertilizer	
35	Gem Lawn Sand	Gem	Ferrous sulphate and fertilizer	

L5 Mosskillers: used to control moss in lawns.

Name	Supplier	Active Ingredient(s)	Details
36 Bio Moss Killer	pbi	Dichlorophen	Can also be used on hard surfaces
37 Green Up Mossfree	Vitax	Ferrous sulphate	
38 Moss Gun	ICI	Dichlorophen	Can also be used on hard surfaces
39 Murphy Super Mosskiller RTU	Levington	Dichlorophen	Can also be used on hard surfaces

L6 Insecticides and Insecticide/Fertilizer Mixes: used to control insect pests in lawns.

Name	Supplier	Active ingredients(s)	Details – Lawn Diseases Controlled
40 Bio Autumn and Winter Toplawn	pbi	Carbaryl and fertilizer	Leatherjackets and earthworms
41 Murphy Lawn Pest Killer	Levington	Carbaryl	Earthworms
42 Sybol	ICI	Pirimiphos-methyl	Use as a drench for leather-jackets and chafer grubs

L7 Biological Control: used to control insect pests in lawns.

Name	Supplier	Active ingredients(s)	Details – Lawn Pests Controlled
43 Biosafe	pbi	Steinernema carpocapsae	Leatherjackets and chafer grubs

L8 Fungicides: used to control diseases in lawns.

	Name	Supplier	Active ingredients(s)	Details – Lawn Diseases Controlled
44	Benlate + Activex 2	ICI	Benomyl with surfactants	
45	Bio Supercarb Systematic Fungicade	pbi	Carbendazim	Red thread, Fusarium and Dollar Spot
46	Bio Moss Killer	pbi	Dichlorophen	Red thread and Fusarium
47	Murphy Super Mosskiller RTU	Levington	Dichlorophen	Also controls liverwort

Paths, Hard Surfaces and Overgrown Areas

P1 Non-Residual Weedkillers: used to control existing weed growth. Refer to product label for specific advice on weeds controlled

	Name	Supplier	Active ingredients(s)	Details
48	Bio Speedweed	pbi	Fatty acids	Contact action. Also kills moss
49	Bio Weed Pencil	pbi	MCPA, mecoprop and dicamba	Systemic, only controls broad- leaved weeds
50	Greenscape Weedkiller	Monsanto	Glyphosate	Systemic action
51	Greenscape Weedkiller Ready to use	Monsanto	Glyphosate	Systemic action
52	Murphy Tumbleweed	Levington	Glyphosate	Systemic action
53	Murphy Tumbleweed	Levington	Glyphosate	Systemic spot treatment

Name	Supplier	Active ingredients(s)	Details
54 Murphy Tumbelweed Spray	Levington	Glyphosate	Systemic action
55 Murphy Weedmaster	Levington	Glufosinate-ammonium	Contact action
56 Murphy Weedmaster RTU	Levington	Glufosinate-ammonium	Contact action
57 Weedol	ICI	Paraquat and diquat	Contact action
58 New Improved Leaf Action Roundup RTU	Monsanto	Glyphosate	Systemic action
59 Roundup GC	Monsanto	Glyphosate	Systemic action
60 Roundup Brushkiller	Monsanto	Glyphosate	Systemic action
61 Roundup Brushkiller Ready to Use	Monsanto	Glyphosate	Systemic action
62 Roundup Tab	Monsanto	Glyphosate	Systemic action

P2 Residual Weedkillers: for long lasting weed control of annual and perennial weeds. Refer to product label for specific advice on weeds controlled.

Name	Supplier	Active ingredients(s)	Details
63 Bio Path and Drive Weedkiller	pbi	Amitrole, ammonium thiocyanate and simazine	Contact, systemic and root absorbed activity
64 Bio Total Weedkiller Granules	pbi	Simazine and diuron	Root absorbed
65 Casoron G4	Vitax	Dichlobenil	Root absorbed

Name	Supplier	Active ingredients(s)	Details
66 Levington Path Weedkiller (soon to be replaced by Pathmaster)	Levington	Amitrole, MCPA and simazine	Contact, systemic root absorbed
67 Gem Sodium Chlorate	Gem	Sodium chlorate	Contact acting
68 Hytrol	Agrichem	Amitrole, 2,4-D, diuron and simazine	Contact, systemic root absorbed
69 Murphy Path Weedkiller	Levington	Amitrole and atrazine	Contact, systemic and root absorbed activity
70 Pathclear	ICI	Paraquat, diquat, simazine and amitrole	Contact, systemic and root absorbed activity

P3 Moss and Algae Control: products which control moss and algae.

Name	Supplier	Active ingredients(s)	Details
71 Bio Mosskiller	pbi	Dichlorophen	Can be used on lawns
72 Bio Speedweed	pbi	Fatty acids	Not for use on lawns
73 Clean-Up	ICI	Tar acids	
74 Moss Gun	ICI	Dichlorophen	
75 Murphy Super Mosskiller RTU	Levington	Dichlorophen	Controls lichen

P4 Difficult and Woody Weeds, and Tree Stumps: products which control difficult and woody weeds, and tree stumps. Refer to product label for specific advice on weeds controlled

Name	Supplier	Active ingredients(s)	Details
76 Bio Ground-clear	pbi	Dicamba, MCPA and dichlorprop	Can be used for stump treatment

	Name	Supplier	Active ingredients(s)	Details
77	Bio Ground-clear Spot	pbi	Dicamba, MCPA and dichlorprop	
78	Murphy Weedmaster	Levington	Glufosinate-ammonium	
79	Murphy Weedmaster RTU	Levington	Glufosinate-ammonium	
80	New Formula SBK Brushwood Killer	Vitax	2,4-D, mecoprop and dicamba	Controls coarse and woody weeds, sapling growth and tree stumps
81	Roundup Brushkiller	Monsanto	Glyphosate	Can be used for stump treatments
82	Roundup Brushkiller Ready to Use	Monsanto	Glyphosate	

Flowerbeds, Shrubberies, Trees and Hedges

F1 Non-Residual Weedkillers: for short-term control of grasses and broadleaved weeds amongst flowers, shrubs, trees and hedges. Refer to product label for specific advice on weeds controlled. Take care to avoid contact with garden plants.

	Name	Supplier	Active ingredients(s)	Details
83	Bio Speedweed	pbi	Fatty acids	Also kills moss
84	Bio Weed pencil	pbi	MCPA, mecoprop and dicamba	
85	Greenscape Weedkiller	Monsanto	Glyphosate	Systemic action
86	Greenscape Weedkiller Ready to Use	Monsanto	Glyphosate	Systemic action
87	Murphy Tumbleweed	Levington	Glyphosate	Systemic action

Name	Supplier	Active ingredients(s)	Details
88 Murphy Tumbleweed Gel	Levington	Glyphosate	Systemic spot treatment
89 Murphy Tumbleweed Spray	Levington	Glyphosate	Systemic action
90 Weedol	ICI	Paraquat and diquat	Contact action
91 Murphy Weedmaster	Levington	Glufosinate-ammonium	Contact action
92 Murphy Weedmaster RTU	Levington	Glufosinate-ammonium	Contact action
93 New Improved Leaf Action Roundup RTU	Monsanto	Glyphosate	Systemic action
94 Roundup GC	Monsanto	Glyphosate	Systemic action
95 Roundup Tab	Monsanto	Glyphosate	Systemic action

F2 Residual Weedkillers: for short-term control of grasses and broadleaved weeds amongst flowers, shrubs, trees and hedges. Refer to product label for specific advice on weeds controlled.

Name	Supplier	Active ingredients(s)	Details
96 Casoron G4	Vitax	Dichlobenil	

F3 Insecticides: to control insect pests on flowers, shrubs, trees and hedges. Refer to product label for specific advice on weeds controlled.

Name	Supplier	Active ingredients(s)	Details
97 Bio BT Caterpillar Killer	pbi	Bacillus thuringiensis	Control of caterpillars
98 Bio Fenitrothion	pbi	Fenitrothion	Contact residual control of pea moth, raspberry beetle, codling moth and other foliar pests

	Name	Supplier	Active ingredients(s)	Details
99	Bio Friendly Pest Pistol	pbi	Horticultural soaps	Contact acting control of aphids, whitefly, red spider mite and scale
100	Bio Liquid Derris	pbi	Rotenone	Contact residual for raspberry beetle, aphids and small caterpillars
101	Bio Long-last	pbi	Dimethoate and permethrin	Combined contact and systemic action for general pest control
102	Bio Malathion	pbi	Malathion	Contact control of aphids and other pests
103	Bio Sprayday	pbi	Permethrin and piperonyl butoxide	Contact acting general purpose
104	Bio Spraydex Greenfly Killer	pbi	Permethrin and bioallethrin	Contact insecticide
105	Bug Gun for Roses and Flowers	ICI	Naturally occurring pyrethrins	Contact acting pest control on flowers
106	Derris Dust	Vitax	Rotenone	Contact insecticide
107	Levington Nature's Answer to Insect Pests on Flowers, Fruit and Vegetables	Levington	Pyrethrum	Contact pest control
108	ICI Derris Dust	ICI	Rotenone	
109	Longer Lasting Bug Gun	ICI	Bioallethrin and permethrin	
110	Murphy Gamma BHC Dust	Levington	Lindane	Contact control of common soil and foliar pests
111	Murphy Liquid Malathion	Levington	Malathion	Contact control of insect pests

Name	Supplier	Active ingredients(s)	Details
112 Murphy Malathion Dust	Levington	Malathion	Contact control of insect pests
113 Murphy Systemic Action Insecticide	Levington	Heptenphos and permethrin	Systemic, contact and fumigant control of foliar insect pests
114 Murphy Tumblebug	Levington	Heptenophos and permethrin	Systemic, contact and fumigant control of foliar insect pests
115 Murphy Bugmaster	Levington	Pyrethrum	Contact insecticide
116 Murphy Derris Dust	Levington	Rotenone	Contact insecticide for control of flea beetle, raspberry beetle, caterpillars and pests
117 Picket	ICI	Permethrin	Kills whitefly, caterpillars and other pests
118 Plant Pin	Phostrogen	Butoxycarboxim	Systemic action
119 Py Garden Insecticide	Vitax	Pyrethrins	Broad spectrum contact control
120 Py Powder	Vitax	Pyrethrins	Broad spectrum contact control
121 Py Spray Garden Insect Killer	Vitax	Pyrethrins	Broad spectrum control
122 Py Spray Insect killer	Vitax	Pyrethins	Broad spectrum contact control
123 Rapid Aerosol	ICI	Pirimicarb	Selective aphid control
124 Rapid Greenfly	ICI	Pirimicarb	Selective aphid control
125 Safer's Rose and Flower	Phostrogen	Natural fatty acids	Contact acting

Name	Supplier	Active ingredients(s)	Details
126 Safer's Garden Insecticide Concentrate	Phostrogen	Natural fatty acids	Contact acting
127 Sybol Aerosol	ICI	Pirimiphos-methyl and synergised pyrethrins	Broad spectrum control
128 Sybol Dust	ICI	Pirimiphos-methyl	Broad spectrum control
129 Sybol	ICI	Pirimiphos-methyl	Controls most garden pests

For slug and snail control see Table GP4 in the General Pest Control section on page 162.

F4 Biological Control of insect pests on flowers, shrubs, trees and hedges.

Name	Supplier	Active ingredients(s)	Details
130 Biosafe	pbi	Steinernema carpocapsae	Control of vine weevil

F5 Fungicides for the control of diseases on flowers, shrubs, trees and hedges. Refer to product label for specific advice on diseases controlled.

Name	Supplier	Active ingredients(s)	Details
131 Benlate + Activex 2	ICI	Benomyl with Activex 2 trace elements and surfacants	Broad spectrum control of most diseases
132 Bio Dithane 945	pbi	Mancozeb	Apple and pear scab, peach leaf curl, leaf spots, downy mildew and rusts
133 Bio Spraydex General Purpose Fungicide	pbi	Copper sulphate and ammonium hydroxide	Apple and pear scab, mildew and blackspot
134 Bio Supercarb Systemic Fungicide	pbi	Carbendazim and activator	Broad spectrum control of most diseases

Name	Supplier	Active ingredients(s)	Details
135 Bio Systhane	pbi	Myclobutanil	Mildew, blackspot and rust on roses
136 Murphy Tumbleblite II	Levington	Penconazole	Systemic control
137 Murphy Traditional Copper Fungicide	Levington	Copper oxychloride	Protective fungicide
138 Nimrod-T	ICI	Bupirimate and triforine	
139 Safer's Garden Fungicide	Phostrogen	Sulphur	Controls powdery mildew

F6 Fungicide/Insecticide Mixtures to control insect pests and diseases on flowers, shrubs, trees and hedges. Refer to product label for specific advice on weeds controlled.

Name	Supplier	Active ingredients(s)	Details
140 Fisons Nature's Answer Fungicide and Insect Killer	Levington	Fatty acids and sulphur	
141 Roseclear	ICI	Bupirimate, triforine and pirimicarb	Aphid and broad spectrum disease control

F7 Fungicide/Insecticide/Foliar Feeds to feed and control insect pests and diseases on flowers, shrubs, trees and hedges. Refer to product label for specific advice on pests and diseases controlled.

Name	Supplier	Active ingredients(s)	Details
142 Bio Multirose	pbi	Permethrin, triforine sulphur and fertilizer	Mildew, blackspot and greenfly

F8 Other Products which may be used on flowers, shrubs, trees and hedges.

	Name	Supplier	Active ingredients(s)	Details
143	Baby Bio Roota	pbi	1-naphthylacetic acid and dicholorophen	For rooting cuttings without rotting
144	Bio Arbrex Pruning Compound	pbi	Bitumen	Seals pruning wounds on trees
145	Bio Boltac Greasbands	pbi	Greasebands	Controls winter moth in fruit trees
146	Bio Strike	pbi and captan	1-naphthylacetic acid	For rooting cuttings. Prevents basal rots
147	Cutlass	ICI	Dikegulac	Controls the growth of hedges and some other wood species
148	Medo	Vitax	Cresylic acid	Pruning compound/ fungal canker paint
149	Murphy Hormone Rooting Powder	Levington	1-naphthylacetic acid and captan	For rooting cuttings without rotting
150	Rooting Powder	Vitax	Captan and 1-napthylacetic acid	For rooting cuttings

Outdoor Fruit and Vegetables

O1 Non-Residual Weedkillers: for short-term control of grasses and broadleaved weeds amongst fruit and vegetables. Refer to product label for specific advice on weeds controlled. Take care to avoid contact with garden plants.

	Name	Supplier	Active ingredients(s)	Details
151	Bio Speedweed	pbi	Fatty acids	Contact action
152	Couch & Grass killer	Vitax	Dalapon	Systemic action
153	Greenscape Weedkiller	Monsanto	Glyphosate	Systemic action

Name	Supplier	Active ingredients(s)	Details
154 Greenscape Weedkiller Ready to Use	Monsanto	Glyphosate	Systemic action
155 Murphy Tumbleweed	Levington	Glyphosate	Systemic action
156 Murphy Tumbleweed Gel	Levington	Glyphosate	Systemic action
157 Murphy Tumbleweed Spray	Levington	Glyphosate	Systemic action
158 Murphy Weedmaster RTU	Levington	Glufosinate-ammonium	Contact action
159 Murphy Weedmaster	Levington	Glufosinate-ammonium	Systemic action
160 New Improved Leaf Action Roundup Ready to Use	Monsanto	Glyphosate	Systemic action
161 Roundup GC	Monsanto	Glyphosate	Systemic action
162 Roundup Tab	Monsanto	Glyphosate	Systemic action
163 Weedol	ICI	Paraquat and diquat	Contact action

O2 Residual Weedkillers for long-term control of grasses and broadleaved weeds amongst fruit and vegetables. Refer to product label for specific advice on weeds controlled.

O3 Insecticides Only for insect pest control on fruit and vegetables. Refer to product label for specific advice on pests controlled. Check harvest interval requirements before applying.

Name	Supplier	Active ingredients(s)	Details – Harvest Interval=HI
164 Bio BT Caterpillar Killer	pbi	Bacillus thuringiensis	Controls caterpillars **HI – None**

Name	Supplier	Active ingredients(s)	Details – Harvest Interval=HI
165 Bio Chlorophos	pbi	Chlorpyrifos and diazinon	Soil applied. Control of root-pests in vegetables
166 Bio Crop Saver	pbi	Permethrin and malathion	Control of foliar pests in vegetables **HI – 1 day**
167 Bio Fenitrothion	pbi	Fenitrothion	Controls raspberry beetle, pea moth, codling moth and sawfly **HI – 14 days, raspberries 7 days**
168 Bio Friendly Pest Pistol	pbi	Horticultral soaps	Contact acting control of aphids, red spider mite, whitefly and scale **HI – None**
169 Bio Liquid Derris	pbi	Rotenone	Contact action. Kills raspberry beetle, aphids and small caterpillars **HI – 1 day**
170 Bio Long-Last	pbi	Dimethoate and permethrin	Combined systemic and contact general purpose **HI – 7 days**
171 Bio Malathion Greenfly Killer	pbi	Malathion	Contact action **HI – 1 day**
172 Bio Sprayday	pbi	Permethrin and piperonyl butoxide	Contact action **HI – None**
173 Bio Spraydex Greenfly Killer	pbi	Permethrin and bioallethrin	**HI – 1 day**
174 Bug Gun for Fruit and Vegetables	ICI	Pyrethrum	Broad spectrum contact control **HI – None**
175 Derris Dust	Vitax	Rotenone	Contact insecticide **HI – 1 day**

Name	Supplier	Active ingredients(s)	Details – Harvest Interval=HI
176 Fisons Nature's Answer to Insect Pests on Flowers, Fruit and Vegetables	Levington	Pyrethrum	Broad spectrum to contact control **HI – None**
177 ICI Derris Dust	ICI	Rotenone	Contact control **HI – 1 day**
178 Longer Lasting Bug Gun	ICI	Bioallethrin and permethrin	**HI – None**
179 Murphy Derris Dust	Levington	Rotenone	Contact control **HI - 1 day**
180 Murphy Gamma BHC Dust	Levington	Lindane	Contact control soil and foliar pests **HI – 14 days**
181 Murphy Liquid Malathion	Levington	Malathion	Contact control **HI – 4 days**
182 Murphy Malathion Dust	Levington	Malathion	Contact control **HI – 4 days**
183 Murphy Systemic Action Insecticide	Levington	Heptenophos and permethrin	Systemic, contact and fumigant control **HI – 1 day**
184 Murphy Tumblebug	Levington	Heptenophos and permethrin	Systemic, contact and fumigant control **HI – 1 day**
185 Murphy Bugmaster	Levington	Pyrethrum	Contact control **HI – None**
186 Picket	ICI	Permethrin	**HI – None**
187 Py Garden Insecticide	Vitax	Pyrethrins	Broad spectrum control insecticide **HI –1 day**
188 Py Powder	Vitax	Pyrethrins	Broad spectrum control insecticide **HI – 1 day**
189 Py Spray Garden Insect Killer	Vitax	Pyrethrins	Broad spectrum control insecticide **HI – 1 day**

Name	Supplier	Active ingredients(s)	Details – Harvest Interval=HI
190 Py Spray Insect Killer	Vitax	Pyrethrins	Broad spectrum control insecticide **HI – 1 day**
191 Rapid Aerosol	ICI	Pirimicarb	Aphid control only **HI – 3 days**
192 Rapid Greenfly	ICI	Pirimicarb	Aphid control only **HI – 3 days** 14 days lettuce under glass
193 Safer's Garden Insecticide Concentrate	Phostrogen	Natural fatty acids	Contact acting **HI – None**
194 Safer's Fruit & Vegetable Insecticide	Phostrogen	Natural fatty acids	Contact acting **HI – None**
195 Sybol	ICI	Pirimiphos-methyl	Broad spectrum control **HI – 7 days**
196 Sybol Aerosol	ICI	Pirimiphos-methyl and Synergised pyrethrins	Broad spectrum control **HI – 7 days**
197 Sybol Dust	ICI	Pirimiphos-methyl	Broad spectrum control **HI – 7 days**

For slug and snail control see Table GP4 in the General Pest Control section on page 162.

O4 Fungicides Only for disease control amongst fruit and vegetables. Refer to product label for specific advice on diseases controlled. Check harvest interval requirements before applying.

Name	Supplier	Active ingredients(s)	Details – Harvest Interval=HI
198 Benlate + Activex 2	ICI	Benomyl with Activex 2 trace elements and surficants	Broad spectrum control **HI – 2–21 days** depending on crop

Name	Supplier	Active ingredients(s)	Details – Harvest Interval=HI
199 Bio Cheshunt Compound	pbi	Copper sulphate and ammonium	For disease control in seedlings only **HI – N/A**
200 Bio Dithane 945	pbi	Mancozeb	Peach leaf curl, potato and tomato blight, downy mildew **HI – 7 days, 21 days lettuce**
201 Bio Liquid Club Root Control	pbi	Thiophanate-methyl	Club root in brassicas **HI – None**
202 Bio Supercarb Systemic Fungicide	pbi	Carbendazim and activator	**HI – None except 14 days** lettuce
203 Bordeaux Mixture	Vitax	Copper sulphate	Controls potato and tomato blights, peach leaf curl, rusts and canker **HI – None**
204 Green and Yellow Sulphur	Vitax	Sulphur	Controls powdery mildew **HI – None**
205 Murphy Traditional Copper Fungicide	Levington	Copper oxychloride	Protective fungicide **HI – None**
206 Nimrod-T	ICI	Bupirimate and triforine	For use on fruit only. **HI – 7 days apple and 14 days blackcurrant/ gooseberry**
207 Safer's Garden Fungicide	Phostrogen	Sulphur	Controls powdery mildew **HI – 1 day**

O5 Fungicides/Insecticide Mixtures to control pests and diseases on fruit and vegetables. Refer to product label for specific advice on pests and diseases controlled. Check harvest interval requirements before applying.

	Name	Supplier	Active Ingredient(s)	Formulation	Details – Harvest Interval = HI
208	Levington Nature's Answer Fungicide and Insect Killer	Levington	Fatty acids and Sulphur	RTU Liquid	**HI – None**

O6 Winter Washes to clean and protect fruit trees.

	Name	Supplier	Active Ingredient(s)	Formulation	Details
209	Murphy Mortegg	Levington	Tar oils	Liquid Conc	Contact control of insect eggs

O7 Other Products for use on outdoor on fruit and vegetables.

	Name	Supplier	Active Ingredient(s)	Formulation	Details
210	Bio Boltac Greasebands	pbi	Grease	RTU Band	To protect against winter moths
211	Baby Bio Roota Liquid	pbi	1-naphthyl-acetic acid and dichlorophen	RTU Rooting Liquid	
212	Bio Arbrex Pruning	pbi	Bitumen	RTU Paint	Sealant for pruning wounds on trees
213	Bio Strike	pbi	1-naphthy-lacetic acid and captan	RTU Powder	Rooting compound. Prevents basal rots
214	Corry's Fruit Tree Grease	Vitax	Grease	RTU Grease	To protect against winter moths

	Name	Supplier	Active Ingredient(s)	Formulation	Details
215	Medo	Vitax	Cresylic acid	RTU Liquid	Pruning compound
216	Murphy Hormone Rooting Powder	Levington	1-naphthy-lacetic acid and captan	RTU Powder	For rooting cuttings without rotting
217	Rooting Powder	Vitax	Captan and 1-naphthylacetic acid	RTU Powder	For rooting cuttings
218	Tomato Setting Spray	Vitax	2-naphthy-loxy acetic acid	RTU Aerosol	

Greenhouses

G1 Insecticides and mite control products for use in the greenhouse. Refer to product label for specific advice on pests controlled. Check harvest interval requirements before spraying.

	Name	Supplier	Active Ingredient(s)	Details – Harvest Interval = HI
219	Bio Crop Saver	pbi	Permethrin and malathion	Control of foliar pests in vegetables **HI – 1 day**
220	Bio Fenitrothion	pbi	Fenitrothion	Controls raspberry beetle, pea moth, codling moth and sawfly **HI – 14 days, raspberries – 7 days**
221	Bio Friendly Pest Pistol	pbi	Horticultural soaps	Contact acting control of aphids, red spider mite, whitefly and scale **HI – None**

	Name	Supplier	Active Ingredient(s)	Details – Harvest Interval = HI
222	Bio Liquid Derris	pbi	Rotenone	Contact action. Kills raspberry beetle, aphids and small caterpillars **HI – 1 day**
223	Bio Malathion Greenfly Killer	pbi	Malathion	Contact action **HI – 1 day**
224	Bio Sprayday	pbi	Permethrin and piperonyl butoxide	Contact action **HI – 1 day**
225	Bio Spraydex Greenfly Killer	pbi	Permethrin and bioallethrin	**HI – 1 day**
226	Derris Dust	Vitax	Rotenone	**HI – None**
227	Levington Nature's Answer to Insect Pests on Flowers, Fruit and Vegetables	Levington	Pyrethrum	Contact insecticide for control of insect pests on flowers, fruit and vegetables **HI – None**
228	Fumite General Purpose Greenhouse Insecticide Smokes	ICI	Pirimiphos-methyl	Control of most pests including red spider mite and whitefly **HI – None**
229	Fumite Whitefly Greenhouse Insecticide Smokes	ICI	Permethrin	Controls whitefly, caterpillars and other pests **HI – None**
230	ICI Derris Dust	ICI	Rotenone	**HI – 1 day**
231	Keri Spray Insect	ICI	Pyrethrins	
232	Longer Lasting Bug Gun	ICI	Bioallethrin and permethrin	**HI – None**
233	Murphy Derris Dust	Levington	Rotenone	Contact insecticide for control of flea beetle, raspberry beetle, caterpillars and wasps **HI – 1 day**

Name	Supplier	Active Ingredient(s)	Details – Harvest Interval = HI
234 Murphy Liquid Malathion	Levington	Malathion	Contact insecticide for control of insect pests on flowers, fruit and vegetables **HI – 4 days**
235 Murphy Malathion Dust	Levington	Malathion	Contact insecticide for control of insect pests on flowers, fruit and vegetables **HI – 4 days**
236 Murphy Systemic Action Insecticide	Levington	Heptenophos and permethrin	Systemic, contact and fumigant control of foliar insect pests on flowers, fruit and vegetables **HI – 1 day**
237 Murphy Tumblebug	Levington	Heptenophos and permethrin	Systemic, contact and fumigant control of foliar insect pests on flowers, fruit and vegetables **HI – 1 day**
238 Murphy Gamma BHC Dust	Levington	Lindane	Contact insecticide for control of common soil and foliar pests around flowers, fruit and vegetables **HI – 14 days**
239 Murphy Bugmaster	Levington	Pyrethrum	Contact insecticide for control of insect pests on flowers, fruit and vegetables **HI – None**
240 Picket	ICI	Permethrin	**HI – None**

Name	Supplier	Active Ingredient(s)	Details – Harvest Interval = HI
241 Py Powder	Vitax	Pyrethrins	Contact insecticide for home and garden use **HI – 1 day**
242 Py Spray Garden Insect Killer	Vitax	Pyrethrins	Contact insecticide for home and garden use **HI – 1 day**
243 Py Spray Insect Killer	Vitax	Pyrethrins	Contact insecticide for edible and ornamental crops **HI – 1 day**
244 Py Spray Garden Insecticide	Vitax	Pyrethrins	Contact insecticide for edible and ornamental crops **HI – 1 day**
245 Rapid Aerosol	ICI	Pirimicarb	Selective aphid control on all plants **HI – 3 days**
246 Rapid Greenfly	ICI	Pirimicarb	**HI – 7 days**
247 Safer's Garden Insecticide Conc	Phostrogen	Natural fatty acids	Contact acting **HI – None**
248 Safer's Rose and Flower	Phostrogen	Natural fatty acids	Contact acting **HI – None**
249 Sybol	ICI	Pirimiphos-methyl	Pest control on
250 Sybol Aerosol	ICI	Pirimiphos-methyl and synergised pyrethins	all plants including cucurbits
251 Sybol Dust	ICI	Pirimiphos-methyl	(cucumbers, melons) **HI – 7 days**

G2 Biological Control of insect pests in the greenhouse.

Name	Supplier	Active Ingredient(s)	Details
252 Biosafe	pbi	Steinernema carpocapsae	Control of vine weevil

G3 Fungicides to control diseases in the greenhouse. Refer to product label for specific advice on pests controlled. Check harvest interval requirements before applying.

Name	Supplier	Active Ingredient(s)	Details – Harvest Interval = HI
253 Benlate & Activex 2	ICI	Benomyl with trace elements and surfacants	Disease control on all types of plants **HI – 2–21 days** depending on crop
254 Bio Cheshunt Compound	pbi	Copper sulphate and ammonium carbonate	**HI – N/A**
255 Bio Dithane	pbi	Mancozeb	**HI – 7 days, except lettuce – 14 days**
256 Bio Spraydex General Purpose Insecticide	pbi	Copper sulphate and ammonium hydroxide	**HI – None**
257 Bio Supercarb Systemic Fungicide	pbi	Carbendazim and activator	**HI – None, except lettuce – 14 days**
258 Bordeaux Mixture	Vitax	Copper Sulphate	Controls tomato blight **HI – None**
259 Green and Yellow Sulphur	Vitax	Sulphur	Controls powdery mildew **HI – None**
260 Murphy Traditional Copper Fungicide	Levington	Copper oxychloride	Protective fungicide for control of peach leaf curl, potato blight, bacterial canker, rust and leaf spot and prevents damping off of seedlings
261 Nimrod-T	ICI	Bupirimate and triforine	Protective control o on fruit and flowers **HI – 7 days**

Name	Supplier	Active Ingredient(s)	Details – Harvest Interval = HI
262 Safer's Garden Fungicide	Phostrogen	Sulphur	Controls powdery mildew **HI – 1 day**

G4 Fungicide/Insecticide Mixtures for controlling pests in the greenhouse. Refer to product label for specific advice on pests and diseases controlled. Check harvest interval requirements before applying.

Name	Supplier	Active Ingredient(s)	Details – Harvest Interval = HI
263 Levington Nature's Answer Fungicide and Insect Killer	Levington	Fatty acids and sulphur	**HI – None**
264 Roseclear	ICI	Bupirimate, triforine and pirimicarb	**For use only on flowers**

G5 Washes and Cleansing for greenhouse hygiene.

Name	Supplier	Active Ingredient(s)	Details
265 Murphy Mortegg	Levington	Tar oils	Contact control of insect eggs, dormant fruit trees

G6 Other Products for use in the greenhouse.

Name	Supplier	Active Ingredient(s)	Details
266 Baby Bio Roota	pbi	1-naphthylacetic acid and dichlorophen	
267 Bio Strike	pbi	1-naphthylacetic acid and captan	Prevents basal rots

	Name	Supplier	Active Ingredient(s)	Details
268	Murphy Hormone Rooting Powder	Levington	1-naphthylacetic acid and captan	For rooting cuttings without rotting
269	Rooting Powder	Vitax	Captan and 1-naphthylacetic acid	For rooting cuttings
270	Tomato Setting Spray	Vitax	2-naphthyloxy acid	

Indoor House Plants

I1 Insecticides to control insect pests on indoor house plants. Check product label for specific advice on pests controlled.

	Name	Supplier	Active Ingredient(s)	Details
271	Baby Bio Flydown	pbi	Permethrin	Contact action
272	Bio Sprayday	pbi	Permethrin and piperonyl butoxide	Contact action
273	Baby Bio Spraydex Houseplant Spray	pbi	Permethrin and bioallethrin	Contact action
274	Levington Insect Spray for Houseplants	Levington	Permethrin	Contact action
275	House Plant Pest Killer	Vitax	Pyrethrins and resmethrin	Controls red spider mite, aphids and other insect pests
276	Keri Insect Spray	ICI	Pyrethrins	
277	Kerispray	ICI	Pirimiphos-methyl and synergised pyrethrins	Broad spectrum control
278	Plant Pin	Phostrogen	Butoxycarboxim	Systemic action
279	Py Spray Insect Killer	Vitax	Pyrethrins	Broad spectrum contact action
280	Safer's House-plant	Phostrogen	Natural fatty acids	Contact acting

I2 Biological Control of insect pests on indoor house plants.

	Name	Supplier	Active Ingredient(s)	Details
281	Biosafe	pbi	Steinernema carpocapsae	Control of vine weevil

F3 Fungicides to control insect diseases on indoor house plants. Refer to product label for specific advice on diseases controlled.

	Name	Supplier	Active Ingredient(s)	Details
282	Benlate + Activex 2	ICI	Benomyl and surfactants	Disease control on all types of plants

General Pest Control

GP1 Insecticides and Antkillers: Refer to product label for specific advice on pests controlled.

	Name	Supplier	Active Ingredient(s)	Details
283	Ant Gun	ICI	Bioallethrin and permethrin	Control of crawling pests outside
284	Antkiller Dust	ICI	Pirimiphos-methyl	Control of crawling pests inside and outside
285	Bio Anti-Ant Dust	pbi	Pyrethrum	Indoor and outdoor control of ants
286	Baby Bio Flydown	pbi	Permethrin	Controls household pests
287	Bio Kybosh	pbi	Permethrin and synergised pyrethrins	Household aerosol for control of flying and crawling pests
288	Bio Wasp Nest Destroyer	pbi	Carbaryl	Puffer pack for wasps in the nest
289	Bio Spraydex Insect Killer	pbi	Permethrin and bioallethrin	

	Name	Supplier	Active Ingredient(s)	Details
290	Creepy Crawly Gun	ICI	Bioallethrin and permethrin	Control of a wide range of insect pests in the home
291	Murphy Kil-Ant	Levington	Phoxim	Control of ants, earwigs, woodlice and other creeping and crawling pests both indoors and outdoors
292	Murphy Kil-Ant RTU	Levington	Cypermethrin	Control of ants, earwigs, woodlice and other creeping and crawling pests both indoors and outdoors
293	Murphy Kil-Ant Powder	Levington	Bendiocarb	Control of ants, earwigs, woodlice and other creeping and crawling pests both indoors and outdoors
294	Nippon Ant and Crawling Insect Killer	Vitax	Permethrin and tetramethrin	Contact and residual insecticidal surface spray for use in and around the home
295	Nippon Ant Killer Liquid	Vitax	Borax	Insecticidal bait for control of ants' nests
296	Nippon Ant Killer Powder	Vitax	Permethrin	Contact and residual
297	Nippon Fly Killer Spray	Vitax	Tetramethrin and permethrin	Aerosol space spray to control flies, wasps and other insects
298	Nippon Ready to Use Ant and Crawling Insect Killer	Vitax	Permethrin	Contact and residual surface spray for use in and around the home

	Name	Supplier	Active Ingredient(s)	Details
299	Py Powder	Vitax	Pyrethrins	Controls household and garden insect pests
300	Py Spray Garden Insect Killer	Vitax	Pyrethrins	Controls household and garden insect pests
301	Waspend	ICI	Pirimiphos-methyl and synergised pyrethrins	Control of all types of domestic pests

GP2 Rat, Mouse and Mole Control

	Name	Supplier	Active Ingredient(s)	Details
302	Bio Racumin Mouse Bait	pbi	Coumatetralyl	
303	Bio Racumin Rat Bait	pbi	Coumatetralyl	
304	Mouser	ICI	Brodifacoum	Controls up to 10 mice/box
305	Murphy Mole Smoke	Levington	Sulphur	Outdoor use only
306	Ratak	ICI	Difenacoum	Control of mice and rats with bait in garden and house

GP3 Deterrents

	Name	Supplier	Active Ingredient(s)	Details
307	Bio Pepper Dust	pbi	Pepper	Deters cats and dogs
308	Pepper Dust	Vitax	Pepper	
309	Scent Off Buds	Vitax	Naphthalene and volatile oils	Training aids for cats and dogs
310	Scent Off Pellets	Vitax	Naphthalene and volatile oils	Training aids for cats and dogs
311	Stay-Off	Vitax	Aluminium ammonium sulphate	Garden pet and bird deterrent

GP4 Slug and Snail Control

	Name	Supplier	Active Ingredient(s)	Details
312	Bio Slug Guard	pbi	Methiocarb	Slug and snail control in wet weather
313	Bio Slug Mini Pellets	pbi	Metaldehyde	
314	Slug Xtra	ICI	Metaldehyde	
315	Murphy Slugit Liquid	Levington	Metaldehyde	
316	Murphy Slugits	Levington	Metaldehyde	

Disposal of Garden Chemicals

● Do not buy more than you need; enough for one year is sufficient.

● Garden chemicals should be used up preferably within two years of purchase.

● Before buying more garden chemicals, check what products you have; read their labels to make sure you do not have a suitable alternative product already in stock.

● Consider buying a ready-to-use product if the right garden chemical for the job is available in this form.

● Mix too little rather than too much. Think in advance what you will do with surplus spray.

● Do not store surplus spray solution, unless it is in a ready-to-use pack; these are labelled and designed to be stable in storage.

● Never dispose of garden chemicals or their wastes down drains, sinks or lavatories or in watercourses or ditches. Take care to protect water, wildlife and natural habitats from contamination by garden chemical waste.

● Unwanted garden chemicals (undiluted): Small quantities (e.g. less than 125ml or 5fl oz) can be diluted as if for use and disposed of by spraying onto bare soil or gravel paths or drives as recommended for surplus spray solution above.

● To dispose of larger quantities, contact your local Waste Regulation Authority. The number will be listed in the telephone book. Some councils offer a free collection service for difficult household waste, others will make a reasonable charge.

Addresses

British Agrochemicals Association Ltd
4 Lincoln Court, Lincoln Road,
Peterborough PE1 2RP
Tel: (01733) 349225

BAA members supplying chemicals

Agrichem International Ltd
Fenland Industrial Estate, Station
Road, Whittlesey, Cambridgeshire
PE7 2EY
Tel: (01733) 204019 *Fax*: (01733)
204162

Boots Company plc
Leisure Business Centre, The
Frontage, Queen Street, Nottingham
NG2 3AA
Tel: (0115) 986 6671 *Fax*: (0115) 986
0695
Telex: 378431

Gem Gardening
Brookside Lane, Oswaldthwistle,
Accrington, Lancashire BB5 3NY
Tel: (01254) 393321 *Fax*: (01254)
236775

ICI Garden Products
Fernhurst, Haslemere, Surrey
GU27 3JE
Tel: (01428) 645454 *Fax*: (01428)
657222

Levington Horticulture Ltd
Horticulture Division, Paper Mill
Lane, Bramford, Ipswich, Suffolk
IP8 4BZ
Tel: (01473) 830492 *Fax*: (01473)
830046
Telex: 98168

Monsanto Garden Care
Thames Tower, Burleys Way,
Leicester LE1 3TP
Tel: (0116) 262 0864 *Fax*: (0116) 253
0320
Telex: 34658

Pan Britannica Industries
Britannica House, Waltham Cross,
Hertfordshire EN8 7DY
Tel: (01992) 623691 *Fax*: (01992)
26452
Telex: 23957

Phostrogen Ltd
Corwen, Clwyd LL21 0EE
Tel: (01490) 412662 *Fax*: (01490)
412177

Vitax Ltd
Owen Street, Coalville, Leicestershire
LE6 2DE
Tel: (01530) 510060 *Fax*: (01530)
510299

Pest and disease control permitted by the Soil Association

Mechanical controls using traps,
    barriers and sound
Pheromones
Herbal sprays, homeopathic and
    biodynamic preparations
Waterglass (sodium silicate)
Bicarbonate of soda
Soft soap
Steam sterilization
Biological control with naturally
    occuring organisms
Conventionally grown seed –
    recleaned only
Symbol approved products.

Products for pest and disease control

Some products are particularly recommended for the control of specific pests and diseases. The numbers against each pest or disease refer to the numbered products in the previous pages.

There are, however, some chemical combinations that have a more general use and you might prefer to use one of these. ICI Picket, for example, will kill a wide range of pests, while Bio Systhane will control many fungus diseases. There are many more.

Products for insect control

Ants	283, 284, 285, 291, 292, 293, 294, 295, 296, 298
Aphids	99, 100, 102, 123, 124
Blackfly	141, 142, 168, 169, 191
Greenfly	192, 221, 222, 245, 275
Caterpillars	97, 100, 116, 117, 164, 169, 222, 229
Chafers	42, 43
Codling Moth	98
Earwigs	291, 292, 293
Flies	287, 297, 301
Leaf Miner	223, 234
Leatherjackets	40, 42, 43
Pea Moth	167
Raspberry Beetle	167, 169, 233
Red Spider Mite	168, 221, 228, 249, 275
Sawfly	167, 220
Scale	168, 221
Vine Weevil	130, 252, 281
Wasps	288, 297
Whitefly	99, 117, 168, 221, 228, 229
Woodlice	291, 292, 293

Products for slug, snail and worm control

Slugs & Snails	312, 313, 314, 315, 316
Worms	40, 41

Products for the control of other animals

Birds	311
Cats & Dogs	307, 308, 309, 310
Mice	302, 304, 306
Moles	305
Rats	303, 306

Products for disease control

Apple Scab	132, 133
Blackspot	133, 135, 142
Canker	203, 260
Club Root	201
Lawn Diseases	44, 45
Leaf Spot	132, 262
Mildew (downy)	132, 133, 135, 200
(powdery)	142, 204, 207, 259
Peach Leaf Curl	132, 200, 203, 260
Pear Scab	132, 133
Potato Blight	200, 203, 259
Rose Rust	132, 135, 203, 260
Tomato Blight	200, 203, 258

Controlling Insect Pests with Biological Controls

I nstead of using potentially harmful chemicals, many garden and green-house pests can now be controlled by importing their natural enemies. Generally, these predators are specific to the pest so pose no danger to other insects. Most are extremely effective, very easy to use and, in the case of vine weevil, the only alternative available to gardeners. They are more expensive than chemicals and by using them, particularly in the greenhouse, it becomes essential to stop using chemicals completely. As an indication of their effectiveness, they are now becoming so popular with commercial growers that all tomatoes in this country are kept pest-free with biological controls.

Pest	Control	Supplier
Whitefly	Encarsia formosa	Green Gardener Defenders Zeneca (Nature's Friends) English Woodlands Applied Horticulture Wyebugs Chase
Red Spider Mite	Phytoseiulus	English Woodlands Wyebugs Green Gardener Zeneca (Nature's Friends) Defenders Chase
Aphids (under glass)	Aphidius	Green Gardener English Woodlands Chase
Vine Weevil	Nematodes	Zeneca (Nature's Friends) Wyebugs Applied Horticulture English Woodlands Green Gardener PBI. (Biosafe) Chase

Pest	Control	Supplier
Leatherjackets	Nematodes	PBI. (Biosafe)
Chafer Grubs	Nematodes	PBI. (Biosafe)
Mealy Bug	Cryptolaemus	Green Gardener English Woodlands Chase
Sciarid Fly Caterpillars	Nematodes Bacillus thuringiensis (Dipel)	Green Gardener Wyebugs English Woodlands Chase
Slugs	Nematodes	Chase Defenders

Addresses

Applied Horticulture, Fargro Ltd,
Toddington Lane, Littlehampton,
West Sussex BN17 7PP
Tel: (01903) 721591

Chase Organics,
The Organic Gardening Catalogue,
Coombelands House, Coombelands
Lane, Addlestone, Surrey KT15 1HY
Tel: (01932) 820958

Defenders Ltd,
PO Box 131, Wye, Ashford, Kent
TN25 5TQ
Tel: (01233) 813121

English Woodlands Biocontrol,
Hoyle Depot, Graffham, Petworth,
West Sussex GU28 0LR
Tel: (01798) 867574.

Green Gardener Ltd,
41 Strumpshaw Road, Brundall,
Norfolk NR13 5PG
Tel: (01603) 715096

PBI – Available at Garden Centres.

Wyebugs,
Wye College, Ashford, Kent
TN25 5AH
Tel: (01233) 812401

Zeneca – Available at Garden
Centres.

Nutrients

A ll plants require nutrients in the form of chemical salts which they absorb in solution. There are three major elements – nitrogen, phosphorus and potassium which are needed in relatively large amounts. The so-called 'trace elements' are needed in smaller quantities, but are essential.

The amount of each major element contained in compound fertilizers is marked on the bag, using the chemical symbols N for nitrogen, P for phosphorus and K for potassium. Often there are only figures showing the percentage of each element but always in that order. So, a bag of fertilizer marked '7.5.6.' contains 7% nitrogen, 5% phosphorus and 6% potassium.

Trace elements are not marked on the bag and indeed, many chemical fertilizers don't contain them. However, soils that are rich in organic matter in the form of regularly applied compost or manure are unlikely to be short. Deficiencies can generally be rectified by feeding with seaweed.

The Need for Feed

Major plant nutrients

NITROGEN (N)
Nitrogen controls the rate of growth, protein development and photosynthesis.
Deficiency symptoms: stunted growth, pale leaves with yellow or red tints, fruit smaller and highly coloured.
Treatment: top dress with nitrogenous fertilizer. Also add compost or manure when digging.

PHOSPHORUS (P)
Phosphorus in phosphates encourages healthy root growth as well as the ripening of fruit.
Deficiency symptoms: poor growth (especially roots), blue or purple-tinted leaves, low fruit yields.

Treatment: top dress with superphosphate or, alternatively, balanced fertilizer.

POTASSIUM (K)
Potassium in the form of potash aids the usefulness of nitrogen, enhances the colour and quality of fruit and flowers, and sustains general good health overall.
Deficiency symptoms: poor quality produce, low yields, leaf mottling, or marginal scorching.
Treatment: dress with sulphate of potash or balanced fertilizer before sowing.

CALCIUM (Ca)
Calcium adjusts soil acidity/alkalinity and helps the assimilation of nitrogen and the formation of plant cell walls.
Deficiency symptoms: growing tips scorched or die back, fruit disorders

(bitter pit in apples, tomato blossom end rot).
Treatment: lime acid soils, spray affected fruit with calcium nitrate solution and avoid irregular watering.

MAGNESIUM (Mg)

Magnesium aids chlorophyll production and seed germination.
Deficiency symptoms: dead or discoloured patches between leaf veins, orange, brown or red tints on foliage, fall of young leaves.
Treatment: lime with magnesium limestone (dolomite) if calcium also deficient; use 1oz Epsom salts (magnesium sulphate) in 1 gal water/sq yd.

Minor plant nutrients

These plant nutrients, often called trace elements, are only needed in very small quantities, but are vital for healthy growth.

IRON (Fe)

Iron helps the formation of chlorophyll.
Deficiency symptoms: complete leaves pale or whitish/yellow (chlorosis), especially in very alkaline soils.
Treatment: apply sequestered iron and guard against excessive liming.

MANGANESE (Mn)

Manganese is thought to help form chlorophyll.
Deficiency symptoms: chlorosis between veins which become bright green, leaf rolling.
Treatment: avoid over-liming, spray affected plants with manganese sulphate.

BORON (B)

Boron helps the movement of nutrients within plants.
Deficiency symptoms: rough patches on fruits and leaves, brown hearts in vegetables.
Treatment: correct soil deficiency by raking in borax at 1oz/10sq yd.

MOLYBDENUM (Mo)

Molybdenum is linked to nitrogen absorption.
Deficiency symptoms: distorted leaf blades and growing tips, whiptail in cauliflowers on acid soils.
Treatment: lime acid soils before growing susceptible plants such as brassicas.

COPPER (Cu)

Copper has an uncertain nutritional role.
Deficiency symptoms: wilt and death of young leaves and shoots, often on peaty soils.
Treatment: difficult – foliar feed with complete fertilizer containing trace elements.

ZINC (Zn)

Zinc aids starch production and balanced growth.
Deficiency symptoms: leaf and shoot distortion, brown buds, usually on light soils.
Treatment: as for copper, and avoid over-liming.

Fertilizers

Fertilizers are available in several forms. Firstly there are solid, liquid and soluble fertilizers: solids are generally longer-lasting but, since they can only be taken up in solution, are somewhat slower acting. Liquids are more readily available but more quickly leached out of the soil, while soluble fertilizers come in the form of a powder which is dissolved in water to form a liquid fertilizer.

Controlled-release fertilizers are now also available to amateur gardeners and they can be extremely useful. They consist of granular feeds which are treated to allow the release of the nutrients generally as temperatures rise. So, when the roots are not growing actively in low temperatures, the fertilizer is unavailable. When soil temperatures increase, so the fertilizer becomes more available. It's possible to buy formulations which remain available for 3–4 months and others for 6–9 months, so saving much labour in hand feeding.

Fertilizers are also bought either as 'straights', delivering just one of the three main nutrients, nitrogen, phosphorus or potassium, or as 'general' fertilizers containing all three in various formulations. A high nitrogen fertilizer is used, for example, to stimulate growth while a high potassium (or potash) feed is used to encourage flowering and fruiting.

Finally, there are organic and chemical fertilizers. While plants take up minerals in the same form, regardless of whether the source is organic or chemical, there are differences.

Organic fertilizers generally do no harm to soil organisms which are needed to break down the materials and make them available to plant roots. For this reason most are also longer lasting but not so immediately available.

Chemical fertilizers tend to depress the activity of soil organisms and it's thought that they can eventually deplete the soil of them entirely. However, they are more readily available but are leached out of the soil faster.

So, organic fertilizers are used to gradually increase fertility in the soil and require the presence of organic matter to sustain the organisms that break them down. Chemical fertilizers feed the plant directly and will work in completely mineral soils or even in hydroponic systems.

Key
O = organic. C = chemical.
L = liquid. S = solid. Sol. = soluble.
SM = several manufacturers.

GC = available at garden centres.
BT&T= Barnsdale Tried and Tested.

General Fertilizers

Acid-lovers Fertilizer
see Ericaceous Fertilizers.

African Violet Fertilizer
C   S   Garden Direct, Geddings
Road, Hoddesdon, Hertfordshire
EN11 0LR
Tel: (01992) 441888

Azalea, Rhododrendron and Heather Fertilizer
J. Arthur Bowers   GC.

Blood, fish and bone meal
O   S   SM   GC.   BT&T.

Bonsai Tree Fertilizer
C   S   Garden Direct.

Cactus and Succulent Fertilizer
C   S   Garden Direct.

Calcified seaweed
O   S   SM   GC.   BT&T.

Carnation Base
C   S   Garden Direct.

Chempak Multipurpose Base
C   S   Garden Direct.

Chempak Potting Base
C   S   Garden Direct.   BT&T.

Chempak Seed Base
C   S   Garden Direct.   BT&T.

Chempak Soluble Plant Foods (4 formulations)
C   Sol.   Garden Direct.   BT&T.

Chicken Manure (pelletted)
O   S   Levington Origins
Range.   GC.   BT&T.
Garden Direct.   Greenvale Farm,
Wonastow Road, Monmouth
NP5 3XX
Tel: (01677) 422953   BT&T.

Coir Liquid Feed
C   L   ICI   GC.   BT&T.

Controlled Release Fertilizer
C   S   Osmocote.   Garden
Direct.   BT&T.

Controlled Release Fertilizer
C   S   Levington
Unifeed.   GC.   BT&T.

Controlled Release Houseplant Fertilizer
C   S   Levington Long Lasting
Feed.   GC.

Ericaceous Base
C   S   Garden Direct.

Ericaceous Fertilizer
C   S   J. Arthur Bowers.   GC.

Ericaceous Fertilizer
C   Sol.   ICI
Miracid.   GC.   BT&T.

Foliar feed
C   L   PBI Fillip.   GC.

Flower and Bedding Plus
C   S   ICI   GC.

Flower and Fruit Fertilizer
C   S   Garden Direct.

Flower Fertilizer
C   L   Bio Flower Maker.   GC.

Foliage Fertilizer
C   L   Bio Leaf Maker.   GC.

Green Foliage Fertilizer
C   S   Garden Direct.

Growmore
C   L   SM   GC.   BT&T.

Growmore
C   S   SM   GC.   BT&T.

Houseplant Fertilizer
C   L   SM   GC.

Humic and Fulvic Acid Booster
O   L   Bio Humigro.   GC.

John Innes Base
C   S   SM   GC.   BT&T.

Morgro
O   S   Garden Direct.

Orchid Fertilizer
C   S   Garden Direct.

Organic Garden All Purpose Fertilizer
O   S   Arthur
Bowers.   GC.   BT&T.

Plant Food Tablets
C   S   Phostrogen.   GC.

Rhododendron Plus
C   S   ICI   GC.   BT&T.

Rose Fertilizer
C   S   SM   GC.   BT&T.

Rose Fertilizer
C   L   SM   GC.   BT&T.

Seaweed Meal
O   S   Garden Direct.   BT&T.

Seaweed Extract
O   L   SM   GC.   BT&T.

Shrub and Tree Plus
C   S   ICI   GC.

Soluble General Fertilizer
C   Sol.   Phostrogen.   GC.   BT&T.

Variegated Foliage Fertilizer
C   S   Garden Direct.

Vegetable Plus
C   S   ICI   GC.   BT&T.

Lawn Fertilizers

Autumn Lawn Food
C   S   SM   GC.

Controlled Release Lawn Food
C   S   Scotts.   GC.   BT&T.

Spring and Summer Lawn Food
C   S   SM   GC.   BT&T.

Spring and Summer Lawn Food
C   L   SM   GC.   BT&T.

Organic Lawn Food
O   S   Levington
Origins.   GC.   BT&T.

Lawn Weed and Feed

Lawn Weed and Feed
C   L   SM   GC.

Lawn Weed and Feed
C   S   SM   GC.   BT&T.

Trace Elements

Sequestered Trace Elements
C   L   Garden Direct.

Trace Element Frit
C   S   Garden Direct.   BT&T.

Kieserite (magnesium)
O S Garden Direct.

Magnesium Sulphate
C S Garden Direct.

Manganese Sulphate
C S Garden Direct

Sequestered Iron
C S Murphy
Sequestrine. GC. BT&T.

Sodium Molybdate
C S Garden Direct

Straights

Aluminium Sulphate (blueing agent)
C S SM GC. BT&T.

Ammonium Nitrate
C Sol. Garden Direct.

Bonemeal
O S SM GC. BT&T.

Borax
C Sol. Garden Direct.

Calcium Nitrate
C L Garden Direct.

Chelated Iron
C Sol. Garden Direct.

Chempak Fish Emulsion
O L Garden Direct.

Chilean Nitrate of Potash
O S Garden Direct.

Dolomite Lime
O S SM GC. BT&T.

Dried Blood
O S SM GC. BT&T.

Epsom Salts
C S Arthur
Bowers. GC. BT&T. Garden
Direct.

Fish Meal
O S SM GC. BT&T.

Hoof and Horn
O S SM GC. BT&T.

Mono Ammonium Sulphate
C S Garden Direct.

Muriate of Potash
C S Garden Direct. BT&T.

Nitrate of Soda
C S SM GC.

Nitrochalk
C S Garden Direct. BT&T.

Rock Potash
O S SM GC. BT&T.

Sulphate of Ammonia
CS SM GC. BT&T.

Sulphate of Iron
C S SM GC.

Sulphate of Potash
C S SM GC. BT&T.

Superphosphate
C S SM GC. BT&T.

Triple superphosphate
C S Garden Direct.

Organic Fertilizers permitted under Soil Association standards

Rock Phosphate

Feldspar

Magnesium Limestone (dolomite)

Calcium Sulphate (gypsum)

Ground Chalk and Limestone

Seaweed (free from non-approved products)

Unadulterated Seaweed and Plant-based Foliar sprays

Calcified Seaweed

Basic Slag

Rock Potash

Symbol approved organic fertilizers/liquid feeds

Wood Ash

Meat, Bone, Hoof and Horn meals

Fish meal

Unadulterated Fish Blood and Bone meals

Calcined Aluminium Phosphate

Fertilizers restricted under Soil Association standards

Proprietary organic fertilizers and liquid feeds without symbol approval

Dried blood – in spring or on overwintered crops

Wool Shoddy, Hop Waste

Leather Meal

Sulphate of Potash – only where exchangeable K levels are low and clay content is less than 20%

Sulphate of Potash – magnesium

Kieserite

Borax

Epsom salts

Composts and Soil Conditioners

A s a result of our concern for the conservation of peat bogs and the many letters from viewers urging us to take a lead in finding alternatives, much work has been done at Barnsdale to assess various products. It has generally been accepted that there is no need to use peat as a soil conditioner.

Finding a suitable compost for sowing and potting in the greenhouse proved more difficult and the work is still progressing.

It should be pointed out that, just as gardeners needed to get used to peat after using soil-based composts, new media may need different treatment. Some of our trials have been very successful and some have failed, but we don't suggest that this implies that those materials which proved less successful are worthless. More time is needed to ensure that we are using them to their best advantage, and the trials will continue. The composts listed here are those that have proved successful so far.

Soil Conditioners and Mulches

GC = Available at Garden Centres.

Cambark Horticultural Products (a range of bark products)
GC.

Danu Organic Soil Conditioner
Earthcare Products, Dromiskin, Dundalk, Eire. (and GC)
Tel: (00353) 4 272219

Levington Composted Bark
GC.

Levington Woodland Chipped Bark
GC.

Good Gardener All Purpose Bark
Garden Direct, Geddings Road, Hoddesdon, Hertfordshire
EN11 0LR
Tel: (01992) 441888

Heritage Soil Enricher
Waste Refineries International, Unit 3, The Home, Bishopscastle, Shropshire SY9 5HU
Tel: (01588) 650492

ICI Forest Bark
GC.

ICI Forest Mulch
GC.

J. Arthur Bowers Mulch and Mix
GC.

J. Arthur Bowers Horse Manure Compost
GC.

J. Arthur Bowers Rose Ultra Bark

J. Arthur Bowers Conifer Ultra Bark

J. Arthur Bowers Ericaceous Ultra Bark

J. Arthur Bowers Composted Ultra Bark

J. Arthur Bowers Decorative Bark Chips
GC.

John McLaughlan Horticulture, (wood fibre products)
50A, Market Place, Thirsk, North Yorkshire YO7 1LH
Tel: (01845) 525585

Lady Muck, (cow slurry soil conditioner)
Marshwood House, Whitegate, Forton, Chard, Somerset TA20 4HL (and GC).
Tel: (01460) 20822

Melcourt Industries, (a range of bark mulches and soil conditioners)
Eight Bells House, Tetbury, Gloucestershire GL8 8JG
Tel: (01666) 502711

Sunshine of Africa Cocoashell
Garden Direct, Geddings Road, Hoddesdon, Hertfordshire EN11 0LR (and GC).
Tel: (01992) 441888

UF Soil Conditioner

UF Tree Planting and Shrub Compost

UF All Purpose Mulch

UF Decorative Mulch

UF Chip and Bark Mulch

UF Manure
UF Horticulture, Stallard Common, Great Ellingham, Attleborough, Norfolk NR17 1JF
Tel: (01953) 456487

Composts

Chempak Coir

Chempak Coir Compost
Garden Direct, Geddings Road, Hoddesdon, Hertfordshire EN11 0LR
Tel: (01992) 441888

Fisons Multipurpose Peat-free Compost
GC.

Goldengrow Multipurpose Cocofibre Compost.

Goldengrow Ericaceous Cocofibre Compost
Goldengrow Ltd, Firth Road, Lincoln LN6 7AH
Tel: (01522) 537561

Godwins Fruit of the Earth Compost
GC.

Heritage Multipurpose Compost

Heritage Coconut Fibre
Waste Refineries International, Unit 3, The Home, Bishopscastle, Shropshire SY9 5HU
Tel: (01588) 650492

John Innes Composts
GC.

New Horizon Grow In Bag

New Horizon Multipurpose Compost

New Horizon Tree & Shrub Compost
GC.

Wessex Cococompost
GC.

Using coir composts

Coir composts look like peat but have very different properties, so you'll need to get used to a slightly different technique. The following points should be considered:

1. Its water-holding capacity is very good, but the top 15mm (½ in) or so tends to dry out quickly. To avoid the temptation to overwater, push your fingers down below the top of the compost to test for moisture until you get used to it.

2. Ideally, rest the pots and seed trays on capillary matting and keep that wet so that water is drawn up from the bottom.

3. Start to feed much earlier than you have done with peat composts. They often need it in the second or third week after potting. Feed with a special liquid feed or with a controlled release fertilizer incorporated into the compost before use.

Making your own composts

John Innes Seed and Potting composts are still excellent for growing a wide range of plants. Indeed, many gardeners still prefer them. Ideally, the loam used should be derived from stacked turf but good garden soil will give satisfactory results.

Soil can be sterilized in small quantities in the microwave oven or with boiling water but, if you're prepared to pick out a few weeds, it's not really necessary.

The original formula uses peat but I have successfully substituted coir compost, leaf-mould or sieved garden compost.

Seed compost

2 parts loam, 1 part leaf-mould or compost, 1 part sharp sand. Add to each bushel (4 two-gallon buckets), 1½ oz. superphosphate, ¾ oz. lime.

Potting compost

JOHN INNES NO. 1
7 parts loam, 3 parts leaf-mould or compost, 2 parts sharp sand. Add to each bushel (4 two-gallon buckets), 4oz. John Innes Base Fertilizer, ¾ oz lime.

JOHN INNES NO. 2
This is used for plants that will be in the pots rather longer and is made in the same way except that the amount of fertilizer is doubled.

JOHN INNES NO. 3
This is for long-term potting and here the fertilizer is trebled.

Alpine compost

Alpines require a very well-drained compost. I make mine using equal parts of soil, garden compost and coarse horticultural grit. No fertilizer is added. Lime may be necessary if your soil is acid.

Planting Charts for Flowering Bulbs, Aquatic Plants and Bedding Plants

Flowering Bulbs

By planting a range of bulbs, it's possible to have colour right through the year with the possible exception of late December/early January.

Bear in mind that many summer bulbs must be lifted in late summer and stored for the winter. Most spring-flowering species can remain in the ground where they'll multiply year on year.

To increase the drainage of the soil, plant at a depth that will cover the bulb with twice its own depth of soil. That means that a 7.5cm (3 in) high daffodil bulb will need a hole 23 cm (9in) deep.

Botanical Name	Common Name	Flowering Time	Colour
Acidanthera	Peacock orchid	Late spring–early autumn	White, maroon
Allium	Ornamental onion	Late spring–mid summer	Various
Amaryllis belladonna	Belladonna lily	Early–late autumn	Pink
Anemone	Windflower	Mid spring–mid summer	Various
Anomatheca laxa		Mid summer	Red, lilac or white
Brodiaea	Spring star flower	Mid–late spring	Blue, mauve
Calochortus	Butterfly tulip	Late spring–early summer	Various
Camassia	Camass	Early summer	Blue
Chionodoxa	Glory of the snow	Early–mid spring	Blue
Colchicum	Autumn crocus	Early–mid autumn	Various
Convallaria	Lily of the valley	Mid–late spring	White
Crinum		Late summer–early autumn	White, pink
Crocosmia		Mid–late summer	Yellow, orange or red
Crocus		Mid autumn–early spring	Various
Cyclamen (hardy varieties)		Mid autumn–late spring	White, crimson
Dierama pulcherrimum	Angel's fishing rod		Pink-purple
Eranthis	Winter aconite	Mid–late winter	Yellow
Erythronium	Dog's tooth violet	Early–late spring	Various

Height	Planting Time	Depth
90cm (3ft)	Late spring	8cm (3in)
30–120cm (1–4ft)	Autumn	10cm (4in)
60–90cm (2–3ft)	Late summer	10–15cm (4–6in)
22–30cm (9–12in)	Mid autumn–mid spring	5–8cm (2–3in)
15–20cm (6–8in)	Spring	3–4cm (¾–1½in)
15–23cm (6–9in)	Autumn	5–7cm (2–3in)
15–60cm (6–24in)	Mid–late autumn	8cm (3in)
60–70cm (24–28in)	Autumn	6–7cm (2½–3in)
10–15cm (4–6in)	Autumn	8cm (3in)
8–20cm (3–8in)	Late summer	2cm (1in)
15cm (6in)	Late autumn–early spring	2–5cm (1–2in)
90–120cm (3–4 ft)	Early spring	22cm (9in)
60–80cm (24–32in)	Early spring	5–8cm (2½–3in)
7–15cm (3–6in)	Late summer–mid autumn	8–10cm (3–4in)
10–15cm (4–6in)	Late summer–early autumn	1cm (½in)
1–1.5m (3–4½ft)	Spring	10cm (4in)
5cm (2in)	Autumn	5cm (2in)
15–30cm (6–12in)	Autumn	8cm (3in)

Botanical Name	Common Name	Flowering Time	Colour
Fritillaria imperialis	Crown imperial	Late spring	Yellow, red
Fritillaria meleagris	Snakeshead fritillary	Mid–late spring	Purple, white
Galanthus	Snowdrop	Late autumn–late winter	White
Galtonia	Spire lily	Mid–late spring	White
Gladiolus		Early spring–late autumn	Various
Hyacinthus	Hyacinth	Mid–late spring	Various
Ipheion uniflorum	Spring star-flower	Spring	Blue
Iris		Mid winter–mid summer	Various
Ixia	African corn lily	Early summer	Various
Leucojum	Snowflake	Mid winter–late spring late autumn	White
Lilium	Lily	Early summer–early autumn	Various
Muscari	Grape hyacinth	Mid–late spring	Blue
Narcissus	Daffodil Lent lily	Late winter–late spring	White, yellow
Nerine		Autumn	Pink
Ornithogalum	Star of Bethlehem	Late spring–early summer	White
Puschkinia	Striped squill	Mid spring	Blue, white
Ranunculus asiaticus	Turban ranunculus	Late spring–early summer	Various
Schizostylis	Kaffir lily	Mid–late autumn	Pink, scarlet
Scilla	Bluebell	Early spring–early summer	Blue, white, pink

Height	Planting Time	Depth
60–90cm (2–3ft)	Autumn	10–12cm (4–5in)
15–30cm (6–12in)	Autumn	5–8cm (2–3in)
10–20cm (4–8in)	Autumn	10cm (4in)
60–90cm (2–3ft)	Autumn	15cm (6in)
60–150cm (2–5ft)	Early–mid spring	10cm (4in)
22–35cm (9–15in)	Mid–late autumn	12–15cm (5–6in)
15cm (6in)	Autumn	4–5cm (1½–2in)
15–75cm (6–30in)	Autumn	8cm (3in)
60cm (2ft)	Autumn	5cm (2in)
10–45cm (4–18in)	Late spring–early autumn	8cm (3in)
45–350cm (1½–12ft)	Autumn	2–20cm (1–8in)
10–20cm (4–8in)	Autumn	5–8cm (2–3in)
10–60cm (4–24in)	Autumn	5–8cm (2–3in)
45–70cm (18–28in)	Early autumn	8cm (3in)
30–45cm (4–24in)	Autumn	10cm (4in)
15cm (6in)	Autumn	8cm (3in)
22cm (9in)	Late autumn–early spring	5cm (2in)
45cm–(18in)	Early–mid spring	8cm (3in)
8–35cm (3–15in)	Autumn	8–15cm (3–6in)

Botanical Name	Common Name	Flowering Time	Colour
Sparaxis	Harlequin flower	Late spring Early summer	Various
Sternbergia	Lily of the field	Mid–late autumn	Yellow
Tigridia	Tiger flower	Mid–late summer	Various
Tulipa	Tulip	Early–late spring	Various
Watsonia	Bugle lily	Late summer– early autumn	Various
Zephyranthes	Flower of the west wind	Early autumn	White

Aquatic Plants

A pond gives you a chance to grow a completely different range of plants in the garden. But, you need to be careful when you're choosing the plants.

If the pond is small, avoid really vigorous marginal plants and particularly natives. There's plenty of choice including many beautiful and less vigorous species.

NB. Planting depth: depth of water which should cover crown

Botanical name	Common name	Planting depth
Acorus gramineus	Sweet rush	0–8cm (0–3in)
Acorus calamus	Sweet flag	8–12cm (3–5in)
Alisma plantago aquatica	Water plantain	8–12cm (3–5in)
Aponogeton distachyos	Water hawthorn	15–45cm (6–18in)
Butomus umbellatus	Flowering rush	8–12cm (3–5in)
Calla palustris	Bog arum	5–10cm (2–4in)
Eichhornia crassipes	Water hyacinth	Floating
Eriophorum angustifolium	Cotton grass	2–8cm (1–3in)
Hottonia palustris	Water violet	Floating
Iris laevigata	Water iris	5–10cm (2–4in)
Iris pseudacorus	Yellow flag	8–12cm (3–5in)

Height	Planting Time	Depth
30cm (1ft)	Autumn	5cm (2in)
10cm (4in)	Late summer	10cm (4in)
45cm (18in)	Mid–late spring	5cm (2in)
15–75cm (6–30in)	Autumn	10–12cm (4–5in)
90–120cm (3–4ft)	Mid spring	8cm (3in)
15cm (6in)	Spring	8–10cm (3–4in)

It's vital to plant them at the right depth. With aquatic plants, the planting depth refers to the amount of water that covers the crown of the plant. Some shallow marginal plants will 'drown' if they're in water that's too deep, while the more vigorous water lilies will not survive in shallow water.

Height	Description
15–20cm (6–8in)	Grass like foliage
75cm (2½ft)	Dark green aromatic foliage, greenish yellow flowers
75cm (2½ft)	Broad leaves, pink & white flowers
10cm (4in)	Floating leaves, white flowers
75cm (2½ft)	Triangular foliage, pink flowers
23cm (9 in)	Glossy leaves, white flowers, red berries
Floating	Shiny leaves, blue flowers
30cm (12in)	Rush-like leaves, cotton-like seeds
Floating	Mauve flowers, ferny leaves
60cm (2ft)	Blue or white flowers
90cm (3ft)	Yellow flowers

Botanical name	Common name	Planting depth
Lemna trisulca	Ivy-leaved duckweed	Floating
Menyanthes trifoliata	Bogbean	8–12cm (3–5in)
Nymphaea pygmaea	Water lily	5–23cm (2–9in)
Nymphaea		15–60cm (6–24in)
Orontium aquaticum	Golden club	15–30cm (6–12in)
Pontederia cordata	Pickerel weed	8–12cm (3–5in)
Sagittaria sagittifolia	Arrowhead	8–12cm (3–5in)
Schoenoplectus tabernaemontani	Zebra rush	12–18cm (3–5in)
Typha minima	Reedmace	5–10cm (2–4in)
Typha stenophylla	Reedmace	30cm (1ft)

Summer and spring bedding

The Victorians loved it, a few 'upmarket' gardeners consider it vulgar, but there's no doubt that for colour, you can't beat spring and summer bedding.

Whether it's in the borders, in tubs, baskets or window boxes, you can grow a bright, colourful display of summer bedding from the late spring to the first frosts. Then it's removed and replaced with spring bedding to provide a little winter colour and a mass display from early to late spring.

For a summer show you use either hardy annuals, (abbreviated in the following lists as HA), half-hardy annuals (HHA), biennials (B) or tender perennials (TP).

Hardy annuals can be sown direct outside in early spring or some varieties even in the autumn. They're certainly the best way to provide the cheapest colour.

Half-hardy annuals are killed by

Botanical name	Common name	Colour
Abutilon		p r
Acroclinium (Helioterum)	Everlasting flower	p r w
Ageratum	Floss flower	b w
Agrostemma	Corncockle	l-p
Alyssum	Sweet alyssum	p w
Amaranthus	Love-lies-bleeding	purple

Height	Description
Floating	Light green leaves
23cm (9in)	Floating leaves, white flowers
15cm (6in)	Pink, white, yellow or red flowers
15cm (6in)	Pink, white, yellow or red flowers
25cm (10in)	Glaucous leaves, yellow flowers
60cm (2ft)	Lance-shaped leaves, blue flowers
45cm (1½ft)	Arrow-shaped leaves, white flowers
1m (3ft)	Long narrow striped leaves
30cm (1ft)	Long narrow leaves
1m (3ft)	brown, poker-like heads

frost, so they're either raised under glass or on the windowsill or bought as plants from the garden centre. Make sure you do not plant out until all danger of frost has passed.

Tender perennials are also frost-tender so the same rules apply. The difference is that, provided they're lifted and brought inside before the first frosts at the end of the year, or cuttings are taken, they can be kept going from year to year without the need to buy more plants.

Summer Bedding

Colour codes
b blue
c cream
g green
l lilac
m mauve
p pink
r red
v violet
w white
y yellow
gr grey
o orange

Height	Spacing	Type
90–120cm (3–4ft)	Spot plant	T P
30–38cm (12–15in)	30–38cm (12–15in)	H H A
20–25cm (8–10in)	23–30cm (9–12in)	H H A
90–120cm (3–4ft)	60–75cm (2–2½ft)	H A
7.5–15cm (3–6in)	15–23cm (6–9in)	H A
		H H A

Botanical name	Common name	Colour
Anchusa	Summer forget-me-not	b l p w
Arctotis	African daisy	o r w y
Antirrhinum	Snapdragon	o p r w y
Aster	Tahoka daisy	b p r w
Bartonia	Blazing star	y
Begonia		p r w
Brachycome	Swan river daisy	b p w
Browallia		b
Calceolaria	Slipper flower	o r y
Calendula	Pot marigold	o y
Callistephus	China aster	m p
Canna	Indian shot	p r
Centaurea	Cornflower	b p
Chrysanthemum		m o r w y
Cineraria		Silver leaves
Clarkia		p w
Convolvulus	Dwarf morning glory	b p w
Cordyline	Cabbage tree	Bronze leaves
Coreopsis	Annual tickseed	b r y
Cosmos		p r w
Dahlia		p r w y
Delphinium	Larkspur	b c p
Dianthus barbatus	Sweet William	p r w
Dianthus caryophyllus	Carnation	
Dianthus chinensis	Pink	
Diascia barberae		p
Dimorphotheca	Star of the veldt	o w y
Echium	Viper's bugloss	b m p w
Eschscholzia	Californian poppy	o p r w y

Height	Spacing	Type
23–30cm (9–12in)	30cm (12in)	H A
30–38cm (12–15in)	30cm (12in)	H H A
15–60cm (6–24in)	23–30cm (9–12in)	H H A
45–90cm (1½–3ft) also dwarf 22–30cm (9–12in)	23–30cm (9–12in)	
30–45cm (1½–2ft)	23–30cm(9–12in)	H A
15–25cm (6–10in)	20cm (8in)	H H A
15–23cm (6–9in)	23–30cm (9–12in)	H H A
20–25cm (8–10in)	23–30cm (9–12in)	H H A
23–30cm (9–12in)	23–30cm (9–12in)	H H A
23–30cm (9–12in)	23cm (12in)	H A
30–90cm (1–3ft)	60–90cm (2–3ft)	
90cm (3ft)	Spot plant	T P
30–90cm (1–3ft)		
60cm (2ft)	60–90cm (2–3ft)	T P
23–30cm (9–12in)	23–30cm (9–12in)	T P
30–38cm (12–15in)	30cm (12in)	H A
30cm (12in)	23–30cm (9–12in)	H A
60cm (2ft)	Spot plant	T P
25–45cm (10–18in)	30cm (12in)	H H A
60–90cm (2–3ft)	38–60cm (15–24in)	H H A
30–90cm (1–3ft)	30–90cm (12–36in)	T P
60–90cm (2–3ft)	45–60cm (18–24in)	H H A
15–30cm (6–12in)	23–30cm (9–12in)	H
20–60cm (8–24in)	23–30cm (9–15in)	H H A
15–45cm (6–18in)	23–38cm (9–15in)	H H A
30–38cm (12–15in)	20–60cm (12–24in)	H H A
15–30cm (6–12in)	23–30cm (9–12in)	H A
30cm (12in)	30–38cm (12–15in)	H A
25–30cm (10–12in)	30–38cm (12–15in)	H A

Botanical name	Common name	Colour
Gaillardia	Blanket flower	r y
Gazania	Treasure flower	o p r
Geranium		p r
Godetia		m p r
Gomphrena	Globe amaranth	m o r w
Gypsophila	Baby's breath	p w
Helichrysum	Everlasting flower	o p r w y
Heliotrope	Cherry pie	v
Iberis coronaria	Candytuft	m p w
Impatiens	Busy lizzie	p r w
Lathyrus	Sweet pea	m p r w
Lavatera	Mallow	p w
Layia	Tidy tips	y
Legousia	Venus's looking glass	b
Leptosiphon	Stardust	o p r w
Limnanthes	Poached-egg plant	y
Limonium	Statice	b p w y
Linaria	Toadflax	r
Lobelia		b r w
Lonas	African daisy	y
Malcolmia	Virginian stock	m r w y
Matricaria	Feverfew	y
Matthiola	Night-scented stock	m
Mesembryanthemum	Livingstone daisy	o p r y
Mimulus	Monkey flower; musk	o p r y
Moluccella	Bells of Ireland	g
Nemesia		l p r w y
Nemophila	Baby blue eyes	b
Nicotiana	Flowering tobacco	g m r w
Nierembergia	Cup flower	w
Nigella	Love-in-a-mist	b p w

Height	Spacing	Type
30–45cm (12–18in)	45–60cm (18–24in)	H H A
23–35cm (9–14in)	23–30cm (9–12in)	T P
22.5–30cm (9–15in)	30–38cm (12–15in)	T P
15–90cm (6–30in)	23–60cm (9–24in)	H A
50–60cm (20–24in)	45–60cm (18–24in)	H H A
15cm (18in)	30–45cm (12–18in)	H A
30–38cm (12–15 in)	30–38cm (12–15in)	H H A
30–38cm (12–15in)	30–38cm (12–15in)	T P
23–45cm (9–15in)	15–23cm (6–9in)	H A
10–15cm (4–6in)	15–23cm (6–9in)	
30–150cm (12in–6ft)	30cm (12in)	H A
60–120cm (2–4ft)	60–90cm (24–36in)	H A
30–38cm (12–15in)	23–30cm (9–12in)	H A
25cm (10in)	23–30cm (9–12in)	H H A
10–15cm (4–6in)	15–23cm (6–9in)	H A
15cm (6in)	15–23cm (6–9in)	H A
30–38cm (12–15in)	30–38cm (12–15in)	H H A
20–45cm (12–18in)	30–38cm (12–15in)	H A
15cm (6in)	15–23cm (6–9in)	H H A
45cm (18in)	30–38cm (12–15in)	H H A
23cm (9in)	23–30cm (9–12in)	H A
20cm (8in)	23–30cm (9–12in)	H H A
30cm (12in)	23–30cm (9–12in)	H H A
7.5–30cm (3–12in)	15–23cm (6–9in)	H H A
15–30cm (6–12in)	15–23cm (6–9in)	H H A
60cm (2ft)	23–30cm (9–12in)	H H A
20–30cm (8–12in)	23–30cm (9–12in)	H H A
15cm (6in)	15–23cm (6–9in)	H A
23–30cm (9–12in)	30–38cm (12–15in)	H H A
12.5–30cm (5–6in)	30–23cm (6–9in)	H H A
45cm (18in)	23–30cm (9–12in)	H A

Botanical name	Common name	Colour
Nolana		b w
Penstemon	Beard tongue	m p r w
Papaver	Poppy	o r y
Petunia		b m p w
Phacelia		b
Phlox		m p r
Polygonum	Knotweed	p
Portulaca	Sun plant, Rose moss	m p r w y
Pyrethrum		Gr/y foliage
Reseda	Mignonette	g r
Ricinus	Castor oil plant	g r folige
Rudbeckia	Cone flower	o
Salpiglossis	Painted tongue; velvet flower	m r p y
Salvia horminum	Clary	b p w foliage
Salvia splendens	Scarlet sage	m r p w
Sanvitalia	Creeping zinnia	y
Scabiosa	Scabious; pincushion flower	b
Silene	Catchfly	p/w
Tagetes erecta	African marigold	o y
Tagetes patula	French marigold	r o y
Tagetes signata	Tagetes	o y
Tolpis		y
Tropaeolum	Nasturtium	o p y
Verbena		b m r w
Viola	Pansy	m y
Xeranthemum	Immortelle	m p w
Zinnia		o p r y

Height	Spacing	Type
30cm (12in)	15–23cm (6–9in)	H H A
45–50cm (18–20in)	23–30cm (9–12in)	T P
30–90cm (1–3ft)	30–38cm (12–15in)	H A
23–30cm (9–12in)	23–30cm (9–12in)	H H A
23–30cm (9–12in)	23–30cm (9–12in)	H A
15–30cm (6–12in)	23cm (9in)	H H A
10–15cm (4–6in)	15–23cm (6–9in)	H H A
10–15cm (4–6in)	15–23cm (6–9in)	H H A
10cm (4in)	15–23cm (6–9in)	H H A
30cm (12in)	23–30cm (9–12in)	H A
105cm (3½ft)	Spot plant	H H A
20–90cm (8–36in)	30–38cm (12–15in)	H H A
30cm (12in)	30–38cm (12–15in)	H H A
45cm (18in)	30–38cm (12–15in)	H H A
15–60cm (6–24in)	30–35 cm (12–14in)	H H A
25–27.5cm (10–11in)	15–23cm (6–9in)	H H A
12.5–23cm (5–9in)	23–30cm (9–12in)	H H A
15cm (6in)	23–30cm (9–12in)	H H A
75cm (2½ft)	30–38cm (12–15in)	H A
23cm (9in)	23–30cm (9–12in)	H A
10–15cm (4–6in)	15cm (6in)	H A
23cm (9in)	15–23cm (6–9in)	H A
45–60cm (8–24in)	30–38cm (12–15in)	H H A
23cm (9in)	23–30cm (9–12in)	H H A
15–23cm (6–9in)	15–23cm (6–9in)	H P/B
60cm (2ft)	23–30cm (9–12in)	H H A
30–90cm (12–36in)	23–30cm (9–12in)	H H A

Spring Bedding

Botannical name	Common name	Colour
Alyssum saxatile	Gold dust	y
Arabis	Rock cress	p w
Aubrieta		m p
Bellis perennis	Daisy	p w
Campanula	Canterbury bell	m p w
Cheiranthus	Wallflower	o r y
Digitalis	Foxglove	p w
Myosotis	Forget-me-not	b
Viola	Pansy	c m p r y
Primula polyantha	Polyanthus	y p w r
Primula vulgaris	Primrose	y

Height	Spacing	Type
23cm (9in)	23–30cm (9–12in)	H P
22.5cm (9in)	23–30cm (9–12in)	H P
7.5cm (3in)	23–30cm (9–12in)	H P
15cm (6in)	15–23cm (6–9in)	H B
30cm (12in)	38–60cm (15–24in)	H B
30–45cm (12–18in)	30–38cm (12–15in)	H B
120–150cm (4–5ft)	38–60cm (15–24in)	H B
15–23cm (6–9in)	23–30cm (9–12in)	H B
15–23cm (6–9in)	15–23cm (6–9in)	H B /P
15cm (6in)	15–23cm (6–9in)	H P
15–23cm (6–9in)	15–23cm (6–9in)	H P

Planting Lists

The very first rule for successful planting is to ensure that you choose the right plant for each particular situation.

There's never a place in the garden that won't grow anything. Even the darkest, driest spot will support some form of life though in extreme cases the choices are naturally fewer.

Always start by trying to alleviate the problem as far as possible. Try to prune overhanging trees judiciously to improve light admission. Improve heavy soil with plenty of coarse grit and light, dry soil with barrowloads of bulky organic matter.

Naturally, it always pays to give the plants the best possible chance so you should also make sure that you coddle them with loving care until they're established with a big enough root system to look after themselves.

Plants for Moist Shade

Trees

Acer cappadocicum
 – griseum
 – negundo
 – platanoides
 – pseudoplatanus
 – saccharinum
Alnus
Betula nigra
 – pendula
Cercidiphyllum japonicum
Crataegus, all forms
Fraxinus in variety
Ilex aquifolium
× altaclerensis
Populus
Prunus padus forms
Pterocarya
Quercus
Salix
Sorbus

Shrubs

Acer palmatum
 – – 'Atropurpureum'
Aucuba japonica
 – – 'Picturata'
 – – 'Salicifolia'
 – – 'Variegata'
Camellia
Cephalotaxus harringtonia drupacea
Cercidiphyllum japonicum
Clethra alnifolia paniculata
Cornus varieties
Danäe racemosa
Daphne laureola
Decaisnea fargesii
Elaeagnus angustifolia
 – commutata
 – × ebbingei
 – pungens 'Maculata'
 – umbellata var. parvifolia
Euonymus fortunei

Fatsia japonica
Fothergilla major
– monticola
Gaultheria procumbens
– shallon
Hamamelis
Hydrangea
Hypericum calycinum
Ilex
Ligustrum
Osmanthus × *burkwoodii*
– decorus
Pachysandra terminalis
Pernettya
Pieris
Prunus laurocerasus
Rhododendron
Rubus cockburnianus
– thibetanus 'Silver Fern'
– tricolor
– Tridel Benenden
– ulmifolius 'Bellidiflorus'
Ruscus aculeatus
Salix
Sambucus
Sarcococca humilis
Skimmia
Spiraea thunbergii
– × vanhouttei
Stachyurus praecox
Staphylea in variety
Symphoricarpos
Viburnum davidii
– opulus
– rhytidophyllum

Conifers

Metasequoia
Picea
Taxus

Herbaceous perennials

Alchemilla mollis
Aruncus sylvester
Asplenium scolopendrium
Astilbe
Athyrium filix-femina
Caltha palustris 'Plena'
Cimicifuga
Convallaria majalis Dicentra
Dryopteris pseudomas
Endymion nonscriptus
Erythronium revolutum
Gentiana asclepiadea
Haberlea rhodopensis
Helleborus
Hosta
Iris sibirica
Ligularia przewalskii
Lilium martagon
Lythrum
Matteuccia struthiopteris
Monarda
Peltiphyllum peltatum
Polygonum
Polystichum setiferum
Primula (candelabra types)
Ramonda
Rodgersia
Sasa veitchii
Saxifraga fortunei
Smilacina racemosa
Symphytum
Tricyrtis (Toad lily)
Trollius
Uvularia
Vinca
Viola

Plants for Dry Shade

Trees

Acer campestre
– *ginnala*
– *platanoides* in variety
– *pseudoplatanus*
Aesculus
Alnus
Amelanchier lamarckii
Betula
Caragana arborescens
Crataegus prunifolia
Gleditsia triacanthos
Populus
Quercus cerris
– *ilex*
Robinia (except 'Frisia')
Sorbus aucuparia

Shrubs

Amelanchier lamarckii
Aucuba
Berberis
Buxus sempervirens
Cotoneaster
Danäe racemosa
Euonymus
Garrya elliptica
Hippophae rhamnoides
Ilex
Lonicera pileata
Mahonia
Osmanthus decorus
Pachysandra terminalis
Pittosporum tenuifolium
Prunus laurocerasus
Rubus calycinoides
– × 'Betty Ashburner'
– *tricolor*
– *ulmifolius* 'Bellidiflorus'
Ruscus aculeatus
Skimmia
Symphoricarpos

Conifers

Cephalotaxus
Juniperus media 'Pfitzeriana'
Podocarpus
Taxus

Perennials

Acanthus
Ajuga
Alchemilla mollis
Aquilegia
Arum
Arundinaria
Astrantia
Bergenia
Brunnera macrophylla
Campanula
Carex
Cortaderia
Corydalis
Cyclamen neapolitanum
Dicentra eximia
– *formosa*
Digitalis
Epimedium perralderianum
Euphorbia amygdaloides var. *robbiae*
Geranium macrorrhizum
– *nodosum*
– *phaeum*
Helleborus
Heuchera
Holcus mollis 'Variegatus'
Iris foetidissima
Lamium
Liriope muscari
Lunaria annua

Meconopsis cambrica
Melissa
Milium
Polygonatum
Polypodium vulgare (fern)
Pulmonaria
Salvia
Sambucus
Santolina
Smyrnium perfoliatum
Tellima grandiflora
Teucrium
Thalictrum
Tiarella
Tolmiea
Valeriana
Vinca
Viola labradorica
Waldsteinia ternata

Plants for Seaside Areas

Trees

Acer pseudoplatanus
Arbutus unedo
Atriplex halimus
Castanea sativa
Crataegus all forms
Escallonia 'Crimson Spire'
– ingramii
Eucalyptus gunnii
– niphophila
Fraxinus angustifolia
– excelsior
Fuchsia
Griselinia littoralis
Ilex × altaclerensis
– aquifolium
Laurus nobilis
Phillyrea latifolia
Populus alba
– canescens

– tremula
Prunus padus
Quercus cerris
– ilex
– petraea
– robur
– × turneri
Rosmarinus officinalis
Salix
Sorbus aria
– aucuparia

Shrubs

Arbutus
Arundinaria
Atriplex canescens
– halimus
Aucuba
Baccharis halimifolia
– patagonica
Buddleia davidii forms
– globosa
Bupleurum fruticosum
Chamaerops humilis
Choisya ternata
Cistus
Colutea
Coprosma lucida
Cordyline australis
– indivisa
Corokia cotoneaster
– × virgata
Cotoneaster
Cytisus
Elaeagnus 5 ebbingei
– commutata
– glabra
– pungens
Ephedra
Erica arborea alpina
– lusitanica
– × veitchii

Escallonia
Euonymus fortunei
  – japonicus
Fabiana imbricata 'Prostrata'
Fuchsia magellanica
Garrya elliptica
Genista
Griselinia
Halimium
Halimodendron halodendron
Hebe
Hippophae rhamnoides
Hydrangea macrophylla
Ilex aquifolium
Lavandula spica
Lavatera olbia
Leycesteria formosa
Lonicera pileata
Lycium
Myrica cerifera
Olearia
Ozothamnus
Pachysandra insignis
Parahebe
Phormium tenax
Pittosporum
Prunus spinosa
Pyracantha
Rhamnus alaternus
Ribes
Rosa
Rosmarinus officinalis
Salix
Sambucus racemosa
Santolina
Senecio
Sibiraea laevigata
Spartium
Spiraea
Tamarix
Ulex
Viburnum
Yucca

Conifers

Cupressus arizonica
  – macrocarpa
Juniperus
Picea omorika
Pinus nigra var. maritima
  – sylvestris

Herbaceous perennials

Achillea
Allium
Alstroemeria
Anthemis
Anthericum
Artemisia
Aster
Bergenia
Campanula
Centaurea
Colutea
Crocosmia
Dianthus
Dierama pulcherrimum
Echinops
Elymus arenarius
Erigeron
Erodium
Eryngium
Euphorbia
Filipendula hexapetala
Geranium
Gypsophila
Heuchera
Iris
Libertia
Limonium
Linaria
Lychnis flos-jovis
Melissa
Mimulus
Morina

Nerine
Oenothera
Origanum
Penstemon
Phygelius
Physostegia
Potentilla
Pulsatilla
Ruta
Salvia
Santolina
Scabiosa
Schizostylis
Scrophularia
Sedum
Sisyrinchium
Stachys
Stokesia
Tritonia
Veronica
Zantedeschia

Plants for Hot, Sunny and Dry Places

Trees

Acer campestre
Calocedrus decurrens
Genista aetnensis
Gleditsia triacanthos

Shrubs

Abelia
Artemisia arborescens
Atriplex halimus
Berberis
Buddleia
Buxus
Caryopteris
× clandonensis

Ceanothus
Ceratostigma willmottianum
Cistus
Clerodendrum trichotomum
Colutea arborescens
Convolvulus cneorum
Corokia cotoneaster
Coronilla glauca
Cotoneaster
Cytisus
Dorycnium hirsutum
Elsholtzia stauntonii
Escallonia
Euonymus
Genista
Hebe
Hedysarum multijugum
Hibiscus syriacus
Hippophae rhamnoides
Kolkwitzia amabilis 'Pink Cloud'
Lavandula
Olearia
Perovskia 'Blue Spire'
Philadelphus
Phlomis fruiticosa
Phormium in variety
Phygelius capensis
Piptanthus laburnifolius
Potentilla
Prunus amygdalus
 – tenella
Rhus
Ribes
Rosmarinus
Sambucus
Santolina
Senecio
Spartium junceum
Spiraea
Symphoricarpos
Tamarix
Teucrium fruticans
Ulex
Yucca

Conifers

Juniperus communis
 – media
Pinus mugo
Taxus baccata
Thuja

Herbaceous perennials

Acaena
Acanthus spinosus
Achillea
Agapanthus
Allium
Alstroemeria aurantiaca
Alyssum saxatile 'Compactum'
Anaphalis margaritacea
Antennaria
Anthemis tinctoria
Arabis
Armeria
Artemisia
Asphodeline lutea
Ballota
Bergenia
Bupleurum falcatum
Calamintha
Carex morrowii 'Evergold'
Catananche caerulea 'Major'
Centaurea dealbata
Centranthus
Cerastium
Ceratostigma plumbaginoides
Cestrum
Chamaemelum nobile
Cheiranthus
Chrysanthemopsis hosmariense
Cichorium
Cirsium rivulare
Commelina
Convolvulus sabatius
Coreopsis
Cotula

Crambe cordifolia
Crepis incana
Crinum
Crocosmia Cynara
Dianthus
Diascia
Dictamnus
Dierama
Draba aizoides
Echinops ritro
Epilobium canum
Eriophyllum
Erodium
Eryngium
Erysimum
Euphorbia coralloides
 – characias subsp.
 – cyparissias
 – dulcis
 – myrsinites
 – polychroma
 – seguieriana
Ferula communis
Foeniculum
Galactites tomentosa
Gaura
Geranium
Gladiolus papilio
Glaucium
Grindelia Gypsophila
Haplopappus
Helianthemum
Helichrysum lanatum
Hypericum
Iberis 'Snowflake'
Incarvillea delavayi
Indigofera gerardiana
Ipheion uniflorum
Iris foetidissima
 – germanica
 – 'Green Spot'
 – pallida
 – unguicularis
Kniphofia

Leptinella squalida
Liatris 'Kobold'
Libertia formosa
– grandiflora
– peregrinans
Linaria
Linum Lychnis coronaria
– flos-jovis
Marrubium
Melissa
Minuartia
Moltkia petraea
Nepeta gigantea
– mussinii
Nerine bowdenii
Oenothera
Onopordum
Origanum rotundifolium
Osteospermum
Othonnopsis
Papaver orientale
Penstemon barbatus
Phlox douglasii
– subulata
Potentilla
Pulsatilla vulgaris
Raoulia
Romneya
Rosmarinus officinalis
Ruta graveolens
Salvia patens
Santolina corsica
Saponaria ocymoides
Sedum
Sempervivum
Sideritis
Silene maritima
Sisyrinchium striatum
Stachys
Stipa
Strobilanthes
Thymus
Tulipa
Verbascum

Cold and Windy

Trees

Acer campestre
– negundo
– platanoides
'Cleveland'
'Drummondii'
'Globosum'
'Laciniatum'
'Olmstead'
'Royal Red'
'Schwedleri'
– pseudoplatanus
'Erectum'
'Leopoldii'
'Spaethii'
'Worleei'
Alnus glutinosa
– incana
Betula
Carpinus betulus
– 'Fastigiata'
– 'Purpurea'
Corylus
Crataegus
Fagus sylvatica
– 'Asplenifolia'
– 'Dawyck'
Fraxinus excelsior
Gleditsia triacanthos
Laburnum
Populus
Quercus
Sorbus aria
– aucuparia
– intermedia
Tilia cordata
Ulmus angustifolia
– 'Cornubiensis'

Shrubs

Actinidia kolomikta
Arctostaphylos uva-ursi
Arundinaria japonica
Berberis
Buddleia
Calluna vulgaris
Caragana arborescens
Chaenomeles
Chamaedaphne calyculata
Clematis viticella
Clethra alnifolia
Colutea arborescens
Cornus
Corylus
Cotinus coggygria
Cotoneaster
Deutzia
Elaeagnus
Euonymus alatus
Gaultheria shallon
Hamamelis virginiana
Hippophae rhamnoides
Hydrangea paniculata 'Grandiflora'
Hypericum calycinum
Ilex
Jasminum nudiflorum
Kalmia angustifolia
– latifolia
Kerria
Lavatera olbia
Ledum groenlandicum
Leucothïe fontanesiana
Ligustrum ovalifolium
Lonicera involucrata
– pileata
Mahonia
Myrica gale
Pachysandra terminalis
Pernettya
Philadelphus
Pieris floribunda
Potentilla

Prunus spinosa
Rhododendron caucasicum
– ponticum
– yakushimanum
Rosa rugosa
Ruscus
Salix
Sambucus nigra
Spartium junceum
Spiraea
Symphoricarpos
Tamarix
Ulex
Viburnum lantana
– rhytidophyllum ·
Wisteria floribunda

Conifers

Chamaecyparis nootkatensis
– obtusa
– pisifera
Cryptomeria japonica
Cupressocyparis leylandii
Ginkgo biloba
Juniperus
Picea abies
– breweriana
– omorika
Pinus
Taxus
Thuja
Tsuga canadensis

Herbaceous perennials

Acaena
Achillea filipendulina
Ajuga reptans
Allium
Anemone × hybrida
Arundinaria
Bergenia
Campanula carpatica

Cimicifuga foetida
Coreopsis verticillata
Dryas octopetala
Echinops ritro
Helleborus niger
Hesperis matronalis
Iris sibirica
Malva moschata
Miscanthus
Nepeta × faassenii
Osmunda regalis
Phalaris arundinacea
Phlox subulata
Polygonum affine
Primula
Pulmonaria saccharata
Sempervivum
Stipa gigantea
Tanacetum vulgare
Tiarella wherryi

Waterlogged Sites

Trees

Acer negundo
Alnus
Amelanchier
Betula
Crataegus oxyacantha
Fraxinus
Liquidambar
Liriodendron
Magnolia virginiana
Mespilus germanica
Nothofagus antarctica
Parrotia
Populus
Pterocarya
Pyrus
Quercus palustris
Salix
Sorbus aucuparia

Shrubs

Amelanchier lamarckii
Andromeda polifolia
Aronia
Calycanthus
Cephalanthus occidentalis
Clethra
Cornus alba
– baileyi
– stolonifera
Gaultheria shallon
Hippophae rhamnoides
Ilex verticillata
Lindera benzoin
Myrica cerifera
– gale
Neillia longiracemosa
Parrotia persica
Pernettya
Philadelphus
Photinia villosa
Physocarpus opulifolius
Prunus spinosa
Rhamnus frangula
Rhododendron Hardy Hybrids
Salix × balfourii
– caprea
– humilis
– integra
– purpurea
– repens
Sambucus
Sorbaria
Spiraea × billiardii
– × vanhouttei
– veitchii
Symphoricarpos
Vaccinium
Viburnum dentatum
– lantana
– lentago
– opulus rhytidophyllum

Conifers

Abies
Cedrus deodara
Metasequoia glyptostroboides
Picea sitchensis
Taxodium ascendens
– distichum

Herbaceous perennials

Acorus
Ajuga reptans
Anaphalis margaritacea
Astilbe
Butomus umbellatus
Caltha
Cardamine pratensis
Carex elata 'Aurea'
– pendula
– riparia
Darmera
Dodecatheon meadia
Eupatorium
Euphorbia palustris
Filipendula
Geranium
Glyceria maxima
Gunnera manicata
Hemerocallis
Houttuynia
Inula
Iris ensata
– laevigata
– pseudacorus
– versicolor
Ligularia
Lobelia
Luzula maxima
Lysichiton
Lythrum
Miscanthus
Monarda didyma

Myosotis
Persicaria bistorta
– campanulatum
– milletii
Petasites japonicus
Pontederia
Primula bulleyana
– florindae
– japonica
– pulverulenta
Ranunculus acris –
constantinopolitanus 'Flore Plenus'
Rodgersia
Sasa veitchii
Senecio smithii
Spartina
Thalictrum flavum
Trollius
Verbena corymbosa
Zantedeschia

Acid Soils

Trees

Acer negundo
– rubrum
Ailanthus altissima
Betula
Castanea
Cercidiphyllum japonicum
Cercis
Cornus kousa
Crataegus monogyna
Embothrium coccineum
Eucryphia
Fagus sylvatica
Gleditsia
Halesia
Ilex aquifolium
Koelreuteria paniculata
Liquidambar styraciflua

Populus alba
– canescens
– tremula
Quercus cerris
– robur
Robinia
Sorbus × hybrida
– intermedia

Shrubs

Acer palmatum 'Dissectum'
Amelanchier canadensis
Arctostaphylos
Baptisia australis
Berberis vulgaris
Calluna vulgaris
Camellia
Cassiope
Corylopsis
Cryptomeria japonica 'Vilmoriniana'
 Daboecia cantabrica
Desfontainia
Dicentra
Enkianthus
Erica
Fothergilla monticola
Gaultheria
Halesia
Hamamelis mollis
Ilex aquifolium
Kalmia latifolia
Lapageria rosea
Ledum
Leucothie
Lilium pardalinum
Lycium barbarum
Magnolia stellata
Osmunda regalis
Pachysandra
Parrotia persica
Pernettya
Pieris

Rhamnus frangula
Rhododendron (incl. Azalea)
Salix × balfourii
– caprea
– cinerea
Sambucus nigra
– racemosa
Sarcococca
Skimmia
Staphylea
Tricyrtis
Ulmus pumila
Viburnum opulus

Conifers

Abies
Chamaecyparis
Cryptomeria japonica 'Elegans'
 Juniperus Larix
Lawsoniana
Picea
Pinus nigra
– sylvestris
Taxodium
Taxus baccata

Herbaceous perennials

Corydalis
Dactylorrhiza elata
Disporum smithii
Epimedium
Erythronium revolutum
Gentiana sino-ornata
Kirengeshoma palmata
Lilium davidii
– tigrinum
Liriope muscari
Lupinus 'Russell Hybrids'
Meconopsis betonicifolia
Ourisia

Primula ulgaris
 – vulgaris elatior
Rhodohypoxis
Tricyrtis hirta
Trillium grandiflorum
Tropaeolum

Robinia
Salix
Sophora
Sorbus aria
 – hybrida
 – intermedia
Tilia
Ulmus

Chalky Soils

Trees

Acer campestre
 – cappadocicum
 – griseum
 – negundo forms
 – platanoides
 – pseudoplatanus
Aesculus
Ailanthus
Amelanchier
Betula
Caragana
Carpinus betulus
Catalpa
Cercis siliquastrum
Corylus
Crataegus oxyacantha
Fagus sylvatica
Fraxinus excelsior
 – ornus
Gleditsia
Juglans
Laburnum
Liriodendron
Magnolia kobus
Malus
Morus nigra
Paulownia
Platanus
Populus alba
 – canescens
Prunus all 'Japanese Cherries'
Pyrus

Shrubs

Aesculus parviflora
Arbutus
Arundinaria
Baccharis halimifolia
Berberis
Buddleia davidii
Buxus
Callicarpa
Caragana arborescens
Catalpa
Ceanothus
Choisya
Cistus
Clematis
Clerododendrum trichotomum
Colutea
Cornus mas
Cotoneaster
Cytisus nigricans
Daphne mezereum
 Deutzia
Dipelta floribunda
Elaeagnus
Erica carnea
Escallonia
Eucryphia
Euonymus
Forsythia
Fuchsia
Genista cinerea
Hebe
Hedera

Helianthemum nummularium
Hibiscus syriacus
Hydrangea villosa
Hypericum
Ilex
Indigofera
Kerria
Kolkwitzia amabilis
Laurus nobilis
Ligustrum
Lonicera
Magnolia kobus
Mahonia aquifolium
Olearia
Osmanthus
Paeonia delavayi
– – lutea
Philadelphus
Phillyrea
Phlomis
Photinia serratifolia
Pittosporum
Potentilla fruticosa
Prunus laurocerasus
Pyracantha
Rhus
Ribes
Romneya
Rosa
Rosmarinus
Rubus tricolor
Salix
Sambucus
Santolina
Sarcococca
Senecio
Spartium junceum
Spiraea japonica
– nipponica
Stachyurus praecox
Staphylea
Symphoricarpus
Syringa vulgaris
Tamarix

Teucrium
Ulex
Viburnum
Vinca
Weigela
Yucca

Conifers

Juniperus communis
– media
Pinus mugo
– nigra
Taxus baccata
Thuya

Herbaceous perennials

Acanthus
Alyssum
Anemone
Anthemis cupaniana
Aubrieta deltoidea
Campanula cochleariifolia
– glomerata
Dianthus
Eremurus
Iris germanica
Linaria purpurea
Paeonia
Papaver orientale
Phlomis
Platycodon
Primula veris
Prunella
Pulsatilla vulgaris
Pyrethrum
Salvia sclarea
Saponaria
Saxifraga umbrosa
Scabiosa caucasica
Sedum spectabile

Thymus vulgaris
Tradescantia
Verbascum bombyciferum
Veronica

Plants for Clay Soils

Trees

Acer
Aesculus
Alnus
Betula
Carpinus
Corylus
Crataegus
Eucalyptus
Fraxinus
Ilex
Laburnum
Malus
Ostrya
Populus
Prunus
Pyrus
Quercus
Salix
Sorbus
Tilia

Shrubs

Abelia
Aralia elata
Aronia
Aucuba japonica
Berberis
Chaenomeles
Choisya ternata
Colutea
Cornus Corylus avellana
Cotinus coggygria
Cotoneaster

Crataegus Cytisus
Escallonia
Eucalyptus
Forsythia Genista
Hamamelis
Hedera helix
Hibiscus syriacus
Hypericum
Kerria
Lonicera
Magnolia Mahonia
Osmanthus
Philadelphus
Pieris floribunda
Potentilla
Prunus cistena
– laurocerasus
Pyracantha
Rhamnus frangula
Rhododendron
Ribes sanguineum
Rosa
Rubus
Salix daphnoides
Senecio greyi
Skimmia
Spiraea 'Arguta'
Symphoricarpos
Syringa
Viburnum plicatum
Weigela florida

Conifers

Abies
Chamaecyparis
Juniperus
Larix
Picea breweriana
Pinus
Taxodium distichum
Taxus
Thuja

Herbaceous perennials

Aconitum
Ajuga
Alopecurus
Anemone japonica
– nemorosa
Arundinaria
Aster Camassia leichtlinii
Campanula
Carex
Cephalaria
Crocosmia masonorum
Darmera
Deschampsia
Digitalis
Doronicum plantagineum
Echinops
Epimedium
Eranthis hyemalis
Erigeron
Euphorbia amygdaloides var. robbiae
Filipendula
Gentiana
Geranium
Helenium autumnale Helleborus
Hemerocallis
Hosta
Inula
Iris
Lamium
Levisticum
Ligularia
Lonicera
Lysimachia clethroides
Lythrum
Miscanthus
Molinia
Monarda
Narcissus
Oenothera
Panicum
Peltiphyllum
Persicaria affinis

Petasites
Phyllostachys
Physalis
Physostegia
Podophyllum emodi
Polemonium
Polygonatum
Primula
Prunella webbiana
Ranunculus
Rheum
Rodgersia
Rudbeckia Salvia
Sasa veitchii
Saxifraga 5 urbium
Sidalcea
Solidago
Spartina
Symphytum
Trachystemon
Tradescantia
Waldsteinia

Shrubs and Climbers for North- and East-Facing Walls

Shrubs

Acradenia frankliniae
Agapetes serpens
Azara microphylla
– petiolaris
Berberis × stenophylla
Camellia japonica
– reticulata
– saluenensis
– sasanqua
– × williamsii
Chaenomeles
Choisya ternata

Crinodendron hookerianum
 – patagua
Daphne gnidium
 – × *hybrida*
 – odora
Desfontainea spinosa
Drimys winteri
Eriobotrya japonica
Eucryphia cordifolia
 – × *intermedia*
 – × *nymansensis*
Euonymus fortunei
Garrya elliptica
 – × *thuretii*
Grevillea rosmarinifolia
Ilex georgei
 – insignis
 – latifolia
Illicum anisatum
Itea ilicifolia
Jasminum humile
 – nudiflorum
Kerria japonica
Lomatia myricoides
Mahonia japonica
 – lomariifolia
 – × *media*
Mitraria coccinea
Osmanthus delavayi
 – yunnanensis
Photinia serrulata
Piptanthus laburnifolius
Pyracantha
Ribes laurifolium
Rubus henryi
 – lambertianus
Schima argentea
Viburnum grandiflorum

Climbers

Akebia quinata
Aristolochia macrophylla
Azara microphylla
Berchemia racemosa
Celastrus orbiculatus
 – scandens
Chaenomeles
Cotoneaster horizontalis
Escallonia
Euonymus fortunei
Forsythia suspensa
Garrya elliptica
Hedera canariensis 'Variegata'
 – colchica
 – – 'Dentata Aurea'
 – helix
 – hibernica
Hydrangea anomala
 – petiolaris
Jasminum officinale 'Grandiflorum'
 – × *stephanense*
Lathyrus
Lonicera × *americana*
 – japonica
Muehlenbeckia complexa
Parthenocissus
Pileostegia viburnoides
Polygonum baldschuanicum
Rosa
Schisandra grandiflora
Schizophragma hydrangeoides
 – integrifolium
Vitis

Shrubs and Climbers for South and West Walls

Shrubs

Abeliophyllum distichum
Acacia
Buddleia
Carpenteria californica
Ceanothus
Choisya ternata
Clianthus puniceus
Fremontodendron

Climbers

Abeliophyllum distichum
Abutilon megapotamicum
Acacia dealbata
Actinidia chinensis
 – kolomikta
Akebia quinata
Aristolochia macrophylla
Buddleia colvilei
 – fallowiana alba
Campsis grandiflora
Ceanothus
Chimonanthus
Clematis
Clianthus puniceus
Cobaea scandens
Cytisus battandieri
Eccremocarpus scaber
Escallonia
Humulus lupulus 'Aureus'
Hydrangea petiolaris
Ipomoea
Itea ilicifolia
Leptospermum scoparium
Lippia citriodora
Lonicera 'Dropmore Scarlet'
 – × tellmanniana

Magnolia grandiflora
Myrtus
Passiflora caerulea
Phygelius capensis
Piptanthus laburnifolius
Prunus triloba 'Multiplex'
Solanum crispum 'Glasnevin'
Thunbergia alata
Trachelospermum jasminoides
Viburnum burkwoodii
Vitis
Wisteria

Plants for Scent

Trees

Acacia dealbata
Aesculus hippocastanum
Azara microphylla
Cladrastis lutea
 – sinensis
Crataegus monogyna 'Stricta'
Drimys winteri
Eucryphia Fraxinus sieboldiana
 – ornus
Gordonia Laburnum alpinum
 – vossii
 – watereri
Magnolia fraseri
 – kobus
 – macrophylla
 – obovata
 – salicifolia
Malus angustifolia
 – baccata mandschurica
 – coronaria 'Charlottae'
 – floribunda
 – hupehensis
 – × robusta
Michelia doltsopa
 – figo

Myrceugenia exsucca
Myrtus apiculata
Pittosporum eugenioides
Poliothyrsis sinensis
Prunus 'Amanogawa'
– *conradinae*
– 'Jo-nioi'
– *lusitanica*
– *padus* 'Grandiflora'
– *serrulata*
– 'Shirotae'
– × *yedoensis*
Robinia pseudoacacia
Styrax japonica
Tilia × *euchlora*
– *europaea*
– *oliveri*
– *petiolaris*
– *platyphyllos*
– *tomemtosa*

Shrubs

Abelia chinensis
– × *grandiflora*
– *triflora*
Alangium Azara lanceolata
– *petiolaris*
Berberis buxifolia
– *sargentiana*
– *stenophylla*
– *vulgaris*
Bruckenthalia spiculifolia
Buddleia
Buxus sempervirens
Camellia sasanqua
Ceanothus 'Gloire de Versailles'
Chimonanthus praecox
Chionanthus virginicus
Choisya ternata
Cionura erecta
Citrus

Clematis heracleifolia
Clethra acuminata
– *alnifolia* 'Paniculata'
– *barbinervis*
– *fargesii*
Colletia armata
– *cruciata*
Cordyline australis
Corokia cotoneaster
Coronilla glauca
– *valentina*
Corylopsis
Cytisus battandieri
– 'Porlock'
– × *praecox*
– *purgans*
Daphne
Datura suaveolens
Deutzia compacta
– *5 elegantissima*
Edgeworthia papyrifera
Elaeagnus angustifolia
– *commutata*
– × *ebbingei*
– *glabra*
– *macrophylla*
– *umbellata*
Erica arborea 'Alpina'
– × *darleyensis*
– *lusitanica*
– × *veitchii*
Escallonia 'Donard Gem'
Eucryphia milliganii
Euonymus sachalinensis
Eupatorium ligustrinum
Fothergilla gardenii
– *major*
– *monticola*
Freylinia lanceolata
Gaultheria forrestii
Genista aetnensis
– *cinerea*
– *monosperma*
– *tinctoria*

Hakea microcarpa
Hamamelis mollis
Hoheria glabrata
– lyallii
Itea ilicifolia
– virginica
Jasminum humile 'Revolutum'
– wallichianum
Lavandula
Ligustrum quihoui
Lomatia myricoides
Lonicera
Luculia gratissima
Lupinus arboreus
Magnolia
Mahonia aquifolium
– japonica
– × media
– ̠– 'Charity'
Myrtus communis
Olearia × haastii
– ilicifolia
– macrodonta
– odorata
– rani
Osmanthus
× Osmarea burkwoodii
Paeonia × lemoinei
Paulownia fargesii
– lilacina
Perovskia 'Blue Spire'
Petteria ramentacea
Philadelphus
Pimelea prostrata
Pittosporum patulum
– tenuifolium
– tobira
– undulatum
Poncirus trifoliata
Prunus mume
Ptelea trifoliata
Pterostyrax
Pyracantha
Rhododendron

Ribes alpinum
– fasciculatum
– gayanum
– odoratum
Romneya
Rosa
Rubus 'Tridel Benenden'
Sarcococca
Skimmia japonica 'Fragrans'
– japonica 'Rubella'
– laureola
Spartium junceum
Syringa
Ulex europaeus
Viburnum
Yucca filamentosa
– flaccida
Zenobia pulverulenta

Herbaceous perennials

Adenophora liliifolia
Asphodeline lutea
Calanthe discolor
Cestrum parqui
Clematis heracleifolia var. davidiana
– recta
Convallaria majalis
Cosmos atrosanguineus
Crambe cordifolia
Dianthus
Dictamnus albus
Hemerocallis lilio-asphodelus
Hosta 'Honeybells'
Houttuynia cordata
Iris graminea
– hoogiana
– pallida
– unguicularis
Lonicera japonica 'Halliana'
Lunaria rediviva
Maianthemum Monarda
Paeonia lactiflora

Phlox maculata
– *paniculata*
– *pilosa*
Polygonum polystachyum
Primula vulgaris
Tellima grandiflora rubra
– *odorata*
Verbena
Viola 'Maggie Mott'
– 'Moonlight'
– *odorata*

Climbers

Abeliophyllum distichum
Acacia dealbata
Actindia chinensis
– *polygama*
Akebia quinata
Clematis armandii
– *cirrhosa balearica*
– *flammula*
– *montana*
– *paniculata*
– *rehderiana*
– *uncinata*
Decumaria sinensis
Holboellia latifolia
Itea ilicifolia
Jasminum azoricum
– *beesianum*
– *officinale*
– *polyanthum*
– × *stephanense*
Lardizabala biternata
Lippia citriodora
Lonicera × *americana*
– *caprifolium*
– *etrusca*
– × *heckrottii*
– *japonica* 'Halliana'
– *periclymenum*
– *repens*

– 'Serotina'
Mandevilla suaveolens
Myrtus
Stauntonia hexaphylla
Viburnum × *burkwoodii*
Vitis coignetiae
– *riparia*
Wattakaka sinensis
Wisteria sinensis

Bulbs

Cardiocrinum giganteum
Crinum × *powellii*
Cyclamen hederifolium
– *purpurascens*
Galanthus
Galtonia
Gladiolus tristis
Hermodactylus tuberosus
Hyacinthus orientalis
Lilium
Narcissus

Plants with Aromatic Foliage

Trees

Atherosperma moschatum
Cercidiphyllum japonicum
Cinnamomum camphora
Clerodendrum
Eucalyptus
Juglans
Laurelia serrata
Laurus nobilis
Phellodendron
Populus balsamifera
– *trichocarpa*
Salix pentandra
– *triandra*

Sassafras albidum
Umbellularia californica

Shrubs

Artemisia arborescens
Camphorosma monspeliaca
Caryopteris clandonensis
Choisya ternata
Cistus
Clerodendrum
Coleonema
Comptonia peregrina
Elsholtzia stauntonii
Escallonia illinita
 – *laevis*
 – *macrantha*
 – *rubra*
Eucalyptus gunnii
Gaultheria procumbens
Hebe cupressoides
Helichrysum plicatum
 – *serotinum*
Hypericum hircinum
Illicium
Laurus nobilis
Lavandula spica
Leptospermum liversidgei
Lindera
Lippia citriodora
Myrica

Myrtus communis
Olearia ilicifolia
 – *mollis*
 – *moschata*
Orixa japonica
Perovskia 'Blue Spire'
Phlomis fruticosa
Prostranthera
Ptelea trifoliata
Rhododendron
Ribes sanguineum
 – *viburnifolium*
Rosa eglanteria
Rosmarinus officinalis
Ruta graveolens
Santolina
Tasmannia aromatica

Herbaceous perennials

Agastache foeniculum
Anthemis punctata cupaniana
Delphinium brunonianum
Geranium endressii
 – *macrorrhizum*
Meum athamanticum
Morina longifolia
Nepeta × *faassenii*
Salvia glutinosa
 – *microphylla*
Smilacina racemosa

Plants for Wildlife

Attracting wildlife into the garden helps control pests and will add an enormous amount of colour, movement and interest.

Birds can be attracted with trees and shrubs for perching on and nesting in and with plants to provide food, especially in winter.

Bees, butterflies and many other insects can be brought into the garden by providing food plants in particular. Breeding colonies can best be established on native plants which many of us gardeners class as 'weeds'. So you may prefer to badger the local council into not cutting the grass verges outside rather than filling your garden with stinging nettles. It's much more effective anyway.

Trees and Shrubs that Attract Birds

Trees

Alnus
Amelanchier lamarckii
Betula
Crataegus
Malus
Mespilus Morus
Salix Sambucus
Sorbus
Staphylea
Syringa
Taxus
Viburnum davidii
– lantana
– opulus
– rhytidophyllum

Shrubs

Arbutus unedo
Arctostaphylos uva-ursi
Aucuba japonica
Berberis
Buddleia
Callicarpa
Chaenomeles
Clerodendrum trichotomum
Colutea
Cornus
Corylus avellana
Cotoneaster
Daphne
Decaisnea
Dorycnium
Elaeagnus
Euonymus europaeus cvs
– japonicus 'Latifolius'
– oxyphyllus

– *sachalinensis*
– *yedoensis*
Gaultheria
Hedera
Hippophäe rhamnoides
Hypericum inodorum 'Elstead'
– *forrestii*
Ilex
Lavandula 'Hidcote Purple' and
others that produce seed
Leycesteria formosa
Ligustrum vulgare
Mahonia
Osmanthus
Pernettya
Poncirus trifoliata
Pyracantha
Rhamnus frangula
Rhus typhina
Ribes odoratum
Rubus calycinoides
Ruscus aculeatus
Sambucus
Skimmia japonica 'Foremanii'
– *laureola*
Symphoricarpos
Viburnum
Vitis

Birds are also attracted to many
flower seedheads, including fennel,
teasel, sedum, lemon balm, lavatera,
poppy, antirrhinum, cosmos,
Michaelmas daisy, scabious and
sunflower.

Trees and Shrubs that Attract Bees and Butterflies

Trees

Acer campestre
– *negundo*
– *platanoides*
–'Royal Red'
– *pseudoplatanus*
– 'Atropurpurea'
Aesculus × *carnea* 'Briotii'
– *hippocastanum*
– *indica*
Ailanthus altissima
Alnus glutinosa (pollen)
– *incana and forms* (pollen)
Betula in variety (pollen)
Caragana arborescens
Castanea sativa
Catalpa bignonioides
Crataegus prunifolia
Fagus (pollen)
Fraxinus excelsior (pollen)
Koelreuteria
Liquidambar styraciflua
Liriodendron tulipifera
Malus Mespilus germanica
Nothofagus antarctica (pollen)
Populus nigra (pollen)
– *tremula* (pollen)
Prunus avium
– *padus* 'Grandiflora'
– 'Pandora'
– *sargentii*
– 'Shirotae'
– *subhirtella*
– 'Pendula Rubra'
– 'Tai-Haku'
– 'Ukon'
– 'Umeniko'
– × *yedoensis*

Quercus in variety (pollen)
Robinia pseudoacacia
Salix alba
Sorbus aria
 – aucuparia
 – intermedia
Tilia euchlora

Shrubs

Aesculus parviflora
Arbutus
Berberis darwinii
 – × irwinii
 – 5 stenophylla
 – thunbergii
 – wilsoniae
Buddleia
Buxus
Caryopteris
Ceanothus
Cercis siliquastrum
Chaenomeles speciosa   Cistus
Colutea arborescens
Cornus
Cotoneaster
Cystisus
Daphne mezereum
Elaeagnus
Escallonia
Fuchsia
Hebe
Hypericum androsaemum
 – forestii
Ilex
Laurus nobilis
Lavandula
Ligustrum
Olearia
Perovskia
Physocarpus
Potentilla
Prunus laurocerasus

Pyracantha
Rhamnus frangula
Rhus
Ribes sanguineum
 – speciosum
Salix caprea
 – repens 'Argentea'
Senecio
 Skimmia
Spiraea
Staphylea
Stephanandra
Symphoricarpos
Syringa
Tamarix pentandra
 Ulex europaeus
Viburnum opulus
 – tinus
Weigela

Perennials and Annuals that Attract Bees and Butterflies

Perennials

Achillea
Ajuga
Alyssum
Anaphalis
Arabis
Armeria Aster
Aubrieta
Calamintha
Cardamine pratensis
Centaurea
Centranthus ruber
Cephalaria
Ceratostigma
Cheiranthus
Convolvulus
Dendranthema

Dianthus deltoides
Echinacea
Echinops ritro
Erigeron
Eryngium
Erysimum linifolium
Eupatorium
Hebe
Helenium
Helichrysum
Hesperis matronalis
Hyssopus officinalis
Jasione perennis
Knautia arvensis
Liatris
Ligularia clivorum
Lunaria annua Lychnis
Lysimachia
Lythrum salicaria
Melissa
Mentha
Nepeta faassenii
Persicaria

Phlox
Phuopsis
Primula
Pulicaria dysenterica
Saponaria officinalis
Scabiosa
Sedum spectabile (not 'Autumn Joy')
Solidago
Thymus (not yellow leafed forms)
Verbena bonariensis

Annuals

Alyssum
Calendula
Convolvulus
Dianthus barbatus
Iberis gibraltarica
Limnanthes douglasii
Myosotis
Petunia
Reseda odorata

Plants Resistant to Rabbits and Deer

R abbits and deer feed on a wide range of plants and it's impossible to guarantee that any one plant is immune to attack. These lists are compiled by the Royal Horticultural Society whom we thank for providing them.

Rabbits can be excluded from gardens with 3mm (⅛in) thick wire netting to a height of 1m (3ft).

Fencing against deer is generally too expensive though there are some ingenious electric fences which might be cheaper. Contact Rutland Electric Fencing Co. Ltd, Unit 3, Pillings Rd, Oakham, Rutland LE15 6QF, Tel: (01572) 722558 for advice and the name of your local supplier.

Some chemical repellents are available at garden centres but are quite expensive and time-consuming since they have to be replaced regularly.

My own solution to invasions from deer was to walk my dog round the perimeter of the garden each night. It proved very effective.

Rabbit-Proof Plants – Soft-Wooded

Acanthus spp. (Bear's breeches)
Aconitum spp. (Monkshood)
Agapanthus
Alchemilla mollis (Lady's mantle)
Anaphalis spp.
Anemone coronaria
Aquilegia spp. (Columbine)
Artichoke, globe and Jerusalem
Aster novae-angliae ⎫ (Michaelmas
Aster novi-belgii ⎭ daisy)
Astilbe spp.
Bergenia spp. (Elephant's ears)
Brunnera macrophylla
Cardiocrinum giganteum
Chionodoxa luciliae (Glory of the snow)
Colchicum spp. (Autumn crocus)
Convallaria majalis (Lily of the valley)

Cortaderia selloana (Pampas grass)
Corydalis lutea
Crinum spp.
Crocosmia
Cyclamen spp.
Dahlia
Delphinium
Digitalis purpurea (Foxglove)
Doronicum spp. (Leopard's bane)
Epimedium spp.
Eranthis hyemalis (Winter aconite)
Eryngium spp. (Sea holly)
Erythronium dens-canis (Dog's tooth violet)
Eupatorium cannabinum (Hemp agrimony)
Euphorbia spp. (Spurges)
Galanthus nivalis (Snowdrop)
Gentiana asclepiadea (Willow gentian)
Helenium autumnale
Helianthus spp. (Sunflowers)
Helleborus spp. (not *niger*)
Hemerocallis (Day lily)

Hyacinthoides non-scripta (Bluebell)
Impatiens
Iris spp. (Irises)
Kniphofia (Red hot poker)
Lamium spp. (Dead nettles)
Lavatera trimestris
Leucojum spp. (Snowflakes)
Linum perenne (Flax)
Liriope muscari
Lupinus spp. (Lupins)
Lysimachia clethroides
Macleaya cordata
Malva moschata (Musk mallow)
Melissa officinalis (Bee balm)
Miscanthus sinensis
Myosotis (Forget-me-not)
Narcissus (Daffodil)
Nepeta faassenii (Catmint)
Nicotiana affinis
Orchis, hardy spp. (Orchids)
Papaver spp. (Poppies)
Petasites fragrans (Winter heliotrope)
Phormium tenax (New Zealand flax)
Phytolacca americana (Poke weed)
Polemonium caeruleum (Jacob's ladder)
Polygonatum × *hybridum* (Solomon's seal)
Polygonum spp.
Potato
Primula vulgaris (Primrose)
Pulmonaria spp. (Lungwort)
Rhubarb
Salvia x *superba*
Saxifraga umbrosa (London pride)
Schizostylis coccinea
Sedum spectabile (Ice plant)
Senecio cineraria (Sea ragwort)
Stachys lanata (Lamb's ears)
Tagetes erecta (African marigold)
Tagetes patula (French marigold)
Trillium grandiflorum (Wake robin)
Tritonia crocata

Trollius europaeus (Globe flower)
Tulip
Verbascum thapsus (Mullein)
Verbena spp.
Viola odorata (Violet)
Zinnia elegans

Rabbit-Proof Plants – Trees and Shrubs

Alnus spp. (Alder)
Araucaria araucana (Monkey puzzle tree)
Arbutus menziesii
Arbutus unedo
Arundinaria spp. (Bamboo)
Aucuba japonica
Azalea spp.
Berberis spp. (Barberry)
Betula spp. (Birch)
Buddleia davidii (Butterfly bush)
Buxus sempervirens (Box)
Ceanothus spp.
Chimonanthus praecox (Winter sweet)
Choisya ternata (Mexican orange)
Cistus hybrids
Clematis spp.
Cornus sanguinea (Dogwood)
Cotoneaster spp. (not *simonsii*)
Cryptomeria japonica (Japanese cedar)
Daphne laureola (Spurge laurel)
Daphne mezereum (Mezereum)
Deutzia scabra
Elaeagnus pungens 'Maculata'
Eucalyptus spp.
Euonymus latifolius
Fatsia japonica
Fuchsia magellanica (Hardy fuchsia)
Gaultheria shallon
Hippophae rhamnoides (Sea buckthorn)
Hydrangea spp.

Hypericum calycinum (Rose of Sharon)
Kalmia latifolia (Calico bush)
Laburnum spp.
Laurus nobilis (Bay tree)
Lavatera thuringiaca (Tree mallow)
Ligustrum ovalifolium (Privet)
Lonicera spp. (Honeysuckle)
Olearia x *haastii*
Paeonia spp. (Paeonies – 'tree' types)
Pernettya mucronata
Philadelphus spp. (Mock orange)
Pinus nigra (Corsican pine)
Prunus spinosa (Sloe)
Rhododendron spp.
Rhus typhina (Sumach)
Ribes spp. (Currant – fruiting and
   ornamental types)
Rosa spp. (spiny species Rose, not
   hybrid teas)
Rosmarinus officinalis (Rosemary)
Ruscus aculeatus (Butcher's broom)
Ruta graveolens (Rue)
Sambucus spp. (Elder)
Skimmia japonica
Symphoricarpos albus (Snowberry)
Syringa vulgaris (Lilac)
Viburnum opulus (Snowball bush,
   Guelder rose)
Viburnum tinus (Laurustinus)
Vinca spp. (Periwinkle)
Yucca spp.

PLANTS RELATIVELY RESISTANT TO DEER

Agapanthus
Aquilegia
Azalea (deciduous types)
Bamboo
Berberis (not purple-leaved types)
Box
Buddleia davidii
Chaenomeles
Choisya ternata

Chrysanthemum maximum
Cistus
Clematis spp.
Cotinus coggygria (not purple forms)
Cornus sanguinea
Daphne spp.
Delphinium
Forsythia
Foxglove
Gaultheria shallon
Gooseberry
Hellebores
Hippophae rhamnoides
Honeysuckle
Hydrangea
Jasmine (winter and summer types)
Kerria japonica
Kniphofia
Lavender
Lonicera nitida
Lupins
Magnolias
Mahonia spp.
Narcissus
Pampas grass
Philadelphus
Phormium tenax
Potentilla fruticosa
Rhubarb
Ribes spp.
Robinia pseudoacacia
Romneya coulteri
Rosa rugosa, R. spinosissima
Spiraea japonica
Sweet bay
Viburnum (deciduous types)
Vinca spp.
Weigela
Yucca

For more information contact:
Andrew Halstead, Entomologist,
Royal Horticultural Society, Wisley,
Woking, Surrey GU23 6QB

Poisonous Plants

Deciding which plants are poisonous and which can be safely classed as harmless is an impossible task. If you ate enough of almost anything you'd be ill, while small quantities of quite poisonous plants can actually be used as curatives.

To make matters more difficult, there seems to be good evidence for the problems likely to be experienced from eating or handling some plants, including medical histories and detailed symptoms, while for others the evidence is extremely sketchy.

Certainly the plants marked 'highly dangerous' should be treated with extreme care and kept out of the reach of children. Others would only cause harm if large quantities were consumed, or if they were eaten by very young children, or older people with already failing health.

You should certainly not be put off growing lupins, for example, but you should avoid eating the seeds. To suggest not growing tomatoes would be ludicrous, but you should be warned against eating the leaves. Armed with the following warnings and a little common sense, you should have no problems.

* = weeds

Common name	Latin name
Amaryllis	*Amaryllis belladonna*
Anemone	*Anemone* spp.
Angel's trumpet (*see* Thorn apple)	
Aquilegia (*see* Columbine)	
Aubergine	*Solanum melongena*
Autumn crocus	*Colchicum autumnale*
Belladonna lily (*see* Amaryllis)	
*Black bryony	*Tamus communis*
Black hellebore (*see* Christmas rose)	
*Black nightshade	*Solanum nigrum*
Bluebell	*Endymion*
Box	*Buxus sempervirens*
Buckthorn	*Frangula alnus*
*Buttercup	*Ranunculus* spp.
Brugmansia (*see* Thorn apple)	
Castor oil plant	*Ricinus communis*
Christmas rose	*Helleborus niger*
Columbine	*Aquilegia* spp.
Corncockle	*Agrostemma githago*
Cotoneaster	*Cotoneaster* spp.
Crinum	(as Amaryllis)
*Cuckoo pint	*Arum maculatum*
Daffodil	*Narcissus* spp.
Daphne	*Daphne mezereum*
Datura (*see* Thorn Apple)	

Poisonous parts	Effect
bulb	Gastroenteritis.
all parts esp. in flower	Juice is an irritant. Blisters mouth. Gastroenteritis.
leaves	Gastroenteritis.
all parts	Highly dangerous. Gastroenteritis. Convulsions. Respiratory failure.
all parts esp. fruit	Burning mouth. Gastroenteritis.
all parts	Highly dangerous. Delirium. Cardiac and respiratory failure.
bulb	Gastroenteritis.
leaves	Sap is irritant. Sore mouth. Gastroenteritis.
all parts esp. seeds	Burning mouth. Gastroenteritis.
all parts esp. when in flower	Burning mouth. Gastroenteritis.
all parts	Highly dangerous. Sap is irritant. Gastroenteritis. Damages digestive tract, liver and kidneys.
all parts	Diarrhoea and dehydration.
seeds	Slows breathing and heart rate.
all parts esp. seeds	Heart stimulant.
berries	Gastroenteritis.
berries	Highly dangerous. Sap irritates mouth. Causes convulsions.
bulb	Gastroenteritis.
all parts esp. berries	Highly dangerous. Sap irritates mouth. Gastroenteritis and convulsions.

Common name	Latin name
*Deadly nightshade	*Atropa belladonna*
Delphinium	*Delphinium* spp.
Dumbcane	*Dieffenbachia sequine*
Egg plant (*see* Aubergine)	
Euphorbia (*see* Spurge)	
Foxglove	*Digitalis purpurea*
Greater celandine	*Chelidonium majus*
Hellebore (*see* Christmas rose)	
*Hemlock (*see* Spotted hemlock)	
*Hogweed	*Heracleum sphondylium*
Holly	*Ilex aquifolium*
Hyacinth	*Hyacinthus* spp.
Ivy	*Hedera helix*
King cup	*Caltha*
Laburnum	*Laburnum anagyroides*
Larkspur (*see* Delphinium)	
Lily of the valley	*Convallaria majalis*
*Lords & ladies (*see* King cup)	
Lupin	*Lupinus* spp.
Marsh marigold (*see* King cup)	
Mezereum (*see* Daphne)	
Mistletoe	*Viscum album*
Monkshood	*Aconitum napellus*
Morning glory	*Ipomoea*

Poisonous parts	Effect
all parts	Highly poisonous. Delirium. Heart and respiration failure.
all parts esp. seeds	Abdominal pain, vomiting, constipation.
sap	Irritates lips and mouth and tongue swells.
all parts	Highly dangerous. Abdominal pain. Diarrhoea and vomiting. Heart failure.
all parts	Highly dangerous. Irritating sap. Gastroenteritis.
all parts	Highly toxic. Skin irritant. Heart failure.
berries	Gastroenteritis.
bulb	Gastroenteritis.
berries and leaves	Respiratory problems. Gastroenteritis.
all parts esp. in flower	Sap is irritant. Gastroenteritis.
seeds and pods	Highly dangerous. Vomiting. Convulsions. Asphyxia.
all parts	Abdominal pain. Diarrhoea. Heart failure.
seeds	Irritant sap. Gastroenteritis.
leaves and berries	Gastroenteritis. Heart and lung failure.
all parts esp. root	Highly dangerous. Gastroenteritis. Convulsions. Cardiac and respiratory failure.
all parts	Hallucinogenic.

Common name	Latin name
Oleander	*Nerium oleander*
Poke weed	*Phytolacca americana*
Poinsettia	*Euphorbia pulcherrima*
Potato	*Solanum tuberosum*
Primula	*Primula* spp.
Privet	*Ligustrum* spp.
Rue	*Ruta graveolens*
Rhubarb	*Rheum* spp.
Snowberry	*Symphoricarpos* spp.
Snowdrop	*Galanthus nivalis*
Spindletree	*Euonymus* spp.
*Spotted hemlock	*Conium maculatum*
Spurge	*Euphorbia*
Stinking hellebore	*Helleborus foetidus*
Sweet pea	*Lathyrus odoratus*
Thorn apple	*Datura stramonium* *Brugmansia*
Tomato	*Lycopersicon esculentum*
Virginia creeper	*Parthenocissus quinquefolia*
Winter cherry	*Solanum capsicastrum*
Wisteria	*Wisteria floribunda*
*Woody nightshade	*Solanum dulcamara*
Yew	*Taxus baccata*

Poisonous parts	Effect
all parts	Highly toxic. Skin irritant. Heart failure.
root	Gastroenteritis.
leaves and sap	Irritant sap causes skin blisters. Gastroenteritis. Delirium.
leaves, stem, fruits, green tubers and sprouts	Burning mouth. Gastroenteritis.
leaves and sap	Irritates skin.
leaves and berries	Drowsiness. Gastroenteritis.
leaves and sap	Irritates skin.
leaves	Abdominal pain. Vomiting.
berries	Gastroenteritis.
bulb	Gastroenteritis.
leaves and fruit	Highly dangerous. Mental confusion. Respiratory failure. Gastroenteritis.
all parts	Highly dangerous. Respiratory failure.
all parts	Sap irritates skin, eyes and mouth. Gastroenteritis.
all parts	Diarrhoea. Dehydration. Convulsions.
seeds	Gastroenteritis.
all parts	Highly dangerous. Delirium. Heart and lung failure.
leaves and stems	Burns throat. Gastroenteritis.
berries	Gastroenteritis.
berries	Gastroenteritis.
pods and seeds	Abdominal pain. Vomiting and diarrhoea.
all parts	Highly dangerous. Abdominal pain. Gastroenteritis. Paralysis.
all parts	Highly dangerous. Gastroenteritis. Heart failure.

Fruit Trees

You can do almost anything with fruit trees and, over the years, many different ways of training them have been developed. By using modern rootstocks (see p 238), trees can be kept very small and, if they're pruned to shape too, they can be grown in quite small spaces. Spacings given are approximate because they'll vary depending on the rootstock and the particular fruit you're growing. They're based on apples on semi-dwarfing rootstocks so, if you're growing a larger tree like a plum or cherry or using a more vigorous rootstock you'll have to adjust the spacing.

OPEN CENTRE BUSH

If you want a free-standing tree, this is a traditional way to grow it. The central shoot is removed to encourage bushy growth and to keep the centre of the tree open. The aim is to produce a shape rather like a goblet. On a dwarfing rootstock, apples and pears grown this way need not be too big, though they'll certainly take up more space than most other methods. Plant about 3.5m (12ft) apart.

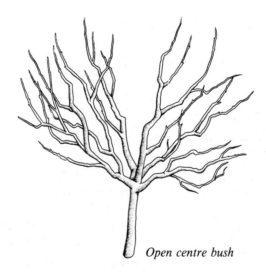

Open centre bush

Dwarf pyramid

DWARF PYRAMID
With this more intensive way of growing, the trees can be planted slightly closer than bushes. The central shoot is maintained and the upper branches are pruned to be somewhat shorter than the lower ones to create a shape rather like a Christmas tree. Plant about 2m (7ft) apart.

STEPOVER
A method that's gaining popularity in small gardens. They're simply single-tier espaliers and are used to edge paths in particular. Plant about 2.5m (8½ft) apart.

ESPALIER
A traditional way to grow apples especially. They make very attractive trees for training on a fence or wall and less often on a post and wire support. Plant about 4.5m (15ft) apart.

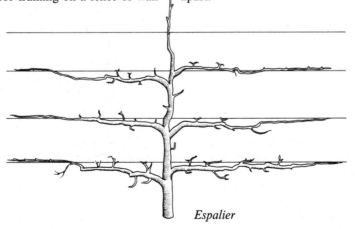

Espalier

CORDON

A popular, space-saving method of training. The trees are grown as a single stem and are planted at an angle to encourage fruiting. The trees are tied in to a wire structure, either free-standing or against a fence or wall. Plant about 75cm (2½ft) apart.

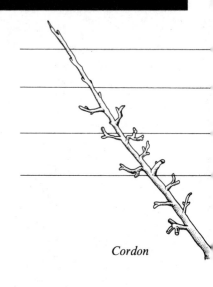

Cordon

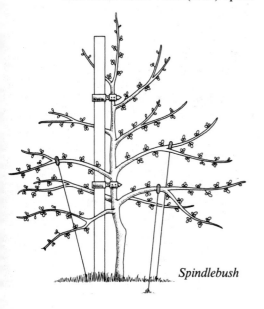

Spindlebush

SPINDLEBUSH

A popular method with commercial growers but not often used in gardens, though there's no reason why not. Instead of pruning, the branches are tied downwards to restrict the flow of sap and so induce heavy cropping early in the life of the tree. Plant about 2m (7ft) apart.

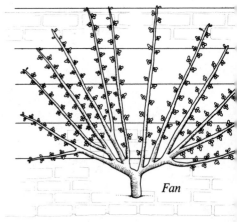

Fan

FAN

Another traditional method used widely for pears, peaches, plums and cherries. Again, they make very attractive wall plants and of course, take up very little space. Plant about 3.5m (12ft) apart.

Pollination

Apples

I t's true to say that no variety of apple will produce a full crop unless it's pollinated by another variety. There is, in fact, a new selection of Cox's Orange Pippin from East Malling Research Station that is self-fertile but that one is, so far, unique.

Generally, apples that flower at the same time will pollinate each other, so choose at least two from the same flowering group. However, there are certain exceptions. Those varieties marked 'T' are triploids and won't pollinate anything. So, if you want to grow, say Bramley's Seedling, you'll have to choose two other varieties from the same group.

Some varieties are also biennial bearing and these are marked 'B'.

Flowering of apples

Group 1
Bolero
Gravenstein (T)
Lord Suffield
Mank's Codling (B)
Polka
Red Astrachan
Stark Earliest (syn. Scarlet
   Pimpernel)

Group 2
Acme
Adam's Pearmain (B)
Baker's Delicious
Beauty of Bath
Beauty of Blackmoor
Ben's Red (B)
Bismarck (B)
Cheddar Cross
Christmas Pearmain (B)
Devonshire Quarrenden (B)
Egremont Russet
George Cave
George Neal
Golden Spire
Idared
Irish Peach
Jerseymac
Kerry Pippin
Keswick Codling (B)
Laxton's Early Crimson
Lord Lambourne
Margil
McIntosh Red
Melba (B)
Merton Charm
Michaelmas Red
Norfolk Beauty
Owen Thomas
Rev. W. Wilks (B)
Ribston Pippin (T)
Ross Nonpareil
St Edmund's Pippin
Striped Beefing
Vista Bella (B)
Warner's King (T)
Washington (T)
White Transparent

Group 3
Acme
Allington Pippin (B)
Arthur Turner
Barnack Orange
Baumann's Reinette (B)
Belle de Boskoop (T)
Belle de Pontoise (B)
Blenheim Orange (TB)
Bountiful
Bowden's Seedling
Bramley's Seedling (T)
Brownlee's Russet
Charles Ross
Cox's Orange Pippin
Crispin (T)
Discovery
Duchess Favourite
Elstar
Emperor Alexander
Emneth Early
  (Early Victoria) (B)
Encore
Epicure
Exeter Cross
Exquisite
Falstaff
Feltham Beauty
Fiesta
Fortuna (B)
Gavin
Goldilocks
Granny Smith
Greensleeves
Grenadier
Hambling's Seedling
Holstein (T)
Hormead Pearmain
James Grieve
John Standish
Jonagold (T)
Jonathan
Jupiter (T)
Karmijn de Sonnaville (T)

Katy (Katja)
Kent
Kidd's Orange Red
King of Tompkins County
King Russet
Lane's Prince Albert
Langley Pippin
Lord Derby
Lord Grosvenor
Lord Hindlip
Malling Kent
Märe de Ménage
Merton Knave
Merton Prolific
Merton Russet
Merton Worcester
Miller's Seedling (B)
Monarch
New Hawthornden
Newton Wonder
Norfolk Royal Russet
Ontario
Peasgood's Nonsuch
Queen
Red Charles Ross
Red Victoria (B)
Redsleeves
Reinette du Canada (T)
Rival (B)
Rosemary Russet
Rubinette
Shoesmith
St Cecilia
St Everard
Spartan
Stirling Castle
Sturmer Pippin
Sunset
Taunton Cross
Tom Putt
Tydeman's Early Worcester
Wagener (B)
Waltz
Wealthy

Worcester Pearmain
S.T. Wright
Wyken Pippin

Group 4
Annie Elizabeth
Ashmead's Kernel
Autumn Pearmain
Barnack Beauty
Bountiful
Chiver's Delight
Claygate Pearmain
Cornish Gillyflower
Cox's Pomona
D'Arcy Spice
Delicious
Duke of Devonshire
Dumelow's Seedling
   (Wellington)
Ellison's Orange
Elstar
Encore
Gala
George Carpenter
Gladstone (B)
Gloster 69
Golden Delicious
Golden Noble
Hawthornden
Herring's Pippin
Howgate Wonder
Ingrid Marie
Jester
Joybells
King's Acre Pippin
Lady Henniker
Lady Sudeley
Lanes Prince Albert
Laxton's Pearmain
Laxton's Superb (B)
Lord Derby
Mannington's Pearmain
Monarch (B)
Orleans Reinette
Pixie

Sir John Thornycroft
Tydeman's Late Orange
Winston
Woolbrook Russet
Yellow Newtown (B)

Group 5
Coronation (B)
Edward VII
Gascoyne's Scarlet (T)
King of the Pippins (B)
Merton Beauty
Mother (American)
Newton Wonder
Northern Spy (B)
Reinette Rouge Etoilée
Royal Jubilee
Suntan (T)
William Crump
Woolbrook Pippin (B)

Group 6
Bess Pool
Court Pendu Plat
Edward VII

Group 7
Crawley Beauty

Pears

Most pears need another variety for full pollination though Conference will set a reasonable crop on its own pollen but the fruits are rather misshapen and elongated. Again, simply choose two varieties from the same group. Here there are also triploids and some varieties that have sterile male flowers and are also useless as pollinators. They're marked 'MS'.

Key
T=triploid
MS=male sterile

Flowering of pears

GROUP 1
Brockworth Park
Maréchal de la Cour (T)
Précoce de Trévoux

GROUP 2
Baronne de Mello
Bellissime d'Hiver
Beurré Alexandre Lucas (T)
Beurré d'Amanlis (T)
Beurré d'Anjou
Beurré Clairgeau
Beurré Diel (T)
Beurré Giffard
Comtesse de Paris
Doyenne d'Eté
Duchesse d'Angoulàeme
Easter Beurré
Emile d'Heyst
Louise Bonne of Jersey
Marguerite Marillat (MS)
Packham's Triumph
Passe Crasanne
Princess
Seckle
St Luke
Uvedale's St Germain (T)
Vicar of Winkfield (T)

GROUP 3
Belle-Julie
Beurré Dumont
Beurré Hardy
Beurré Superfin
Black Worcester
Conference
Doyenne Boussoch (T)
Doyenne George Boucher
Dr Jules Guyot
Duchesse de Bordeaux
Durondeau
Fertility
Fondante d'Automne
Fondante Thirriott
Hessle
Jargonelle (T)
Josephine de Malines
Laxton's Early Market
Laxton's Progress
Laxton's Satisfaction
Le Lectier
Merton Pride (T)
Nouvelle Fulvie
Oliver de Serres
Roosevelt
Souvenir du Congräs
Thompson's
Triomphe de Vienne
Williams' Bon Chrétien

GROUP 4
Beth
Beurré Bedford (MS)
Beurré Mortillet
Bristol Cross (MS)
Calebasse Bosc
Catillac (T)
Clapp's Favourite
Concorde
Doyenne du Comice
Glou Morceau
Gorham
Improved Fertility
Laxton's Foremost
Laxton's Victor
Marie Louise
Napoleon
Nouveau Poiteau
Onward
Pitmaston Duchess (T)
Santa Claus
Winter Nelis
Zépherin Grégoire

The following pears are incompatible: 'Beurré d'Amanlis' with 'Conference' and 'Doyenne du Comicé' with 'Onward'. The following pears are all incompatible with each other: 'Fondante d'Automne', 'Laxton's Progress', 'Louise Bonne of Jersey', 'Précoce de Trévoux', 'Seckle', and 'Williams' Bon Chrétien'.

Triploid and male sterile-pears are ineffective as pollinators for others, so two other pears are required, to pollinate both themselves and the triploid or male-sterile cultivar.

Plums and Damsons

Plums are more complicated than apples and pears. Some varieties are self-fertile setting a full crop with their own pollen. Others are partially self-fertile and another group self-sterile. Both these last two groups need a pollinator which again must come from the same flowering period or an adjacent one.

It's all pretty complicated so to simplify it, we've put the two groups of varieties that need pollinating together into five flowering periods. Bear in mind though, that most of us will only want one tree so a self-fertile one is by far the best bet. Of course, it doesn't matter when they flower unless you want to use one to pollinate a variety in one of the other groups.

Self-fertile plum varieties

GROUP 1
Monarch

GROUP 2
Avalon
Denniston's Superb
Reine-Claude de Bavay
Warwickshire Drooper

GROUP 3
Czar
Laxton's Cropper
Laxton's Supreme
Merryweather Damson
Opal
Pershore Yellow Egg
Purple Pershore
Thames Cross
Victoria

GROUP 4
Blaisdon Red
Bradley's King Damson
Early Transparent Gage
Giant Prune
Ontario
Oulin's Golden Gage

GROUP 5
Belle de Louvain
Marjorie's Seedling
Prune Damson

Cherries

Cherries are by far the most complicated and difficult to match. Many varieties, though flowering at the same time, will not pollinate certain other varieties. So, the only way to sort it out is to put all the incompatible varieties into a group. Then you know that in order to find a pollinator, you need a variety which flowers at the same time yet comes from another group. So, for example, Early Amber will not pollinate Elton Heart or Governor Wood, but all of them will pollinate Merton Premier or Merton Marvel. Fortunately, there are now a few self-fertile varieties and any of these will pollinate all the others that flower at the same time.

Flowering of cherries

	Flowering period 1 (earliest)	Flowering period 2
Universal donors	Noir de Guben Nutberry Black	Merton Glory Merchant
Incompatibility group 1	Early Rivers	Bedford Prolific Knight's Early Black
Incompatibility group 2		Bigarreau de Schrecken Mermat Merton Favourite Waterloo
Incompatibility group 3		
Incompatibility group 4		
Incompatibility group 5		
Incompatibility group 6		Merton Heart
Incompatibility group 7		
Incompatibility group 8		
Incompatibility group 9		
Self-fertile		

Flowering period 3	Flowering period 4	Flowering period 5	Flowering period 6 (latest)
	Summit	Bigarreau Gaucher	
Frogmore Early Merton Bigarreau Merton Bounty Van	Belle Agathe Merton Crane		
Merton Marvel	Emperor Francis Napoleon Bigarreau		
Merton Premier	Kent Bigarreau		
		Late Black Bigarreau	
Early Amber Elton Heart Grovenor Wood			
			Bradbourne Black Géante d'Hedelfinger
Peggy Rivers			
	Merton Reward	Merton Late	
Lapins May Duke	Stella Sunburst	Morello	

Rootstocks

Most fruit trees are grafted or budded onto a rootstock. You can see the join about 30cm(1ft) above the ground where there's a small kink in the stem.

The rootstocks which were developed at government research stations, have the effect of controlling the growth and eventual size of the tree. They also have a marked effect on the time taken for the tree to come into regular fruiting. Dwarfing roostock bring trees into bearing within the second or third year.

If you want a very large tree or your soil is particularly poor, choose a vigorous stock but remember that it will take longer to crop.

If your soil is good and you want a very small tree, choose a very dwarfing stock, while on poor soil a semi-dwarfing one will be best. Remember too that trees on dwarfing stocks will need staking all their lives.

On the good soil at Barnsdale, the larger, bush apple trees are on MM106 stocks while the cordons and espaliers are on M9. These are certainly the two most common stocks found in nurseries and garden centres. There are also some trees in containers and they are on M27 and doing well but they need constant attention to watering and feeding.

All the pears at Barnsdale are on Quince A and the plums, peaches, nectarines, etc, are on Pixy. I would recommend this for all but the very poorest soil.

Cherries are generally budded onto Colt stocks, but bear in mind that they still make big trees. At Barnsdale I compromize by growing them as fans and keeping them smaller by pruning.

Bear in mind that the sizes quoted here are approximate, since growth is also affected by soil and climate. If in doubt, ask the stockist and if they can't tell you the rootstock as well as the variety, go elsewhere.

Apples

MM111
Very vigorous, but good for poor soils. Can be used for standards and half standards, espaliers and fans. Height and spread is 5.5m (20ft), yields from 200–250kg (4–5cwt), crops 5–6 years after planting. Ideal if you want to plant a traditional orchard.

MM106
Semi-dwarfing, for half standards, large bushes, fans, espaliers and cordons on poor soil. Height and spread is 4.6m (15ft), yields around 1 cwt, crops after 3–5 years.

M26
Dwarfing for bushes, cordons and small espaliers. Height and spread is 3.6m (12ft), yields around 75lbs, crops after 3 years.

M9
Very dwarfing rootstock, for bushes and cordons. Needs good soil and permanent staking. Height and spread is 3m (10ft), yields around 18kg (40lbs), crops after 2–3 years.

M27
Extremely dwarfing, for cordons and growing in containers. Needs careful watering and feeding, and some permanent support. Height and spread is 1.8m (6ft), yields around 9kg (20lbs), crops after 2 years.

Pears and some medlars

QUINCE A
Fairly vigorous, common stock, for all garden forms. Height and spread 4.6m (15ft), yields 45.36kg (100lbs), crops after 4 years.

QUINCE C
Semi-dwarfing, used for strong growing types, needs fertile soil. Height and spread 3.6m (12ft), yields 34kg (75lb), crops after 3 years.

Plums, damsons, gages, peaches, nectarines and apricots

ST JULIAN A
Fairly vigorous, best for large

gardens or poor soils. Height and spread 4.6m (15ft), yields 22.68kg (50lbs), crops after 2 years.

PIXY dwarf
Good for heavy soils. Height and spread 2.4m (8ft), yields 9kg (20lbs), crops after 2 years.

Cherries

COLT
Semi-dwarfing, for most soils. Height and spread 4.6m (15ft), yields 9kg (20lbs), crops after 3 years.

INMIL Dwarf
Needs good soil and permanent stakes. Height and spread 3.6m (12ft), yield 6.8kg (15lbs), crops after 3 years.

Mulberries

These are grown on their own roots and generally propagated by cuttings.

Figs

Also grown on their own roots from cutings or layers.

Quinces

QUINCE A
A rootstock of medium vigour for most soils.

QUINCE C
Slightly dwarfer for really good soils.

General Chart Showing Cropping Periods of Fruit

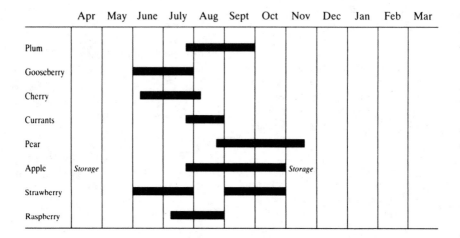

	Apr	May	June	July	Aug	Sept	Oct	Nov	Dec	Jan	Feb	Mar
Plum					▅▅▅▅▅▅▅▅▅						
Gooseberry			▅▅▅▅▅▅▅									
Cherry			▅▅▅▅▅									
Currants				▅▅▅								
Pear						▅▅▅▅▅▅▅▅						
Apple	*Storage*				▅▅▅▅▅▅▅▅			*Storage*				
Strawberry			▅▅▅▅			▅▅▅▅						
Raspberry				▅▅▅								

Vegetables and Herbs

The following tables are designed to help new vegetable and herb gardeners grow a succession of crops. Old hands will have their own favourite varieties, but I would suggest that even they try something new each year. There have been some excellent developments lately that have made many older varieties obsolete.

The sowing dates are deliberately rather vague since they'll vary somewhat in different parts of the country. However, absolute accuracy is unnecessary, though you should bear in mind that no vegetable seeds will germinate at temperatures much below about 7°C (45°F). So for the first sowings in early spring it's better to err on the late side.

The fertilizer rates are based largely on research done at the National Vegetable Research Station at Wellesbourne. Because they have been scientifically produced they are probably too accurate for gardeners but they'll give a good idea of how much to use. It's important not to overdose vegetables with chemical fertilizers and for this reason, organic products are recommended for gardeners who apply it fairly roughly by hand.

To grow a succession of vegetables

Vegetable	Barnsdale recommended varieties	Growmore or chicken manure fertilizer in gms per sq.metre (oz per sq.yd)	Sow in greenhouse or windowsill
Artichoke (Globe)	'Green Globe'	136gm (4½oz)	Late Jan/Feb
Artichoke (Jerusaleam)	'Fuseau'	136gm (4½oz)	
Asparagus	'Sorbonne' 'Franklim'	136gm (4½oz)	
Aubergine	'Black Prince'	Weekly liquid Feeds	Feb/March
Broad Bean	'The Sutton' 'Jubilee Hysor' 'Jade'	102g (3½oz)	Jan/Feb
French Bean	'Daisy' 'Limelight' 'Tendergreen'	136gm (4½oz)	Late March/April
Runner Bean	'Polestar' 'Mergoles' 'Painted Lady'	68gm (2oz)	April
Field Bean (Bush Runners)	'Pickwick'	66gm (2oz)	April
Beetroot	'Boltardy' 'Burpees Golden'	136gm (4½oz)	Feb
Beetroot for storing	'Cylindra' 'Forono'	272gm (9½oz) in 2 applications	
Broccoli	'Early Purple' 'White Sprouting'	272gm (9½oz) in 2 applications	

Sow under cloche	Sow outdoors	Spacing between plants	Spacing between rows	Harvest
	March	As annuals: 45cm (18in) 90cm (3ft) as perennials 90cm (3ft)	90cm (3ft)	June/July as perennials July/August as annuals
	Plant tubers early spring	30cm (12in)	1.5m (5ft)	In winter as required
	Plant grows in June	30cm (12in)	30cm (12in)	May/June from 2nd year
		23cm (9in) pots under glass		August onwards while shiny
Jan/Feb 30cm	March/April	10cm (4m)	Double rows 30cm (12in) apart and 1m (3ft) between double rows	June onwards
Late Mar/ April	April–July (every month)	30cm (8in)	30cm (12in)	July onwards
April	Mid May	30cm (12in)	60cm (24in)	Late July onwards
April	Mid May	30cm (12in)	60cm (24in)	Late June onwards
Mar	April–July (every 3 weeks)	8cm (3in)	30cm (12in)	June onwards
	June/July	15cm (6in)	30cm (12in)	October to store
	April/May	75cm (30in)	75cm (30in)	Feb/April

Vegetable	Barnsdale recommended varieties	Growmore or chicken manure fertilizer in gms per sq.metre (oz per sq.yd)	Sow in greenhouse or windowsill
Brussels Sprouts	'Peer Gynt' 'Fortress' 'Widgeon'	340gm (12oz) in 2 applications	
Cabbage, spring	'April' 'Offenham' 'Durham Early'	272gm (9½oz) in 2 applications	
Cabbage, summer	'Kingspi' 'Primo'	136gm (4½oz)	Feb
Cabbage, autumn/ winter	'Castello' 'January King'	340gm (12oz) in 2 applications	
Calabrese	'Green Comet' 'Mercedes' 'Romanesco'	136gm (4½oz)	
Capsicum (*see* Pepper)			
Carrot, early	'Rondo'	34gm (1oz)	Late Jan/Feb in modules
Carrot, Maincrop	'Berlicum Berjo'	34gm (1oz)	
Carrot, storing	'Autumn King'	34gm (1oz)	
Cauliflower, summer	'Alpha' 'Montano'	136gm (4½oz)	Jan/Feb
Cauliflower, autumn	'Dok Elgon'	272gm (9½oz) in 2 applications	
Cauliflower, winter	'Walcheren Winter' 'Asmer Snowcap March'	272gm (9½oz) in 2 applications	
Celeriac	'Snow White' 'Tellus'	136gm (4½oz)	April

Sow under cloche	Sow outdoors	Spacing between plants	Spacing between rows	Harvest
	March/April	75cm (30in)	75cm (30in)	Oct–March
	July/August	23cm (9in)	45cm (18in)	Early March. Pulling every other plant for greens. Allow rest to heart up.
March	April at monthly intervals	30cm (12in)	30cm (12in)	Late May onwards
	April/May	45cm (18in)	45cm (18in)	October onwards
	April/May	15cm (6in)	30cm (12in)	July onwards
March		7.5cm (3in)	7.5cm (3in)	May
March to July monthly		5cm (2in)	15cm (6in)	June onwards
	June/July	7.5cm (3in)	30cm (12in)	Oct for storing
March	March–May at 3 weekly intervals	50cm (20in)	60cm (24in)	June onwards
	April	60cm (24in)	75cm (30in)	Sept–Nov
	April/May	75cm (30in)	75cm (30in)	March–June
		30cm (12in)	30cm (12in)	Oct to store

Vegetable	Barnsdale recommended varieties	Growmore or chicken manure fertilizer in gms per sq.metre (oz per sq.yd)	Sow in greenhouse or windowsill
Celery, blanched	'Giant Pink' 'Solid White'	136gm (4½oz)	Mar/April
Celery, self-blanching	'Celebrity'	136gm (4½oz)	Mar/April
Chicory, blanched	'Apollo' 'Normato'	136gm (4½oz)	
Chicory Leaf	'Sugar Loaf'	136gm (4½oz)	
Courgette and marrow	'Ambassador' 'Long Green Striped'	272gm (9½oz) in 2 applications	April
Cucumber, in greenhouse	'Athene' 'Brunex'	136gm (4½oz) plus weekly liquid tomato feeding	Mar-May
Cucumber, outside	'Bush Crop' 'Bush Champion'	272gm (9½oz) in 2 applications	April
Endive	'Sally' 'Moss Curled'	68gm (2oz)	
Florence Fennel	'Cantino ' 'Sirio'	136gm (4½oz)	
Garlic	'Long Keeper'	272gm (9½oz) in 2 applications	
Hamburg Parsley (see Parsnip)			
Kale	'Hungry Gap' 'Pentland Brig' 'Dwarf Green Curled'	136gm (4½oz)	
Kohlrabi	'Rowel'	136gm (4½oz)	Feb
Land cress		136gm (4½oz)	

Sow under cloche	Sow outdoors	Spacing between plants	Spacing between rows	Harvest
		in trenches 23cm (9in)	45cm (18in)	Nov onwards
		23cm (9in)	23cm (9in)	Aug to first hard frost
	May	23cm (9in)	30cm (12in)	Autumn through winter for blanching
	June/July	23cm (9in)	38cm (15in)	October onwards
April	Late May	60cm (24in)	60cm (24in)	From July cut courgettes when 15cm (6in) long
		Plant in 23cm (9in) pots or growing bags		Regularly from June
	Mid May	45cm (18in)	45cm (18in)	Regularly from July
	May–August at monthly intervals	30cm (12in)	30cm (12in)	Aug/Sept (blanch 3 weeks before)
	May–August at monthly intervals	20cm (8in)	45cm (18in)	August onwards
	Plant cloves Oct/Nov	15cm (6in)	15cm (6in)	July/August
	April	60cm (24in)	60cm (24in)	Feb–April (take leaves from centre)
eb	March–July at monthly intervals	23cm (9in)	23cm (9in)	June onwards. Pull when roots are 7.5cm (3in) in diameter
	Mar–Aug at 2 monthly intervals	15cm (6in)	30cm (12in)	May–October

Vegetable	Barnsdale recommended varieties	Growmore or chicken manure fertilizer in gms per sq.metre (oz per sq.yd)	Sow in greenhouse or windowsill
Leek	'King Richard' 'Musselburgh' 'Giant Winter'	170gm (6oz)	March
Lettuce	'Tom Thumb' 'Little Gem' 'Saladin' 'Toledo' 'Raisa' 'Sigmaball'	136gm (4½oz)	Feb to March
Lettuce, inside	'Kelly's'	136gm (4½oz)	Nov to Jan
Marrow see courgette			
Melon (greenhouse or frame)	'Ogen' 'Sweetheart'	Weekly liquid tomato feed	April
Onion bulb from seed	'Hygro' 'Rijnsburger' 'Brunswick'	136gm (4½oz)	Feb
Onion bulb from sets	'Ailsa Craig' 'Giant Fen Globe'	136gm (4½oz)	
Onion bulb from early sets	'Unwins First Early'	136gm (4½oz)	
Onion, Japanese	'Imai Early Yellow'	136gm (4½oz) applied in Feb	
Onion, Salad	'White Lisbon' 'Ishikura'	136gm (40oz)	Feb in modules
Parsnip/Hamburg Parsley	'White Gem' 'Gladiator' 'Hamburg Turnip Rooted'	102gm (3oz)	

ow nder loche	Sow outdoors	Spacing between plants	Spacing between rows	Harvest
	March	15cm (6in)	30cm (12in)	All winter
eb to	Mar–Aug at March intervals	15-23cm (6-9in) two weekly (depending on variety)	30cm (12in) (depending on	May to first hard frost
		30cm (12in)	30cm (12in)	April onwards
		in 23cm (9in) pots or growing bag, 2 plants per bag		Aug onwards when soft
	March	7.5cm (3in)	30cm (12in)	Aug to Sept to store
	March	7.5cm (3in)	30cm (12in)	Aug to Sept to store
	Sept–Nov	7.5cm (3in)	30cm (12in)	June–Sept to store
	August	7.5cm (3in) (Thin in spring)	30cm (12in)	June–Sept
	March at monthly intervals	Sow thinly	23cm (9in)	April onwards
	March	15cm (6in)	30cm (12in)	Dec/Jan after frost

Vegetable	Barnsdale recommended varieties	Growmore or chicken manure fertilizer in gms per sq.metre (oz per sq.yd)	Sow in greenhouse or windowsill
Pea	'Douce Provence' 'Cavalier' 'Oregon Sugar Pod' 'Sugar Bon'	None Needed	Feb
Pepper, sweet	'Worldbeater' 'Gypsy' 'Redskin'	Liquid tomato feed weekly	Feb
Pepper, chilli	'Hot Mexican'	Liquid tomato feed weekly	Feb
Potato, Early	'Concorde' 'Foremost' 'Accent' 'Rocket'	170gm (6oz)	
Potato, Maincrop	'Kestrel' 'Sante' 'Romano' 'Pink Fir Apple' 'Ratte'	272gm (9½oz) in 2 applications	April
Pumpkin	'Little Gem' 'Butternut' 'Tivoli'	272gm (9½oz) in 2 applications	April
Radish	'French Breakfast' 'Cherry Belle'	34gm (1oz)	Jan in modules
Ruby or Rhubarb Chard (*see* **Swiss Chard**)			
Salsify Scorzonera	'Mammoth' 'Habil'	136gm (4½oz)	
Silver or Seakale Beet (*see* **Swiss Chard**)			
Shallots (from seed)	'Creation'	136gm (4½oz)	

Sow under cloche	Sow outdoors	Spacing between plants	Spacing between rows	Harvest
eb	March–July at monthly intervals	5cm (2in) in wide drill made with a spade	1.2m (4ft)	June–October. Pick regularly
ant pril		Grow in 20cm (8in) pots		Aug onwards
ant pril		Grow in 20cm (8in) pots		Aug onwards
eb	March	30cm (12in)	30cm (12in)	May–July
	March/April	38cm (15in)	75cm (30in)	Sept to store
pril	April	1m (3ft)	1m (3ft)	Sept–Oct to store
eb	March–Sept at 2 week intervals	Sow thinly	15cm (6in)	April–Nov. Pull selectively to thin
	April	15cm (6in)	30cm (12in)	Oct to Dec
	March/April	15cm (6in)	30cm (12in)	July/Aug to store

Vegetable	Barnsdale recommended varieties	Growmore or chicken manure fertilizer in gms per sq.metre (oz per sq.yd)	Sow in greenhouse or windowsill
Shallots (from sets)	'Dutch Yellow' 'Dutch Red' 'Delicato' 'Topper'	136gm (4½oz)	
Spinach	'Symphony' 'Triathlon' 'Triton'	272gm (9½oz) in 2 applications	Jan/Feb
Spinach Beet	'Perpetual'	272gm (9½oz) in 2 applications	
Swede	'Marian' 'Ruby'	102gm (3½oz)	
Sweetcorn	'Xtra Sweet Improved' 'Sundance'	272gm (9½oz) in 2 applications	April
Swiss Chard	'Fordhook Giant' 'Feurio'	136gm (4½oz)	
Tomato, outdoor bush	'Red Alert' 'Tornado' 'Tumbler'	272gm (9½oz) in 2 applications	March
Tomato, outdoor upright	'Outdoor Girl' 'Yellow Perfection' 'Dario'	272gm (9½oz) in 2 applications	March
Tomato, in greenhouse	'Ailsa Craig' 'Sungold' 'Gardener's Delight' 'Herald'	Liquid tomato feed twice weekly	Feb
Turnip	'Milan Purple Top' 'Golden Ball'	153gm (5oz)	Feb in modules

w der che	Sow outdoors	Spacing between plants	Spacing between rows	Harvest
	Plant Mar/April	15cm (6in)	30cm (12in)	July/Aug to store
b	March–May and Aug–Oct	15cm (6in)	30cm (12in)	May–Nov. Pick few leaves form each plant
	April–Aug then cover with cloches	23cm (9in)	30cm (12in)	July/Aug Mar/April
	May/June	30cm (12in)	45cm (18in)	Oct onwards
ril		60cm (24in)	60cm (24in) sow or plant in a block	Aug–Oct. Harvest when tassels are black
	April–July	30cm (12in)	38cm (15in)	July onwards. Pulling a few leaves as required
		60cm (24in)	60cm (24in)	July onwards. Pick regularly
		60cm (24in)	1m (3ft)	Aug onwards. Pick regularly
			Grow in growing bags, 3 plants per bag in 23cm (9in) pots or 45cm (18in) apart in the border	June. Pick regularly
b	March–July	10cm (4in)	30cm (12in)	June–October. Pull when golf-ball size

To grow a succession of herbs

Common name	Botanical name	Annual/Biennial Perennial	Propagation
Anise	Pimpinella anisum	Half hardy annual	Sow in spring
Angelica	Angelica archangelica	Hardy herbaceous biennial	Sow in autumn
Sweet basil	Ocimum basilicum	Tender annual	Sow indoors in heat late spring
Bay	Laurus nobilis	Evergreen tree	Take stem cuttings or layer in late summer
Bergamot	Monarda didyma	Hardy herbaceous perennial	Divide or take root cuttings in spring
Borage	Borago officinalis	Hardy annual	Sow in spring
Caraway	Carum carvi	Hardy annual	Sow late spring or early autumn
Chamomile	Chamaemelum nobile	Hardy evergreen perennial	Take cuttings in summer; divide in spring or summer
Chervil	Anthriscus cerefolium	Hardy annual	Sow monthly in summer
Chicory	Cichorium intybus	Hardy perennial	Sow early summer
Chives	Allium schoenoprasum	Hardy perennial	Take offsets or divide bulb in autumn or spring
Chinese chives (or Garlic chives)	Allium tuberosum	Hardy perennial	Take offsets or divide bulb in autumn or spring
Comfrey	Symphytum officinale	Hardy herbaceous perennial	Take root offsets spring, summer or autumn

Growing Position	Height	Uses: Aromatic/ Culinary/Medicinal
Well drained, alkaline soil Sunny, sheltered position	45cm 8in	whole plant: c seed: a+m+c
Moist soil Light shade	1–2.5m 3–8ft	leaf: m leaf seed root:a leaf & stem: c+m
Moist, well drained soil Sunny, sheltered position	45cm 18in	leaf: c+m
Rich, well drained, moist soil. Full sun, sheltered position	7m 23ft	leaf: m+a+c
Rich, light, moist soil Sunny position	60cm–1m 2–3ft	leaf: m+c+a
Well drained soil Sunny position	30–75cm 1–2ft 6in	leaf & seed: m flower & leaf: c
Well drained soil Sun	60cm 2ft	root & seed: c seed: m
Well drained soil Full sun	20cm 8in	flower: m+a
Well drained soil Light shade	25–38cm 10-15in	leaf: c+m
Light soil Sunny position	1–1.5m 3–5ft	leaf & root: m chicon & root: c
Rich, well drained soil Sunny position	20–30cm 8–12in	leaf: c+m whole plant: m
Rich, well drained soil Sunny position	20–30cm 8–12in	leaf & flower: c whole plant: m
Soil rich in nitrogen Full sun	1–1.2m 3–4ft	leaf: c+m

Common name	Botanical name	Annual/Biennial Perennial	Propagation
Coriander	Coriandrum sativum	Hardy annual	Sow in autumn or spring
Cotton lavender	Santolina chamaecyparissus	Perennial	Stem cuttings in spring or from midsummer to autumn
Dill	Anethum graveolens	Hardy annual	Sow in spring
English mace	Achillea decolorans	Half hardy	Sow in spring
Everlasting onion	Allium cepa	Hardy perennial	Divide in autumn or spring
Fennel	Foeniculum vulgare	Hardy herbaceous perennial	Sow in late spring, divide in autumn
Garlic	Allium sativum	Hardy perennial	Plant cloves in autumn Sow seed in spring
Horseradish	Armoracia rusticana	Hardy perennial	Sow or divide roots in spring
Hyssop	Hyssopus officinalis	Hardy semi-evergreen shrub	Stem cuttings in summer
Lavender	Lavandula angustifolia	Hardy evergreen shrub	Stem cuttings in autumn or spring–divide or layer
Lemon balm	Melissa officinalis	Hardy herbaceous perennial	Sow in spring spring or autumn
Lemon verbena	Aloysia triphylla	Half hardy shrub	Sow in spring Softwood cuttings late spring
Lovage	Levisticum officinale	Hardy herbaceous perennial	Sow late summer Root cuttings in spring or autumn
Marjoram	Origanum marjorana	Half hardy herbaceous perennial	Sow in spring

Growing Position	Height	Uses: Aromatic/ Culinary/Medicinal
Rich, light soil Full sun	60cm 2ft	leaf: c seed: a+c+m
Well drained soil Sun	60cm 2ft	leaf: a flower & leaf: m
Rich, well drained soil Sunny, sheltered position	60cm–1.5m 2–5ft	seed & leaf: c seed: m
Sandy soil	45cm 18in	leaf: a
Rich, moist soil Sunny position		bulb: c
Well drained soil Full sun	2.1m 7ft	seed, leaf & bulb: c seed: m
Rich, well drained soil Sunny position	30cm 12in	bulb: c+m
Rich, moist soil Sunny position	60cm–1m 2–3ft	root: m+c leaf: c
Well drained alkaline soil Full sun	45cm–1.2m 18in–4ft	leaf & flower: a+c+m
Well drained Sunny, open position	45cm–1m 18in–3ft	flower: a+c+m
Moist soil Sunny position	1m 3ft	leaf: a+c+m
Light, well drained alkaline soil. Full sun, sheltered position	60cm–1.2m 2–4ft	leaf: a+c+m
Rich, moist, well drained soil. Sunny position or partial shade	2.1m 7ft	seed & leaf: c+m
Well drained, rich, alkaline soil. Full sun	60cm 2ft	flower: m leaf: c+a

Common name	Botanical name	Annual/Biennial Perennial	Propagation
Mints **Applemint**	*Mentha suaveolens*	Hardy herbaceous perennial	Root or stem cuttings or divide in spring or autumn
Variegated Applemint	*Mentha suaveolens* 'Variegata'	Hardy herbaceous perennial	Root or stem cuttings or divide in spring or autumn
Corsican mint	*Mentha requienii*	Hardy herbaceous perennial	Root or stem cuttings or divide in spring or autumn
Creeping pennyroyal	*Mentha pulegium*	Hardy herbaceous perennial	Root or stem cuttings or divide in spring or autumn
Curly mint	*Mentha spicata* 'Crispa'	Hardy herbaceous perennial	Root or stem cuttings or divide in spring or autumn
Eau de Cologne mint	*Mentha × piperita* 'Citrata'	Hardy herbaceous perennial	Root or stem cuttings or divide in spring or autumn
Gingermint	*Mentha × gentilis* 'Variegata'	Hardy herbaceous perennial	Root or stem cuttings or divide in spring or autum
Lemon mint	*Mentha × piperita* 'Citrata Lemon'	Hardy herbaceous perennial	Root or stem cuttings or divide in spring or autumn
Moroccan spearmint	*Mentha spicata* 'Moroccan'	Hardy herbaceous perennial	Root or stem cuttings or divide in spring or autumn
Peppermint	*Mentha × piperita*	Hardy herbaceous perennial	Root or stem cuttings or divide in spring or autumn
Red raripila spearmint	*Mentha rubra raripila*	Hardy herbaceous perennial	Root or stem cuttings or divide in spring or autumn
Upright pennyroyal	*Mentha pulegium* 'Upright'	Hardy herbaceous perennial	Root or stem cuttings or divide in spring or autumn

Growing Position	Height	Uses: Aromatic/ Culinary/Medicinal
Rich, moist, well drained alkaline soil. Sun or partial shade	60cm 2ft	leaf: a+c
Rich, moist, well drained alkaline soil. Sun or partial shade	60cm 2ft	leaf: a+c
Rich, moist, well drained alkaline soil. Sun or partial shade	2.5cm 1in	leaf: a+c+m
Rich, moist, well drained alkaline soil. Sun or partial shade	15cm 6in	leaf: a+m
Rich, moist, well drained alkaline soil. Sun or partial shade	40cm 16in	leaf: a+c
Rich, moist, well drained alkaline soil. Sun or partial shade	45cm 18in	leaf: a
Rich, moist, well drained alkaline soil. Sun or partial shade	40cm 16in	leaf: a+c
Rich, moist, well drained alkaline soil. Sun or partial shade	40cm 16in	leaf: a+c
Rich, moist, well drained alkaline soil. Sun or partial shade	60cm 2ft	leaf: a+c+m
Rich, moist, well drained alkaline soil. Sun or partial shade	2.5ft 75cm	leaf: a+c+m
Rich, moist, well drained alkaline soil. Sun or partial shade	60cm 2ft	leaf: a+c+m
Rich, moist, well drained alkaline soil. Sun or partial shade	30cm 12in	leaf: a

Common name	Botanical name	Annual/Biennial Perennial	Propagation
Mustard	Sinapis alba	Hardy annual	Sow in spring for seed or every 3 weeks for salad
Nasturtium	Tropaeolum majus	Hardy annual	Sow late spring
Tree onion (or Egyptian onion)	Allium cepa proliferum	Hardy perennial	Divide bulb in autumn or spring
Welsh onion	Allium fistulosum	Hardy perennial	Divide bulb in autumn or spring
Oregano (Wild marjoram)	Origanum vulgare	Hardy herbaceous perennial	Sow in spring Divide, take stem or root cuttings
Golden marjoram	Origanum vulgare 'Aureum'	Hardy herbaceous perennial	Sow in spring Divide, take stem or root cuttings
Parsley	Petroselinum crispum	Hardy biennial	Sow spring–summer
Pot marigold	Calendula officinalis	Hardy annual	Sow seed in spring in situ or singly in pots
Pot marjoram	Origanum onites	Perennial	Sow in spring. Divide spring or autumn. Take root or stem cuttings late spring to midsummer
Purslane	Portulaca oleracea	Half hardy	Sow monthly summer
Rosemary	Rosmarinus officinalis	Hardy evergreen perennial	Sow in heat in spring or take cuttings or layers
Rue	Ruta graveolens	Hardy evergreen sub-shrub	Divide in spring. Take stem cuttings late summer. Sow in spring
Sage	Salvia officinalis	Hardy evergreen shrub	Sow seed in spring. Take cuttings in summer

Growing Position	Height	Uses: Aromatic/ Culinary/Medicinal
Fertile, well drained soil Sunny position	2.4m 1–8ft	seed & leaf: c seed: m
Well drained soil Full sun or partial shade	30–60cm 1–2ft	leaf & flower & seed: c
Rich, moist, well drained soil	1m 3ft	bulb: c
Rich, moist, well drained soil	30cm 12in	leaf: c
Rich, well drained alkaline soil. Full sun	60cm 2ft	leaf: c+m
Rich, well drained alkaline soil. Full sun	60cm 2ft	leaf: c+m
Rich, moist soil Full sun or light shade	38cm 15in	leaf: c+m
All soils Full sun	30–60cm 1–2ft	flower: c+m
Well drained, alkaline soil	15–60cm 6in–2ft	stem: c leaf: a+c+m flowering top: m
Well drained soil Sunny, sheltered position	15cm 6in	leaf & stem: c+m
Well drained soil Sunny, sheltered position	1–2m 3–6ft	leaf: c+m flower & leaf: a+c leaf: m
Well drained alkaline soil. Full sun	60cm 2ft	leaf: m seed & leaf: c
Light, well drained alkaline soil. Full sun	30–75cm 1–2ft 6in	leaf: c+m flower: c

Common name	Botanical name	Annual/Biennial Perennial	Propagation
Scented geranium Apple scent	*Pelargonium odoratissimum*	Tender evergreen perennial	Take cuttings in summer. Grow in pots
Incense	*P. quercifolium*	Tender evergreen perennial	Take cuttings in summer. Grow in pots
Orange	*P. crispum* 'Prince of Orange'	Tender evergreen perennial	Take cuttings in summer. Grow in pots
Nutmeg	*P. fragrans*	Tender evergreen perennial	Take cuttings in summer. Grow in pots
Rose	*P. capitatum*	Tender evergreen perennial	Take cuttings in summer. Grow in pots
Rose-lemon	*P. radens*	Tender evergreen perennial	Take cuttings in summer. Grow in pots
Peppermint	*P. graveolens* 'Lady Plymouth'	Tender evergreen perennial	Take cuttings in summer. Grow in pots
Sorrel	*Rumex rugosus* *Rumex scutatus*	Hardy perennial	Sow in spring or divide in autumn
Sweet cicely	*Myrrhis odorata*	Hardy herbaceous perennial	Sow outdoors in autumn
Sweet rocket	*Hesperis matronalis*	Hardy biennial	Sow outdoors in spring
Southernwood	*Artemesia*	Perennial	Sow when available Take semi-hardwood cuttings late summer
Tansy	*Tanacetum vulgare*	Perennial	Sow in spring. Divide roots in spring or autumn
French tarragon	*Artemisia dracunculus*	Hardy perennial	Divide roots in spring. Take stem cuttings in summer

Growing Position	Height	Uses: Aromatic/ Culinary/Medicinal
Well drained compost Sunny position	30cm–1m 1–3ft	leaf: a+c+m flower: c
Well drained compost Sunny position	30cm–1m 1–3ft	leaf: a+c+m flower: c
Well drained compost Sunny position	30cm–1m 1–3ft	leaf: a+c+m flower: c
Well drained compost Sunny position	30cm–1m 1–3ft	leaf: a+c+m flower: c
Well drained compost Sunny position	30cm–1m 1–3ft	leaf: a+c+m flower: c
Well drained compost Sunny position	30cm–1m 1–3ft	leaf: a+c+m flower: c
Well drained compost Sunny position	30cm–1m 1–3ft	leaf: a+c+m flower: c
Moist, sunny site. Well drained Full sun. Sheltered position	60cm–1.2m 2–4ft	leaf: c+m
Rich soil Light shade	1m 3ft	seed & leaf: c leaf: m
Rich loam Full sun or light shade	1m 3ft	flower: a+c leaf: c
Light soils Full sun	60cm–1.2m 2–4ft	leaf: c+m
Any soil that is not too wet. Full sun or light shade	60cm–1m 2–5ft	flower & leaf: m leaf: c
Rich, light soil Sunny, sheltered position	60cm–1m 2–3ft	leaf: c+m

Common name	Botanical name	Annual/Biennial Perennial	Propagation
Common thyme	*Thymus vulgaris*	Evergreen shrub	Divide, layer or cuttings in spring, summer or autumn
Wild thyme	*T. praecox arcticus*	Evergreen shrub	Divide, layer or take cuttings in spring, summer or autumn
Lemon-scented thyme	*T. × citriodorus*	Evergreen shrub	Divide, layer or take cuttings in spring, summer or autumn
Golden lemon-scented thyme	*T. × citriodorous* 'Auerus'	Evergreen shrub	Divide, layer or take cuttings in spring, summer or autumn
Winter savory	*Satureja montana*	Hardy evergreen shrub	Sow or divide in spring or autumn

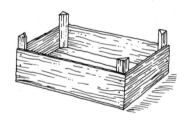

Growing Position	Height	Uses: Aromatic/ Culinary/Medicinal
Light, well drained soil Full sun	30cm 12in	leaf: a+c+m
Light, well drained soil Full sun	10cm 4in	leaf: a+c+m
Light, well drained soil Full sun	15cm 6in	leaf: a+c+m
Light, well drained soil Full sun	15cm 6in	leaf: a+c+m
Well drained, alkaline soil Full sun	38cm 15in	leaf: c+m flower: m

Vegetable Rotation

R otations are a very useful way of ensuring that your resources are used to their best advantage. The idea is to divide the vegetable garden or allotment into three, or more often, four plots. The heavy feeders are grown on the plot that has just been manured or composted. The following year, another area is manured and takes these crops, and in the subsequent year they're moved on again. So with a three year rotation, the entire garden is manured every three years.

That system requires only three plots, of course, and the fourth is used for permanent crops such as rhubarb and asparagus.

In small gardens, there is not much value in practising vegetable rotations as a preventative control of pests and diseases. They'll normally be mobile enough to spread the small distances involved anyway. If you want to be on the safe side, do not follow any crop with one from the same family anyway: there are, in fact, a few soil pests, like eelworm, that *are* relatively immobile, so rotations are of some limited value here.

Otherwise, forget rotations and dress the whole of the vegetable garden with well-rotted manure or compost. Contrary to popular opinion, root crops won't suffer provided the manure is well rotted.

Lime is also used every three years and that goes on the plot which the members of the cabbage family (brassicas) grow.

PLOT A
Cultivation: Double digging incorporating manure in upper and lower levels, plus two handfuls of blood, fish and bone meal per square metre/yard. Some crops in this group may need extra feeding.
Suitable crops: Potatoes, carrots, beetroot, parsnips, onions, shallots, leeks, garlic, tomatoes, courgettes, marrows, pumpkins, celery, Florence fennel, aubergines, peppers, cucumbers, melons, celeriac, Hamburg parsley, salsify, scorzonera.

PLOT B
Cultivation: Single digging and application of blood, fish and bone meal at the rate of two handfuls per square metre/yard, over the whole plot, two or three weeks before sowing the first crops of the season.
Suitable crops: Peas, French beans, runner beans, broad beans, Lima beans, soya beans, peanuts, sweetcorn, okra, spinach, spinach beet, Swiss chard, lettuce, chicory, endive, cresses, globe artichokes.

PLOT C
Cultivation: Single digging and applications of blood, fish and bone meal (as on plot B) and lime to bring the pH level up to 6.5–7.0. Some crops may need extra feeding during the season – refer to specific entries in this chapter.
Suitable crops: Cabbages, Chinese cabbages, Brussels sprouts, cauliflowers, calabrese and broccoli, kale, swedes, turnips, radishes, kohl-rabi.

PLOT D
Space must also be left for the permanent crops, which occupy a plot of their own and do not come within the rotation plan. These are: rhubarb, globe artichokes, Jerusalem artichokes, asparagus, seakale and herbs. (The globe artichokes are included in both plots because they can be grown as perennials or annuals.)

In a small garden it is sensible to grow some of the permanent crops in the ornamental border.

Germination

The following list of germination times and temperatures is, of course, somewhat approximate.

All of them refer to seedlings raised in the greenhouse and, where vegetables are mentioned, these too refer to early crops sown under glass for either growing on in the greenhouse, or for planting out under cloches.

Where seeds need light to germinate, they should be covered with a thin layer of horticultural vermiculite and then with either a sheet of glass or clear polythene.

When the seeds need darkness they can be covered with a thin layer of compost or not at all and then with opaque polythene or kitchen foil.

Those that remain unmarked are not too fussy so it's recommended to cover them with a little vermiculite and then with opaque polythene.

Germination times for seeds sown outside vary so much that there's little point in listing them. But you should be able to get an approximation from this chart used in conjunction with the prevailing weather conditions and soil temperature.

Seeds – Germination

Variety	Germination Days	Light/ Dark	Temperature (°F)
Achillea	21–30	L	60–65
Achimenes	21–30		65–75
Adonis	30–120		60–65
Ageratum	10–14	L	70–75
Alstroemeria	30–365		65–70
Alyssum	7–14	L	55–75
Amaranthus	10–15		70–75
Amaryllis	21–70		65–75
Anchusa	7–30		65–70
Anemone	28–180		65–70
Aquilegia	30–90	L	65–75
Arabis	20–25	L	65–70
Arctotis	21–35		60–70

Variety	Germination Days	Light/ Dark	Temperature (°F)
Arenaria	15–30		55–65
Armeria	14–21		55–60
Artichoke	7–8		65–70
Asparagus	21–30		60–70
Asperula	30–42	L	50–55
Aster	10–14		65–70
Astilbe	40–80		60–65
Atriplex	9–21		50–55
Aubergine	6–7		65–70
Aubrieta	14–21	L	60–65
Basil	7–10		60–70
Beetroot	7–8		60–65
Begonia	15–60	L	70–80
Bellis	10–15	L	60–70
Broad Beans	7–8		60–65
Browallia	14–21	L	70–75
Cabbage	2–3		55–60
Cacti	5–180	L	75–80
Calandrinia	5–14		55–60
Calceolaria	14–21	L	65–75
Calendula	10–14	D	65–70
Campanula	14–28	L	60–70
Candytuft	10–15		68–85
Canna	21–60		70–75
Capsicum	21–30	L	70–75
Carrot	6–7		55–60
Catananche	21–25		65–75
Cauliflower	2–3		55–60
Celery	10–11	L	65–70
Celosia	10–15	L	70–75
Centaurea	7–14	D	60–70
Centranthus	21–30		60–70
Cerastium	5–10		55–60
Cheiranthus	14–21		65–75
Chelone	14–42		55–65
Chrysanthemum	10–18		60–70
Cineraria	14–21	L	65–70

Variety	Germination Days	Light/ Dark	Temperature (°F)
Clarkia	21		50–55
Cleome	10–14	L	70–75
Cobaea	21–30		70–75
Coleus	10–20	L	65–75
Convolvulus	5–14		65–70
Coreopsis	20–25	L	55–70
Corydalis	30–60	L	50–60
Courgette	7		65–70
Craspedia	14–30		70–75
Cucumber	7		70–75
Cuphea	8–10	L	65–70
Cyclamen	30–60	D	55–60
Cynoglossum	5–10	D	65–75
Cyperus	25–30		70–75
Dahlia	5–20		65–70
Delphinium	14–28	D	50–55
Dianthus	14–21		60–70
Digitalis	15–20	L	60–65
Dimorphotheca	10–15	L	60–70
Eccremocarpus	30–60		55–60
Echinops	15–60		60–65
Echium	7–14		65–70
Erigeron	15–20		55–60
Eschscholtzia	14–21		60–65
Eucalyptus	14–90		70–75*
Euphorbia	10–15		65–70
Exacum	15–20	L	70–75
Ferns	30–180	L	65–70
Ficus	15–90	L	70–80
Freesia	25–30		65–75
Fuchsia	21–90	L	70–75
Gaillardia	15–20	L	65–70
Gaura	14–30		65–75
Gazania	8–21	D	60–65
Gentiana	14–180	D	70–75
Geranium	3–21		70–75
Gerbera	15–25	L	70–75

Variety	Germination Days	Light/ Dark	Temperature (°F)
Gesneria	14–21	L	70–75
Geum	21–28+		65–70
Gilia	17		
Gloxinia	15–30	L	65–75
Godetia	7–14		60–65
Gourds	15–28		70–75
Grasses	10–90	L	60–75
Grevillea	20–25	L	75–80
Gypsophila	10–15		65–70
Helianthus	10–14		65–70
Helichrysum	7–10	L	65–75
Helleborus	30–545		60–65
Hesperis	20–25	L	70–80
Heuchera	10–60	L	65–70
Hollyhock	10–12	L	60–70
Hypericum	30–90		50–55
Hypoestes	10–21		70–75
Impatiens	21–30	L	70–75
Incarvillea	25–30		55–65
Ipomoea	15–21		65–70
Jacaranda	10–15		70–85
Jacobaea	8–21		60–65
Kalanchoe	7–30	L	65–75
Kniphofia	10–30		65–70
Kochia	10–15	L	70–75
Larkspur	14–21	D	50–55
Lathyrus	20–30		55–65
Lavatera	15–20		65–70
Lavender	21–90		55–65
Leontopodium	10–42	L	50–55
Leptosiphon	17–21		55–65
Lettuce	4–5	L	60–65
Liatris	20–25		55–75
Lilies	30–365		65–75
Limnanthes	14–2		55–60
Linaria	10–15		55–60
Linum	20–25		55–60

Variety	Germination Days	Light/ Dark	Temperature (°F)
Lithops	10–40	L	75–80
Lobelia	15–20	L	65–75
Lunaria	10–14		65–70
Lupin	15–60	D	55–65
Lychnis	21–30	L	65–70
Marigold	5–14		65–70
Matricaria	5–21	L	65–75
Meconopsis	14–28		55–65*
Melon	7		65–70
Mentzelia	5–21		55–60
Mesembryanthemum	15–20	D	65–75
Mimulus	7–21	L	65–70
Mirabilis	7–21	L	65–70
Moluccella	21–35	L	60–65
Myosotis	14–30	D	65–70
Nasturtium	7–21	D	60–65
Nemesia	7–21	D	55–70
Nemophila	7–21		55–60
Nepeta	7–21		60–70
Nicandra	15–20		70–75
Nicotiana	10–20	L	65–70
Nigella	10–15		65–70
Nolana	14–30		60–70
Onions	2–3		55–60
Pansy	14–21	D	65–75
Papaver	10–30	D	55–60
Passiflora	30–365		70–80
Peas	4–5		60–65
Penstemon	18–21	L	55–60
Petunia	10–21	L	55–65
Phacelia	12–30	D	55–65
Phlox-Annual	10–21	D	55–65
Phlox-Perennial	25–30	D	65–70
Physalis	21–30	L	65–70
Portulaca	14–21	L	70–85
Primula	20–25	L	60–65
Pyrethum	30–60		55–60

Variety	Germination Days	Light/ Dark	Temperature (°F)
Radish	2		55–60
Rhodanthe	14–30		75–80
Ricinus	15–21		70–75
Rudbeckia	5–21	L	65–70
Saintpaulia	30–60	L	70–75
Salpiglossis	15–30	D	70–75
Salvia	10–14	L	68–80
Saponaria	10–21	L	65–70
Saxifraga	15–60		65–75
Scabiosa	10–15		70–75
Schizanthus	7–14	D	60–75
Sedum	15–30		50–55
Silene	15–20		65–70
Solanum	15–21	L	70–75
Spinach	5–6		60–65
Stocks	10–14	L	55–60
Strelitzia	30–180		70–75
Streptocarpus	15–30	L	55–65
Sweet Pea	10–20	D	55–60
Thunbergia	14–21		70–75
Thymus	15–30	L	50–55
Tomato	6–7		65–70
Tropaeolum	10–15		55–65
Turnip	2		55–60
Ursinia	14–30		55–60
Verbascum	14–30		55–60
Verbena	14–90	D	60–65
Veronica	15–30	L	65–70
Vinca	15–30	D	70–75
Viola	14–21	D	55–60
Viscaria	10–21		60–65
Zinnia	10–24		75–80

*After cold treatment

Propagation

I t's not for this book to go into the details of propagation but simply to remind you which plants you can raise from seed or from one of the various forms of vegetative propagation. I have naturally left out annuals, biennials and vegetables which are nearly all raised from seed.

Bear in mind that often the seed can be collected from your own plants. Sometimes hybrids will come true to type (ie. like the parent plant the seed was collected from), as is the case with Crocosmia 'Lucifer' for example, but generally it's best to collect from species or old, established hybrids that are pollinated by insects outside. Never bother with F1 hybrids.

Cuttings are worth experimenting with. On a garden scale there's little to lose so it's worthwhile trying all methods on all plants and seeing what suits you best.

Perennials to raise from seed

Acanthus
Achillea (but not
   hybrids)
Aconitum
Agapanthus
Agastache
Alchemilla
Allium
Alstroemeria
Alyssoides
Anaphalis
Anchusa
Anemone
Anthemis
Anthyllis
Aquilegia
Aruncus
Asclepias
Asphodeline
Aster
Astrantia
Baptisia

Boykinia
Calandrinia
Calceolaria
Campanula
Catananche
Centaurea
Cephalaria
Cimicifuga
Codonopsis
Coreopsis
Corydalis
Crocosmia
Cynoglossum
Delphinium
Dicentra
Dictamnus
Dierama
Digitalis
Dodecatheon
Draba
Eccremocarpus
Echinacea

Echinops
Epilobium
Eremurus
Erigeron
Erinus
Erodium
Eryngium
Euphorbia
Festuca
Filipendula
Francoa
Gaillardia
Galega
Gentiana (some)
Geranium
Geum
Helenium
Helleborus
Hesperis
Heuchera
Hieracium
Hosta

Incarvillea	Miscanthus	Rodgersia
Inula	Nepeta	Rudbeckia
Iris	Oenothera	Salvia
Knautia	Omphalodes	Saponaria
Kniphofia	Ophiopogon	Scabiosa
Lathyrus	Paeonia	Semiaquilegia
Leonurus	Papaver	Sidalcea
Liatris	Paradisea	Silene
Ligularia	Pennisetum	Sisyrinchium
Lilium	Penstemon	Stachys
Limonium	Phlomis	Stipa
Linaria	Physalis	Symphyandra
Linum	Phytolacca	Tellima
Liriope	Phytostegia	Teucrium
Lobelia	Plantago	Thalictrum
Lupinus	Polemonium	Tiarella
Lychnis	Potentilla	Trollius
Malva	Primula	Urospermum
Meconopsis	Prunella	Veratrum
Mimulus	Pulsatilla	Viola

Perennials Suitable for Basal Cuttings

Achillea	Dicentra	Hesperis
Anaphalis	Euphorbia (but	Lupinus
Anthemis	wear gloves to	Lychnis
Campanula	avoid contact	Malva
Chrysanthemum	with irritant sap)	Polygonum
Delphinium	Gypsophila	

Perennials Suitable for Stem Cuttings

Acaena	Ballota	Eriophyllum
Achillea	Bergenia	Euphorbia
Ajuga	Campanula	Euryops
Anthemis	Carnation	Felicia
Argyranthemum	Centaurea	Geranium
Artemisia	Chrysanthemopsis	Gypsophila
Asarina	Dendranthema	Helenium
Aster	Dianthus	Helianthemum
Astilbe	Diascia	Helichrysum
Astrantia	Draba	Iberis

Lavatera
Leucanthemum
Lobelia
Lotus
Lupinus
Lysimachia
Monarda

Osteospermum
Penstemon
Phlomis
Polygonum
Potentilla
Salvia
Saponaria

Sedum
Stachys
Tanacetum
Teucrium
Tolmiea
Veronica
Viola

Shrubs, Conifers and Climbers from Softwood Cuttings

Abies
Actindia
Akebia
Ampelopsis
Andromeda
Aristotelia
Artemisia
Berberis
Buddleia
Buxus
Callicarpa
Calluna
Calycanthus
Camellia
Campsis
Ceanothus
Celastrus
Cephalanthus
Ceratostigma
Cestrum
Chamaecyparis
Choisy
Cistus
Clematis
Convolvulus
Coprosma
Corokia
Coronilla
Cotinus
Cotoneaster
Cryptomeria
Cuphea

Cytisus
Daboecia
Deutzia
Diervilla
Dorycnium
Elaeagnus
Epilobium
Erica
Escallonia
Euonymus
Exochorda
Fatsia
Forsythia
Fuchsia
Garrya
Gaultheria
Genista
Halimiocistus
Hebe
Hedera
Helianthemum
Hibiscus
Humulus
Hydrangea
Hypericum
Ilex
Itea
Jasminum
Juniperus
Kolkwitzia
Lavandula
Lavatera

Laurus
Leycesteria
Ligustrum
Lippia
Lithospermum
Lonicera
Microbiota
Mimulus
Neillia
Olearia
Parthenocissus
Philadelphus
Phlomis
Photinia
Phygelius
Physocarpus
Picea
Pieris
Pileostegia
Pittosporum
Potentilla
Prostanthera
Pyracantha
Rhamnus
Rosa
Rosmarinus
Rubus
Ruta
Salix
Sambucus
Santolina
Sarcococca

Schizophragma
Senecio
Solanum
Spiraea
Syringa

Teucrium
Thuja
Trachelospermum
Tsuga
Ulex

Viburnum
Vinca
Vitis
Weigela
Zenobia

Shrubs from Hardwood Cuttings

Abelia
Azara
Berberis (evergreen)
Buddleia
Buxus
Cornus
Cotoneaster
Desfontainia
Deutzia
Elaeagnus
Escallonia
Forsythia

Garrya
Griselinia
Jasminum
Kerria
Leptospermum
Leycesteria
Ligustrum
Lonicera
Metasequoia
Nandina
Olearia
Osmanthus

Philadelphus
Polygonum
Ribes
Rosa
Salix
Sambucus
Sarcococca
Spiraea
Symphoricarpos
Tamarix
Viburnum (deciduous)
Weigela

Plants Suitable for Root Cuttings

Acanthus
Ailanthus
Anchusa
Anemone hybrida
Arundinaria
Brunnera
Catananche
Clerodendrum

Crambe
Dicentra
Dictamnus
Echinacea
Eryngium
Limonium
Lythrum
Nepeta

Papaver orientale
Phlox
Primula denticulata
Rhus
Robinia
Romneya
Rubus

Plants Suitable for Division

Acaena
Achillea
Alchemilla
Aquilegia
Armeria
Arundinaria
Aster

Astilbe
Astrantia
Bergenia
Brunnera
Campanula
Carex
Centaurea

Coreopsis
Crocosmia
Dactylis
Delphinium
Dendranthema
Dicentra
Doronicum

Echinacea
Echinops
Epimedium
Erigeron
Filipendula
Geranium
Geum
Gladiolus
Helenium
Hemerocallis
Hesperis
Heuchera
Hosta
Koeleria
Iris
Lamium
Leucanthemum

Liatris
Liriope
Luzula
Lysimachia
Miscanthus
Molinia
Oenanthe
Papaver
Phlomis
Phlox
Polygonatum
Polygonum
Potentilla
Primula
Pulmonaria
Rheum
Rodgersia

Rudbeckia
Saponaria
Saxifraga
Schizostylis
Sedum
Sidalcea
Solidago
Stachys
Stipa
Tanacetum
Tellima
Tiarella
Tradescantia
Trollius
Tropaeolum
Veronica
Waldsteinia

Shrubs Suitable for Semi-Ripe Cuttings

Aucuba
Azalea (evergreen)
Berberis
Buddleia
Buxus
Ceanothus
Cedrus
Ceratostigma
Chaenomeles
Chamaecyparis
Choisy
Cistus
Colutea
Convolvulus
Cryptomeria
Cupressocyparis
Cytisus
Daphne
Escallonia

Euonymus
Gaultheria
Genista
Hebe
Hydrangea
Hypericum
Ilex
Indigofera
Itea
Juniperus
Kolkwitzia
Lavatera
Lippia
Lonicera
Myrtus
Pernettya
Phlomis
Philadelphus
Photinia

Picea
Pieris
Pinus
Pittosporum
Potentilla
Prunus (laurels)
Pseudotsuga
Pyracantha
Rhamnus
Rhododendron
Ruta
Santolina
Senecio
Taxus
Thuja
Ulex
Viburnum
Weigela

Trees and Shrubs to Raise from Seed

Acer	Daphne	Liquidamber
Aesculus	Davidia	Liriodendron
Ailanthus	Enkianthus	Morus
Alnus	Eucalyptus	Nothofagus
Amelanchier	Eucryphia	Paeonia
Arbutus	Euonymus	Paulownia
Araucaria	Fatsia	Phormium
Berberis	Fraxinus	Picea
Betula	Gaultheria	Piptanthus
Callicarpa	Genista	Pittosporum
Callistemon	Ginkgo	Prunus (some)
Carpinus	Gleditsia	Quercus
Castanea	Hibiscus	Robinia
Cercidiphyllum	Hippophae	Sorbus
Cercis	Hypericum	Spartium
Colutea	Ilex	Stranvaesia
Cornus (some)	Juglans	Taxus
Corylus	Koelreuteria	Thuja
Cotoneaster	Laburnum	Tilia
Crataegus	Larix	
Cytisus	Leycesteria	

Alpines to Raise from Seed

Acaena	Draba	Linum
Aethionema	Dryas	Lychnis
Alyssum	Erigeron	Papaver
Anacyclus	Erinus	Phlox
Anagallis	Erysimum	Primula
Anchusa	Erythronium	Pulsatilla
Antennaria	Gentiana	Ramonda
Arabis	Geranium	Saponaria
Arenaria	Globularia	Silene
Calamintha	Hepatica	Sisyrinchium
Campanula	Hypericum	Soldanella
Chiastophyllum	Iberis	Thymus
Cotyledon	Leontopodium	Viola
Dianthus	Lewisia	
Diascia	Linaria	

Alpines to Raise from Cuttings

Acantholimon
Achillea
Aethionema
Alyssum
Anagallis
Anchusa
Andromeda
Androsace
Arabis
Armeria
Asperula
Aubrieta
Calamintha
Campanula
Cassiope

Cotyledon
Dianthus
Draba
Dryas
Edraianthus
Erodium
Erysimum
Euryops
Frankenia
Gentiana
Geranium
Gypsophila
Helichrysum
Hypericum
Iberis

Linum
Lithospermum
Parahebe
Phlox
Polygala
Potentilla
Primula
Sagina
Saponaria
Saxifraga
Silene
Thymus
Veronica
Viola

Shrubs and Climbers to Layer

Azalea
Akebia
Camellia
Campsis
Celastrus
Clematis
Cornus
Cotinus

Hedera
Hydrangea (climbing)
Jasminum
Magnolia
Parthenocissus
Rhododendron
Ribes
Rubus

Schizophragma
Syringa
Trachelospermum
Viburnum
Vitis
Wisteria

Hedges

The name of the game with hedges is fast growth so make sure you prepare the soil well before planting. Dig deeply and manure a strip at least 90cm (6ft) wide.

In the following selection hedges that are generally clipped to shape are classified 'formal', while those that are allowed to grow more or less naturally are called 'informal'.

The recommended planting distances err a little on the close side for quick cover but if the budget's small, the plants could be spaced wider though they'll naturally take longer to form an impenetrable screen.

Low Growing Hedges

Plant	Height	Planting Distance
Berberis thunbergii 'Atropurpurea Nana'	45–60cm 1½–2ft	35cm 15in
Berberis verruculosa	1–1.2m 3ft–4ft	60cm 2ft
Buxus sempervirens 'Suffruticosa'	15–20cm 6–8in	15–20cm 6–8in
Hebe	60cm 2ft	45cm 1½ft
Lavandula spica	1–1.2m 3ft–4ft	45cm 1½ft
Lavandula 'Hidcote'	30–60cm 1–2ft	35cm 15in
Lavandula 'Munstead Dwarf'	45–60cm 1–2ft	35cm 15in
Lavandula vera	60–90cm 2–3ft	35cm 15in
Olearia haastii	1.2m 4ft	90cm 3ft
Potentilla 'Farreri'	1–1.2m 3–4ft	60cm 2ft
Potentilla 'Jackman's Star'	1–1.2m 3–4ft	60cm 2ft
Prunus cistena	1.2–1.5m 4–4½ft	60cm 2ft
Santolina chamaecyparissus	45–60cm 1½–2ft	30cm 1ft
Santolina chamaecyparissus 'Nana'	30–45cm 1–1½ft	23cm 9in
Santolina virens	45cm 1½ft	30cm 1ft

Foliage	Flowers/ Berries	Formal/ Informal	Remarks
Reddish purple	—	F	Trim in winter
Glossy green	Golden flowers in May. Attractive fruit	F	Prune in spring Evergreen
Green	—	F	Clip in spring or late summer. Evergreen
Yellowish green	White flowers July–Sept	F	Evergreen. Trim in spring
Grey/Green	Grey/blue flowers July–Sept	F	Evergreen Trim in spring
Silvery	Deep purple/blue flowers	F	Evergreen. Trim in spring
Grey/green	Dark flowers	F	Evergreen. Trim in Spring
Silvery	Soft blue flowers	F	Trim in April Deadhead all season
Greyish Oval	White flowers July onwards	I	Prune after flowering Evergreen
Fern-like	Yellow flowers May–Sept	F	Prune in spring
Fern-like	Brilliant yellow flowers	F or I	Prune in spring
Crimson	White flowers	F or I	Trim after flowering
Feathery Silver	Yellow flowers June–Aug	F or I	Trim after flowering and in April. Evergreen
Feathery Silver	Yellow flowers June–Aug	F or I	Trim after flowering and in April. Evergreen
Bright Green	Lemon yellow flowers	F or I	Trim after flowering and in April

Tall Hedges (Informal)

Plant	Height	Planting Distance
Berberis darwinii	1.2–1.8m 4–6ft	60cm 2ft
Berberis sanguinea	1.2m 4ft	60cm 2ft
Berberis stenophylla	3m 10ft	60cm 2ft
Berberis thunbergii	1.2–1.8m 4–6ft	60cm 2ft
Berberis thunbergii 'Atropurpurea'	1.5–2m 5–6ft	60cm 2ft
Berberis thunbergii 'Erecta'	60cm–1.2m 2–4ft	45cm 1½ft
Berberis thunbergii 'Helmond Pillar'	60cm–1.2m 2–4ft	45cm 1½ft
Berberis thunbergii 'Red Chief'	1.5–2m 5–6ft	60cm 2ft
Cotoneaster lacteus	2.5–3m 8–10ft	90cm 3ft
Cotoneaster simonsii	1.5–2.5m 5–8ft	45cm 1½ft
Escallonia varieties	1.5–1.8m 5–6ft	75cm 2½ft
Euonymus japonicus 'Ovatus Aureus'	1.5–2.5m 5–8ft	45cm 1½ft
Griselinia littoralis	3.5–4.5m 11–14ft	60cm 2ft
Hebe speciosa	1.2m 4ft	60cm 2ft

Foliage	Flowers/ Berries	Formal/ Informal	Remarks
Shield-like shiny green	Orange/yellow flowers April/May Bluish/purple berries	I	Prune after flowering Trim in winter Evergreen Impenetrable
Sea green	Greenish	I	Evergreen
Deep green	Yellow flowers May/June	I	Prune after flowering Evergreen Impenetrable
	Pale-yellow flowers. Bright red fruit	I	Impenetrable
Reddish purple		I	
		I	Stiff vertical habit makes a narrow hedge
Reddish bronze form of 'Erecta'		I	
Wine red form of 'Atropurpurea'		I	
Olive green	White flowers in June Red berries		Prune in summer Impenetrable Evergreen
Turns red in winter	Red berries	I	Trim in winter Evergreen
Green	Pink or white flowers	F or I	Prune after flowering and lightly in spring. Evergreen
Green		I	Good for seaside. Trim in spring. Evergreen
Fresh green		I	Use *only* near sea. Trim early summer
Green above, purple beneath	Pink, red or purple flowers	I	Suitable only for mild areas. Evergreen

Plant	Height	Planting Distance
Hippophae rhamnoides	1.8–2.2m 6–7ft	60cm 2½ft
Ilex aquifolium	1.5m 5ft	90cm 3ft
Osmanthus burkwoodii	1.8–2.4m 6–8ft	60cm 2ft
Pittosporum tenuifolium	1.5–2.5m 5–8ft	45cm 1½ft
Prunus cerasifera 'Pissardii'	1.8–2.5m 6–8ft	60cm 2ft
Prunus lusitanica	1.5–1.8m 5–8ft	60cm 2ft
Prunus laurocerasus 'Rotundifolia'	1.5–1.8m 5–8ft	60cm 2ft
Pyracantha rogersiana	1.2–1.8m 4–6ft	60cm 2ft
Rhododendron luteum	2.2–2.4m 7–8ft	90cm 3ft
Rhododendron ponticum	1.8–3m 6–9ft	90cm 3ft
Rosmarinus officinalis 'Miss Jessop's Upright'	1.2–1.8m 4–6ft	60cm 2ft
Symphoricarpos 'Magic Berry'	1.2–1.5m 4–5ft	1m 3ft
Symphoricarpos 'White Hedge'	1.2–1.5m 4–5ft	1m 3ft
Syringa vulgaris varieties	2.5–3m 8–10ft	1.2m 4ft
Tamarix gallica	1.2–1.5m 4–5ft	60cm 2ft

Foliage	Flowers/ Berries	Formal/ Informal	Remarks
Silvery white	Orange flowers Red berries	I	Good for seaside Trim in spring
Dark green	Red berries	F or I	Trim late summer Impenetrable Evergreen
Lustrous green Toothed	Scented white flowers April/May	I	Trim after flowering Evergreen
Pale shiny green	Purple flowers in May Black berries	I	Prune as required Needs light soil and shelter. Evergreen. Only for mild areas
Purple	Pink flowers in spring	F or I	Trim after flowering
Dark glossy green	Scented white flowers in June Purple berries	I	Prune in April Evergreen
Light green Broad		I	Prune in April. Evergreen
Glossy green	White flowers in June. Red berries		Prune in spring and summer if necessary. Evergreen
Good autumn colour	Scented yellow flowers May/June	I	Needs lime-free soil. Deciduous
Dark glossy green	Purplish pink flowers	I	Evergreen Needs lime-free soil
Dark green White underside	Blue flowers in May	F	Trim in spring Evergreen
Green	Lilac flowers Carmine berries	I	Trim in spring
Green	White berries	I	Trim in spring
Green	White, pink or mauve flowers. May–June	I	Prune after flowering
Feathery Sea green	Pink flowers June–Aug	I	Good for seaside Prune hard in spring

Plant	Height	Planting Distance
Tamarix pentandra	1.2–1.5m 4–5ft	60cm 2ft
Viburnum tinus	1.8–2.5m 6–8ft	60cm 2ft
Viburnum tinus 'Eve Price'	1.8–2.5m 6–8ft	60cm 2ft

Tall Hedges (Formal)

Plant	Height	Planting Distance
Acer campestre	1.8–3m 6–10ft	60cm 2ft
Carpinus betulus	1.5–2.5m 5–8ft	45cm 1½ft
Crataegus monogyna	1.5–2.5m 5–8ft	30cm 12in
Fagus sylvatica	2–3m 7–10ft	45cm 1½ft
Fagus sylvatica 'Riversii'	2–3m 6½–10ft	45cm 1½ft
Ligustrum ovalifolium	1.2–1.8m 4–6ft	30cm 1ft
Ligustrum ovalifolium 'Aureum'	1.2–1.8m 4–6ft	30cm 1ft
Lonicera nitida	1.2–1.8m 4–6ft	30cm 1ft

Foliage	Flowers/ Berries	Formal/ Informal	Remarks
Silvery grey	Rose pink flowers		
Oval Dark glossy green	Pink buds. White flowers. Blue berries Dec–March	I	Evergreen
	Carmine buds. Pink flowers		

Foliage	Flowers/ Berries	Formal/ Informal	Remarks
Red in spring Orange-red in autumn		F	Trim in winter or summer
Green		F	Trim in winter or late summer. Good alternative to beech on wet soil
Green	Scented white flowers	F	A field hedge
Brown leaves last all winter		F	Avoid heavy wet soils
Light red turning to purple		F	Avoid heavy wet soils
Green		F	Semi-Evergreen. Trim in April and August
Yellow		F	Semi-Evergreen. Trim in April and August
Glossy Small Green		F	Trim April and August. Evergreen

CONIFEROUS

Plant	Height	Planting Distance
Chamaecyparis lawsoniana 'Alumii'	2.5m 8ft	90cm 3ft
Chamaecyparis lawsoniana 'Fletcheri'	2.5m 8ft	90cm 3ft
Chamaecyparis lawsoniana 'Green Hedger'	2.5m 8ft	90cm 3ft
Cupressocyparis × *leylandii*	3.5–4.5m 12–15ft	90cm 3ft
Cupressocyparis × *leylandii* 'Castlewellan'	3.5–4.5m 12–15ft	90cm 3ft
Cupressus macrocarpa 'Gold Crest'	3m 10ft	90cm 3ft
Pinus nigra 'Austriaca'	2.5–3m 8–10ft	1.5m 5ft
Pinus radiata	3.5–4.5m 12–15ft	1.5m 5ft
Taxus baccata (Yew)	1.8m 6ft	60cm 2ft
Thuja occidentalis 'Smaragd'	2.5–3m 8–10ft	90cm 3ft
Thuja plicata 'Atrovirens'	2.5–3m 8–10ft	90cm 3ft

Foliage	Flowers/ Berries	Formal/ Informal	Remarks
Blue-grey and sea green		F	Evergreen
Grey-green Feathery		F	Evergreen
Bright green		F	Evergreen
Grey-green		F	Fast growing Good for coastal areas Evergreen
Golden			
Bright golden		F	Trim with secateurs at first in April and August. Evergreen
Dark green		I	Shape in spring. Good for coast. More used for a windbreak
Grassy green		I	Evergreen. A good windbreak for seaside areas
Dark green		F	Trim late summer. Needs good drainage. Evergreen
Emerald green		F	Evergreen
Bright dark green		F	Fast growing. Trim with secateurs in summer

Pruning Clematis

There are dozens and dozens of varieties of clematis, and each one needs to be pruned in a specific way. It's therefore easy to understand how confusion reigns. In fact, the basic rules are very easy to grasp and the mythical complexities should never be allowed to put you off growing them.

The first rule is that, after planting, all varieties should be pruned to within 30cm (1ft) off the ground to encourage strong, bushy growth to grow right from the base of the plant. This is done in February, cutting back to just above a plump bud. To establish a really strong, bushy framework, it's also recommended that, in the second February or March after planting, all shoots are again cut back to within about 1m (3ft) off the ground, but understandably, few gardeners have the patience to do this.

All varieties fall into three groups, so there are just three methods to grasp.

Group 1
These are the vigorous, small-flowered varieties such as *C. montana* which flower before the end of May. After the initial, post-planting treatment, these varieties are pruned immediately after flowering, simply cutting out weak or dead stems and trimming with shears where the plant is growing in a place where it's not wanted.

Group 2
Early-flowering varieties like 'Nelly Moser' flower before the end of June, producing single flowers from buds in the leaf joints. Naturally, pruning really hard would cut off most of those buds so, in this case, you leave the main framework of branches and cut the sideshoots hard back to a plump bud. The job's best done in February or March.

Group 3
Late-flowering varieties like 'Jackmanii Superba' are also pruned in February or March but this time, the plant has all season to make its growth and then produce flowers on the shoots it has made during the season. To encourage strong, vigorous growth, the plants are cut back hard to just above a bud about 75cm (30in) above soil level.

Feeding

All plants, with the possible exception of the vigorous, early-flowering species that are growing too rampantly, should be fed at the same time as pruning. Use a couple of handfuls of organic fertilizer per square metre to cover an area at least 2m (6ft) square around the base of established plants.

Group 1

alpina; armandii; chrysocoma; cirrhosa; forsteri; gracilifolia; macropetala; japonica; montana; montana rubens; napaulensis; patens; paniculata; rehderiana; terniflorai × *vedrariensis.*

Group 2

'Allanah'; 'Alice Fisk'; 'Anna Lousie'; 'Asao'; 'Barbara Dibley'; 'Barbara Jackman'; 'Beauty of Richmond'; 'Beauty of Worcester'; 'Bees' Jubilee'; 'Belle Nantaise'; 'Belle of Woking'; 'Bracebridge Star'; 'Capitaine Thuilleaux'; 'Carnaby'; 'Corona'; 'Countess of Lovelace'; 'Crimson King'; 'Daniel Doronda'; 'Dawn'; 'Dr Ruppel'; 'Duchess of Edinburgh'; 'Duchess of Sutherland'; 'Edith'; 'Edomuraski'; 'Elsa Späth'; 'Empress of India'; 'Etoile de Malicorne'; 'Fair Rosamund'; 'Fairy Queen'; 'Fireworks'; 'Florida'; 'General Sikorski'; 'Gillian Blades'; 'Glenderek'; 'Guernsey Cream'; 'Hainton Ruby'; 'Haku Ookan'; 'Henryi'; 'H.F.Young'; 'Horn of Plenty'; 'Jackmanii Alba'; *japonica*; 'John Paul II'; 'John Warren'; 'Kathleen Dunford'; 'Kathleen Wheeler'; 'Ken Donson'; 'King Edward VII'; 'Lady Caroline Nevill'; 'Lady Londesborough'; 'Lady Northcliffe'; 'Lasurstern'; 'Lemon Chiffon'; 'Lilactime'; 'Lincoln Star'; 'Lord Neville'; 'Madame le Coultre'; 'Marcel Moser'; 'Maureen'; 'Miss Bateman'; 'Miss Crawshay'; 'Moonlight'; 'Mrs Bush'; Mrs Cholmondeley'; 'Mrs George Jackman'; 'Mrs James Mason'; 'Mrs Spencer Castle'; 'Mrs N. Thompson'; 'Mrs P.B. Truax'; 'Multi-Blue'; 'Myojo'; 'Nelly Moser'; 'Niobe'; 'Peveril Pearl'; 'Pink Champagne'; 'Princess of Wales'; 'Proteus'; 'Ramona'; 'Richard Pennell'; 'Rouge Cardinale'; 'Royality', 'Royal Velvet'; 'Ruby Glow'; 'Scartho Gem'; 'Sealand Gem'; 'Serenata'; 'Silver Moon'; 'Sir Garnet Wolseley'; 'Snow Queen'; 'Sylvia Denny'; 'The President'; 'Twilight'; 'Veronica's Choice'; 'Vino'; 'Violet Charm'; 'Vyvyan Pennell'; 'Wada's Primrose'; 'W.E. Gladstone'; 'Will Goodwin'; 'William Kennett'.

Group 3

'Ascotiensis'; *campaniflora*; 'Comtesse de Bouchaud'; 'Dorothy Walton'; × *durandii*; × *eriostemon*; 'Ernest Markham'; *flammula*; 'Sieboldii'; 'Gipsy Queen'; 'Hagley Hybrid'; *heracleifolia*; 'Huldine'; *integrifolia*; 'Jackmanii Superba'; 'John Huxtable'; *jouiniana*; 'Lady Betty Balfour'; 'Lilacina Floribunda'; 'Madame Baron Veillard'; 'Madame Edouard Andre'; 'Madame Grange'; 'Margaret Hunt'; *orientalis*; *paniculata*; 'Paul Farges'; 'Perle d'Azur'; 'Pink Fantasy'; 'Prince Charles'; 'Prins Hendrik'; *pitcheri*; *potaninirecta*; *serratifolia*; 'Star of India'; *tangutica*; *texensis*; *thunbergii*; 'Victoria'; 'Ville de Lyon'; *vitalba*; *viticella*; 'Voluceau'; 'Warsaw Nike'.

Greenhouse and Conservatory Temperatures

What you grow in your greenhouse or conservatory depends entirely on the temperatures you can maintain during the winter. Bear in mind that it's the minimum temperature that's important and it generally only needs to dip below that recommended at night for the damage to be done. Plants are killed and will not recover.

The easiest and cheapest way is to grow only hardy plants in winter and to move them out in the spring when they can be replaced with more tender plants. This still leaves plenty of scope for, say, alpines in winter and tomatoes and pot plants in summer.

If you decide to add heat in order to keep more tender plants through the winter, you'll naturally extend your scope tremendously. But make sure that you have a back-up in case of really cold nights.

Choose a heater of a size that should produce the correct temperature and supplement that with a small, thermostatically-controlled, extra one. Set it so that it only comes on when the temperature falls below the necessary level and you sleep easy at nights.

The temperatures quoted here are all minimums.

Plants for particular Temperature Regimes

Plants marked C are recommended for conservatories

Temperatures will need to be higher for propagation

BELOW 32°F (0°C)
Hardy bulbs
Most alpines
Hardy perennials and
  shrubs

40°F (47°C)
Abelia
Abutilon C
Acacia
Agapanthus C
Aristolochia C
Bambusa

Callistemon
Camellia C
Clianthus C
Coronilla
Daphne
Desfontainea
Dionaea
Diosma
Eccremocarpus C
Erica
Eriostemon
Erythrina C
Eugenia

Eulalia
Fabiana
Fatsia
Ferns
Habrothamnus
Hymenocallis C
Lagerstroemia C
Lapageria C
Leonotis
Leptospermum C
Leucophyta
Mimulus
Myrtus C

Nertera
Olea
Ophiopogon
Ornithogalum
Oxalis
Passiflora C
Pelargonium
Pittosporum C
Polygala
Punica
Rehmannia
Rhodochiton C
Richardia
Selaginella
Solanum C
Sollya
Sparmannia
Statice
Streptocarpus
Tolmiea C
Trachelium
Vallota C
Vitis C

45°F (7°C)
Aeonium C
Agapetes
Agathaea
Aloe
Alonsoa C
Aloysia C
Anigozanthus
Anthericum
Araucaria
Ardisia
Asclepias
Aspidistra C
Azalea
Begonia C
Billbergia
Boronia C
Bougainvillea C
Bouvardia
Brunfelsia

Burchellia
Calceolaria
Calendula
Campanula
Campsis
Carex C
Carnation
Cassia
Celsia
Centradenia
Ceropegia
Chamaedorea
Chlorophytum C
Choisya C
Chorizema
Cineraria
Cissus
Citrus C
Clarkia
Clematis C
Cobaea C
Colocasia
Cordyline C
Correa C
Cotyledon
Crassula
Crinum
Cuphea
Cymbidium C
Cytisus
Darlingtonia
Datura C
Drosera
Echeveria C
Epacris
Epidendrum
Epiphyllum
Eucalyptus
Eucomis C
Eurya
Euryops C
Eustoma C
Ferns C
Francoa

Freesia
Fuchsia C
Gerbera C
Gesnera
Gilia
Grevillea C
Haemanthus C
Hedychium C
Hibbertia
Hibiscus C
Hoya C
Humea
Isolepis
Jasminum C
Kleinia
Lachenalia C
Lilium
Luculia
Lycoris
Mandevilla C
Manettia
Milla
Mitraria
Nerine
Nerium
Odontoglossum
Opuntia
Pachyphytum
Parodia
Pavetta
Pelargonium
Petrea
Pharbitis C
Pilea
Pimelea
Plumbago C
Polianthes
Portulacaria
Pycnostachys
Reineckea
Reseda
Rhododendron C
Russelia
Salvia

Sarrecenia
Saxifraga
Scutellaria
Selaginella
Selenicereus
Sparmannia
Stenocarpus
Stephanotis C
Streptosolen
Thyrsacanthus
Tibouchina C
Trachelium
Trachelospermum
Tristania
Veronica
Zebrina
Zephyranthes C

50°F (10°C)
Achimenes
Adiantum
Aechmea
Agave C
Aphelandra
Aporocactus
Asparagus C
Begonia
Beloperone C
Browallia
Brunfelsia
Celosia
Coleus
Cryptanthus
Cyclamen
Cyperus
Exacum
Ficus C
Gloriosa C
Gloxinia
Hatiora
Heliotropium

Hippeastrum C
Hylocereus
Impatiens
Jacaranda C
Jacobinia
Kalanchoe
Linaria C
Lotus
Monstera C
Neoregelia
Nidularium
Ochna
Palms C
Persea
Platycerium
Primula
Rhipsalis
Schlumbergera
Sinningia
Strelitzia C
Streptocarpus
Tradescantia
Tropaelolum C
Tulbaghia C
Zantedeschia C

55°F (13°C)
Alpinia
Amasonia
Begonia
 (fibrous-rooted)
Caladium
Calathea C
Chlorophytum C
Clerodendrum C
Clivia C
Codiaeum
Coffea C
Crossandra
Desmodium
Dicentra

Dieffenbachia
Dipladenia
Eranthemum
Eucharis
Euphorbia
Ferns C
 (stove species)
Ficus C
Fittonia
Gardenia C
Gynura
Heliconia
Hoya
 (stove species)
Hydrangea C
Ipomoea C
Ixora
Jasminum
 (stove species)
Justicia C
Lachenalia C
Lantana C
Leea
Maranta
Mussaenda
Pandanus
Panicum
Passiflora
 (stove species)
Pellionia
Peperomia
Plumbago
 (stove species)
Rondeletia
Ruellia
Sanchezia
Sansevieria C
Sonerila
Stigmaphyllon
Strelitzia C
Thunbergia C

Zingiber

60°F (16°C)
Acalypha
Aechmea
Aeschynanthus
Aglaonema
Allamanda
Alocasia
Alonsoa
Ananas
Anthurium
Aphelandra
Aralia
Aristolochia
Azalea C
Bauhinia
Bertolonia
Canna C
Columnea
Cryptanthus
Medinilla
Musa
Nidularium
Philodendron
Phyllanthus
Saintpaulia
Schismatoglottis
Strobilanthes
Tabernaemontana
Tillandsia
Trevesia
Vriesia

65°F (18°C)
Dracaena
Ipomoea (some)
Nepenthes

Easy Greenhouse Pot Plants

I t's possible to fill your greenhouse with colour quite cheaply and provide a succession of colouful pot plants for the house. All the following plants can be easily raised from seed or bulbs.

Plants to raise from seed in the cool greenhouse

For germination times and temperatures see Germination section
Colours: b-blue, c-cream, g-green, m-mauve, o-orange, p-pink, r-red, w-white, y-yellow

Botanical name	Common name	Colour	Height
Achimenes	Hot water plant, Cupid's bower	m r	15–22cm (6–9in)
Asparagus plumosus nanus sprengeri	Asparagus fern	g foliage	30cm (12in) trailing
Begonia semperflorens	Begonia, fibrous-rooted	p r w y	22–30cm (9–12in)
Browallia		b w	30cm (12in)
Calceolaria	Slipper flower, Lady's slipper	r y	15–60cm (6in–2ft)
Calendula	Pot marigold	y	30-60cm (1–2ft)
Campanula isophylla	Bell flower	b w	Trailing
pyramidalis	Chimney bell flower		90–120cm (3–4ft)
Celosia	Cockscomb	ry	30cm (12in)
Cineraria		m p r w	30cm (12in)
Coleus	Flame nettle	g o r foliage	30–45cm (1–1½ft)
Cuphea	Mexican cigar flower	r y	30cm (12in)
Cyclamen F[1]		m p r w	23–30cm (9–12in)
Eustoma	Prairie gentian	p	60cm (2ft)

Flowering season	Sowing season	Cultivation
Late summer	Spring	Water with warm water. Support with twigs. Light shade. Keep moist
Year round interest	Spring	Light shade. Keep moist
Summer	Mid–late winter	Light shade
Autumn	March/Apr	Humid atmosphere
Spring and Summer	June in cold frame	Bring inside late Sept. Light shade
Summer	Spring	Pinch when 7½–10 cm (3–4in) high. Remove dead flowers
June onwards	April	Water well while in flower
Summer–autumn	March	Light, moist warmth
Winter–spring	June in cold frame	Bring inside end Sept. Water carefully
Summer and autumn	Feb	Pinch out flowers. Light shade
July onwards	March	Moist, light shade. Pinch out tips
Nov onwards	Feb	Poisonous. Soak seeds
Summer	Feb	Shade and stake. Long lasting cut flower

Botanical name	Common name	Colour	Height
Exacum	Persian violet	b	15–30cm (6–12in)
Fuchsia		p r	45cm (18in)
Gerbera	Transvaal daisy	o p r w	20–60cm (8–24in)
Gloxinia (*Sinningia*)		r/w	30cm (12in)
Hypoestes	Polka dot plant	g foliage p or w markings	15–22cm (6–9in)
Kalanchoe	Flaming Katie	r y	30cm (12in)
Mimosa pudica	Sensitive plant	g foliage	30cm (12in)
Pelargonium zonal	Geranium	p r w	30cm (12in)
Primula			20–30cm (8–12in)
kewensis		y	
malacoides		m p r w	
obconica		b p r w	
sinensis		m p	
Salpiglossis	Painted tongue, Velvet flower	o r y	45–60cm (1½–2ft)
Schizanthus	Butterfly flower, Poor man's orchid	m p r/w	30–45cm (12–15in)
Solanum capsicastrum	Winter cherry	o r y	22–30cm (9–12in)
Streptocarpus	Cape primrose	m p r w	22–30cm (9–12in)

Flowering season	Sowing season	Cultivation
Late summer	March	Scented. Shady, moist atmosphere
July–Oct	April	Partial moist shade
March onwards	March	Do not overwater. Long lasting cut flower
Summer	Feb	Warm, moist, shady conditions
Summer–autumn	March	
Spring and summer	March	Good drainage needed
Year round interest	March	Soak seeds. Leaves fold when touched
Summer	Jan–Feb	Dry atmosphere. Scented leaves
Winter–spring		Keep cool in summer
	March	Bring inside end of September
	Apr–June	
	Apr/May	Can cause skin rash
	Apr/May	
Summer and autumn	March	Pinch out. Water carefully
July onwards	March	
Winter	March	Poisonous. Keep outside in summer
Summer onwards	March	Moist, cool shade

Climbers

Botanical name	Common name	Colour	Height
Cobaea	Cathedral bells, Cup and saucer vine	m p	5m(16ft)
Eccremocarpus	Chilean glory flower	o r y	5m (16ft)
Ipomoea	Morning glory	b	5m (16ft)
Luffa	Loofah		4m (13ft)
Thunbergia	Black-eyed Susan	c-o	3m (10ft)
Tropaeolum	Canary creeper	y	4m (13ft)

Flowering season	Sowing season	Cultivation
Summer and autumn	March	Moist warmth. Large pot or greenhouse border
Summer and autumn	March	Large pot
Summer and autumn	April	Soak seeds. Grow in sun. Large pot or border
Summer and autumn	March	Large pot or border
Summer and autumn	March	12.5cm (5in) pot, moist shade
Summer and autumn	March	15cm (6in) pot

Greenhouses and Greenhouse Equipment

The products listed here have all been tried and tested at Barnsdale and are considered good value for money. However, exclusion from the list does not necessarily imply that a product is inferior.

(GC = obtainable at garden centres)

Greenhouses

Banbury Homes & Gardens Ltd, PO Box 17, Banbury, Oxfordshire OX17 3NS

Cambridge Glasshouse Co, Barton Rd, Comberton, Cambridgeshire CB3 7BY
Tel: (01223) 262395

CW Whitehouse Ltd, Buckhurst Works, Bells Yew Green, Frant, Tunbridge Wells, Kent TN3 9BN
Tel: (01892) 750247

Norfolk Greenhouses, PO Box 22, Watton, Norfolk IP25 6PA
Tel: (01638) 510568

Parklines, Birmingham B5 7BR
Tel: (0121) 446 6030

Robinsons Greenhouses Ltd, Robinson's House, First Avenue, Millbrook, Southampton SO15 0LG
Tel: (01703) 703355

Samuel Wernick, Russel Gardens, Wickford, Essex SS11 8BL
Tel: (01268) 561199

Polythene tunnels
LBS Polythene, Cottontree, Colne, Lancashire BB8 7BW
Tel: (01282) 871777

Greenhouse equipment

Automatic ventilators
Bayliss Precision Components, Lysander Works, Blenheim Rd, Airfield Industrial Estate, Ashbourne, Derbyshire DE6 1HA
Tel: (01335) 42981

Jemp Engineering, Canal Estate, Station Rd, Langley, Berkshire SL3 6EG
Tel: (01753) 548327

Thermoforce, Heybridge Works, Maldon, Essex CM9 7NW
Tel: (01621) 858797

Disinfectant
Jeyes Fluid. GC.

Fertilizers
Levington Liquinure. GC.
Levington Tomorite. GC.
Phostrogen. GC.

Heaters
Jemp Engineering Ltd, Canal Estate, Station Rd, Langley, Berkshire SL3 6EG
Tel: (01753) 548327 (electric).

George H. Elt Ltd, Eltex Works, Bromyard Rd, Worcester WR2 5DN (Paraffin and gas).
Tel: (01905) 422377

Autoheat from: Findlay, Irvine Ltd, Bog Road, Penicuik, Lothian EH26 9BU
Tel: (01969) 672596 – or GC.

Parwin Power Heaters, Holmes Road, Yaxley, Peterborough PE7 3NA
Tel: (01733) 240699

Hormone rooting liquid
PBI Roota. GC.

Instruments (thermometers etc) Diplex, PO Box 172, Watford, Hertfordshire WD1 1BX
Tel: (01923) 231784

Insulation
Nortene. GC.

Lighting
Sunlight Systems, 3, St. Mary's Works, Burnmoor St, Leicester LE2 7JJ *Tel*: (0116) 247 0490

Misting systems
Access Garden Products, Crick, Northampton NN6 7XS
Tel: (01788) 822301

Modules – Plastics
PG Horticulture, Street Farm, Thornham Magna, Eye, Suffolk IP23 8HB *Tel*: (0137) 971515

– Polystyrene
AP Propapacks, (polystyrene). GC.

Propagators
George Ward (Moxley) Ltd, Heathfield Lane, Darlaston, West Midlands WS10 8QZ. GC.
Tel: (01902) 491991

Propagating blanket to make heated bench
Prylorn Ltd, Elmhurst Yard, High St, Chatteris, Cambridgeshire PE16 6NP
Tel: (01354) 695779

Seed trays
George Ward (Moxley) Ltd, Heathfield Lane, Darlaston, West Midlands WS10 8QZ. GC.
Tel: (01902) 491991

Shading
PBI Coolglass. GC.

Soil warming cable
Jemp Engineering Ltd, Canal Estate, Station Rd, Langley, Berkshire SL3 6EG
Tel: (01753) 548327

Sprayers
Hozelock-ASL. GC.

Staging and accessories
Two Wests and Elliott, Unit 4, Carrwood Rd, Sheepbridge Industrial Estate, Chesterfield, Derbyshire S41 9RH
Tel: (01246) 541077

Terracotta Pots
Whichford Pottery, Whichford, Nr Shipston-on-Stour, Warwickshire CV36 5PG
Tel: (01608) 684416
Olive Tree. GC.

Watering cans
Haws, 120 Beakes Rd, Smethwick, Warley, West Midlands B67 5AB
Tel: (0121) 420 2494
Geeco. GC.

Watering systems (automatic)
Hozelock-ASL. GC

Concrete

The following mixes have been used at Barnsdale and other gardens over the years and have proved successful over a long term. All measurements are by volume and note that it's absolutely essential to use fresh cement.

For the base to paving:
8 parts all-in ballast.
1 part Portland cement.
Mix dry and spread at least 7.5cm (3in) thickness, Consolidate by treading.

Mortar for laying paving:
3 parts builders sand.
1 part Portland cement.
Mix quite dry.

For setting fence posts:
4 parts all-in ballast.
1 part Portland cement.
Mix on the dry side consistent with ease of tamping down. Ideally concrete in metal sockets to take the wooden posts.

For foundations of walling and areas of exposed concrete:
4 parts all-in ballast.
1 part Portland cement.
Mix as dry as possible consistent with ease of laying. In freezing weather use liquid antifreeze in gauging water as instructions on can. If required, colouring powder can also be added.

Mortar for laying brick and stone walling:
2 parts builders' sand.
1 part masonry cement.
For bricks, mix the mortar quite wet but make it much drier for stone.

For building concrete pools:
4 parts all-in ballast.
1 part Portland cement.
Concrete waterproofer used as instructions on the can.
Use this for the main structure of the pool and then skim over the top with a screed of:
3 parts sharp sand.
1 part Portland cement.
Liquid waterproofer added to gauging water as instructions on can.

For making 'hypa-tufa' troughs or covering glazed sinks:
2 parts sieved coir compost.
2 parts sharp sand.
1 part Portland cement.

ADDITIVES:
A variety of concrete additives is available for colouring, to protect against frost, to speed drying, to increase hardening and to plasticize mortar for easy and clean brickwork. Ask at any builders' merchant.

Measuring and Ordering Materials

W hen ordering materials for the garden, especially for unfamiliar landscape jobs, it's sometimes quite tricky to work out exactly how much of any particular material you need. Since delivery or even collection costs are often the biggest factor in the price, you should always make sure you have enough to finish the job without having to re-order. So, though you would always expect to order a little too much rather than too little, you won't want to go over the top. The following methods of measuring are meant to be a rough guide.

Measuring areas.
Most materials these days are sold by metric measurements, so measuring areas in metres and centimetres instead of yards and inches will greatly simplify the job. In fact, even old fellers like me have found metric much easier to work out once you get used to it. Younger gardeners will know no other way. If it's absolutely out of the question, work it out in imperial and hope your supplier can convert it for you. Alternatively, use the tables starting on p.330.

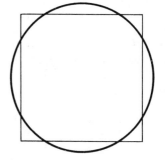

Rectangles and squares. Simply measure the length and the breadth and multiply the two together. For example, an area 5m × 10m = 50 sq.m.

Circles. Turn the circle into a square as illustrated. For garden jobs it's quite accurate enough.

Uneven areas. Often, lawned areas need to have curved edges so use the same method to work out an average and add about 5% for safekeeping.

Cubic measurements. To work out how much soil is needed for a given

area, measure the area in square metres and multiply by the depth required in centimetres. i.e. an area 6m long × 5m wide = 30 sq.m. If you want a 5cm thickness of soil, multiply by 5 = 150 and divide by 100 = 1.5cu.m.

To calculate the amount of grass seed
Grass seed should be sown at 50 g per square metre. Simply measure the area and multiply by 50 to obtain the number of grams needed. There are 1000 g per kilogram.

To calculate amounts of turf
Turves are generally 30cm wide and 100cm long. So three turves make up near enough a square metre. I'm afraid that turves are also sometimes measured in imperial measurements, being 1ft wide by 3ft long so here three turves make up a square yard. Measure the area and multiply by three to give the number of turves needed. Alternatively, give the supplier the area in yards or metres and he'll work it out.

To calculate amounts of ballast and cement.
Measure the amount of ballast needed for concreting by the same method recommended for soil. Don't add anything for the cement you put in because this makes up for the sinkage of the ballast when it's tamped down. Again, add 5% to be on the safe side.

For a normal ballast/cement mix of 4:1, you'd need 6 bags of cement for each cu.m of ballast. For small jobs, you might buy the ballast by weight in bags. In that case you need 300kg of ballast to 1 bag of cement.

Use Portland cement and always ensure that it's fresh.

To calculate amounts of sand and cement.
If you're building a wall, you use a 4:1 mix of builders' sand and masonry cement. For large jobs you'll need 10 bags of cement for every cubic metre of sand. For smaller jobs use 1 bag of cement to 200 kg of sand. This will be enough to lay about 500 bricks.

If you would like further information, The British Cement Association have two helpful books. *Build it with Concrete* costs £5.58 and *Concrete around your House and Garden* costs £3.50. Add £1 post and packing for each. Obtainable from The British Cement Association, Century House, Telford Avenue, Crowthorne, Berkshire RG11 6YS.

Ordering rectangular paving.
If you're using one size of slab only, nothing could be simpler. Measure the area and ask for so many square metres.

But if you're laying the paving in a random pattern of different sized slabs and you have no predetermined plan, remember to order equal *areas* of each slab size rather than equal *numbers* or you'll finish up with too many large ones.

Ordering pond liners.
Measure the length and width of the pond and its depth and add twice the depth plus 30cm (1ft) to allow for an overlap at the edges. So, if the pool measures 6m long and 4m wide and it's 1m. deep, the liner should be 6m + 2m + 30cm = 8.3m long and 4m + 2m + 30cm = 6.3m wide.

Landscape Gardening Equipment

The manufacturers and suppliers mentioned here are those who have provided materials for work carried out at Barnsdale or one of our other projects shown on *Gardeners' World*.

GC = available at garden centres.

Arbours and garden buildings
The English Basket and Hurdle Centre, The Willows, Curload, Stoke St Gregory, Taunton, Somerset TA3 6JD
Tel: (01823) 698418

Stuart Garden Architecture, Lydeard St Lawrence, Burrow Hill Farm, Wiveliscombe, Somerset TA4 2RN
Tel: (01984) 667458

Brick Pavers
The York Handmade Brick Co. Ltd, Forest Lane, Alne, North Yorkshire YO6 2LU
Tel: (01347) 838886

Chicken coops
George Carter, Silverstone Farm, North Elmham, Norfolk NR2 5EX
Tel: (01362) 668130

Concrete Pavers
Marshalls Mono, Southowram, Halifax, West Yorkshire HX3 9SY
Tel: (01422) 366666

Fencing
The English Basket Centre, The Willows, Curload, Stoke St Gregory, Nr. Taunton, Somerset TA3 6JD
Tel: (01823) 698418

(Willow hurdles).
Forest Fencing Ltd, Stanford Court, Stanford Bridge, Nr Worcester WR6 6SR
Tel: (018865) 451

Larch-Lap Ltd, PO Box 17, Lichfield St, Stourport-on-Severn, Hereford & Worcester DY13 9ES
Tel: (01299) 823232

Picket – Blenheim Estates Sawmills, Combe Witney, Oxon OX8 8ET
Tel: (01993) 881206

Fruit cages and arches
Agriframes, Charlwoods Rd, East Grinstead, West Sussex RH19 2HG
Tel: (01342) 318181

Knowle Nets, East Rd, Bridport, Dorset DT6 4NX
Tel: (01308) 424342

Furniture
Andrew Crace Designs, 49 Bourne Lane, Much Hadham, Hertfordshire SG10 6ER
Tel: (01279) 842685

Barlow Tyrie Ltd, Springwood Industrial Estate, Rayne Rd, Braintree, Essex CM7 7RN
Tel: (01376) 322505

Barnsley House GDF, Barnsley House, Cirencester, Glous. GL7 5EE
Tel: (01285) 74561

Chatsworth Carpenters, Estate Office, Edensor, Bakewell, Derbyshire DE45 1PJ
Tel: (0124) 6582242

Frolics of Winchester, 82 Canon Street, Winchester SO23 9JQ
Tel: (01962) 856384

Geebro Ltd, South Rd, Hailsham, East Sussex BN27 3DT
Tel: (01323) 840771

Pepe Garden Furniture, Burhill, Buckland, Nr Broadway, Worcs. WR12 7LY
Tel: (01386) 858842

Seat-table, Unit D3, Plumtree Farm Industrial Estate, Bircotes, Doncaster, South Yorkshire DN11 8EW
Tel: (01302) 750243

Grass seed
W W Johnson and Son, London Rd, Boston, Lincolnshire PE21 8AD
Tel: (01205) 365051

Unwins Seeds Ltd, Mail Order Dept, Histon, Cambridgeshire CB4 4ZZ
Tel: (01945) 588522

Gravel, decorative
Border Hardcore and Rockery Stone Co., Middletown Quarry, Welshpool, Powys SY21 8DJ
Tel: (01938) 570375

Love Seat
Woodworks, 7 North Street West, Uppingham, Rutland LE15 9SF
Tel: (01572) 823131

Manhole covers
Drainplanters, Quigley Plastics, Newtown Industrial Estate, Cross Keys, Newport, Gwent NP1 7PZ

Ornaments
Chilstone Garden Ornaments, Sprivers Estate, Lamberhurst Rd, Horsmonden, Kent TN12 8DR
Tel: (01892) 723266; from Jan. 1996: (01892) 740110

Haddonstone Ltd, The Forge House, East Haddon, Northamptonshire NN6 8DB
Tel: (01604) 770711

Minsterstone Ltd, Station Rd, Ilminster, Somerset TA19 9AS
Tel: (01460) 52277

Paving and walling
Bradstone Garden Products, Okus Trading Estate, Swindon, Wiltshire SN1 4JH
Tel: (01793) 512288

Marshalls Mono, Southowram, Halifax, West Yorkshire HX3 9SY
Tel: (01422) 366666

The Marley Paving Co. Ltd, Lichfield Rd, Branston, Burton upon Trent, Staffordshire DE14 3HD
Tel: (01283) 713877

Pergolas
Forset Fencing – GC
Larchlap – GC

Pond liners, pumps, lighting
Hozelock – GC

Pools and pool liners
Stapeley Water Gardens Ltd, 92 London Rd, Stapeley, Nantwich, Cheshire CW5 6HE
Tel: (01270) 623868

Lotus Water Garden Products,
PO Box 36, Junction St, Burnley,
Lancashire BB12 0NA
Tel: (01282) 20771

Hozelock – GC

Printed Concrete
Creteprint, Auckland House, Perry
Way, Witham, Essex CM8 3SX
Tel: (01376) 517766

Stones, boulders, chippings etc.
Border Stone, Middletown Quarry,
Welshpool, Powys SY21 8DJ
Tel: (01938) 570375

Stone, Natural
Border Stone, Middletown Quarry,
Welshpool, Powys SY21 8DJ
Tel: (01938) 570375

J. Brailsford Turf Ltd, Thrang End
Farm, Yealand Redmayne,
Carnforth, Lancashire LA5 9TE
Tel: (01524) 781952

Stonecraft, Burgh Rd, Aylesham,
Norfolk NR11 6AR
Tel: (01263) 733322

Trellis and treillage
Stuart Garden Architecture, Lydeard
St Lawrence, Burrow Hill Farm,
Wiveliscombe, Somerset TA4 2RN
Tel: (01984) 667458

Frolics of Winchester, 82 Canon St,
Winchester, Hampshire SO23 9JQ
Tel: (01962) 856384

Hickson Landscape Structures,
Wheldon Rd, Castleford, West
Yorkshire WF10 2JT
Tel: (01977) 556384

See also 'Fencing'.

Tubs and troughs
(plastic): Grosfillex UK Ltd, 10
Chandos Rd, London NW10 6NF
Tel: (0181) 965 2268

(glazed ceramic): Woodlodge
Products, 21B Rydens Rd, Walton-
on-Thames, Surrey KT12 3AB
Tel: (01932) 223412

(terracotta): Whichford Pottery,
Whichford, Nr Shipston-on-Stour,
Warwickshire CV36 5PG
Tel: (01608) 684416

Turf
Rolawn (Turf Growers) Ltd,
Elvington, Yorkshire YO4 5AR
Tel: (01904) 85661

Victorian edging tiles
The Bulmer Brick and Tile Co. Ltd,
Bulmer, Nr, Sudbury, Suffolk
CO10 7EF
Tel: (01787) 269232

Wall decorations
Frolics of Winchester, 82 Canon
Street, Winchester SO23 9JQ
Tel: (01962) 856384

Wood stain
Sadolin – builders' merchants

Seasonal Gardening Jobs

I t's difficult to advise accurately times to carry out gardening jobs, simply because the weather and climate vary so much. Cold, exposed areas could be as much as two, three or even four weeks behind warmer places. So the jobs are listed in seasons rather than months. You'll soon get used to your own timings and can use this list as a reminder. As a guide, the following months apply to Barnsdale which is in a relatively exposed spot in the East Midlands.

Winter – November to late January.
Early spring – February to late March.
Spring – April to late May.

Early summer – June to early July.
Summer – July to late August.
Autumn – September to late October.

WINTER

Kitchen garden
Protect all members of the cabbage family with netting against hungry birds.

● Order seed catalogues.

● Clear away debris and make regular slug and snail-hunting sorties.

● Plant fruit trees and bushes.

● Lift a few parsnips and leeks and put them into a corner in garden compost in case the ground freezes hard.

● Winter prune bush apples and pears.

● Remove the top netting of the fruit cage in case it snows.

● Keep strawberries in pots outside but put them on their sides to prevent waterlogging.

● Protect cauliflower curds from frost by snapping a few leaves over them.

● Continue winter digging and manuring.

● Remove all weeds to the compost heap.

● Remove stumps of brassicas immediately after harvesting and shred them if possible.

● Plant new rhubarb crowns.

● Cover a piece of ground with clear polythene for the early crops.

Flower garden
● Sweep up fallen leaves and put them into a container.

● Cover alpines that resent winter wet.

● Clear all debris from the borders and lightly fork over spreading manure or compost at the same time.

● Winter prune deciduous shrubs.

● Plant trees and shrubs.

● Be prepared to protect plants in the cold-frame against frost by covering.

● Sow seeds of berried shrubs and alpines and put the pots outside or in the frame.

● Check stakes and ties on trees and replace or loosen as necessary.

● Brush snow off trees and shrubs if it threatens to damage them. Otherwise leave them covered as insulation.

● Remove all weeds to the compost heap.

● Shrubs that are in the wrong place can now be moved.

● Protect tender plants with cloches.

● Take hardwood cuttings.

Greenhouse, windowsill and potting shed
● Ventilate as much as possible during the day but leave only the smallest chink at night. Some heating may be necessary to maintain frost-free conditions.

● Insulate with bubble polythene to save heating costs.

● If you have border space sow broad beans, early peas and winter lettuce.

● Examine stored fruit and vegetables and remove any showing signs of rotting.

● If your seed order arrives, store it in a cold, dry place.

● Check dahlia tubers in store.

● Sow cyclamen if you can maintain a temperature of 18 °C (64 °F).

● Clean pots and boxes in very hot water with a little household bleach added.

● Take advantage of sunny days to do any greenhouse repairs.

● Plant figs, vines, peaches and nectarines and pot up citrus fruits.

● Put greasebands on the staging legs to protect against vine weevils.

● Set up potato tubers to sprout.

● Towards the end of the period, sow hardy annuals in modules.

● Sow broad beans, cabbage, carrot cauliflower, celery, celeriac, lettuce, spinach, onion, pea, salad onion and turnip.

● Take root cuttings of perennials.

General
● Check tools, repair them if necessary and put them away.

● Take the mower to be serviced.

● Buy in manure and stack it.

● Check the garden centre for winter bargains and try to buy the next season's requirements all at once while they're a bit cheaper.

EARLY SPRING

Kitchen garden

● Try to finish off the winter digging as soon as possible.

● Put out cloches for early vegetables at least 2 weeks in advance of sowing or planting.

● Plant potatoes.

● Test for lime and spread it if necessary.

● Feed fruit trees and bushes.

● Plant Jerusalen artichokes.

● Cover strawberries with cloches.

● When the soil has warmed up sufficiently under cloches, sow broad bean, carrot, cabbage, cauliflower, lettuce, early peas, salad onions, spinach and turnips. If you sowed the same crops in the greenhouse, plant them out at the same time.

● Plant onion sets and shallots outside if the weather and soil conditions are favourable.

● Protect peaches from rain to avoid peach leaf curl fungus.

● Prune autumn fruiting raspberries.

● Net blackcurrants against bullfinches which eat the buds.

● Feed spring cabbage with a high nitrogen fertilizer.

● Sow parsnips and hamburg parsley.

● Plant perennial herbs.

● Towards the end of the period, sow winter cabbage, cauliflower, kale, brussels sprouts, sprouting broccoli and leeks in a seed-bed.

● Plant out globe artichokes and onion sets towards the end of the period.

● Lift, divide and replant chives, garlic chives and sorrel.

● Graft apples and pears.

Flower garden

● Prune deciduous shrubs that flower later in the year on the current season's growth.

● Prune hypericums back to the ground if they were infected with rust disease.

● Prune late-flowering clematis.

● Lift and transplant snowdrops, snowflakes and aconites.

● Sow sweet peas or transplant those raised inside from an earlier sowing.

● Towards the end of the period, sow hardy annuals or plant out seedlings raised earlier inside.

● Prune roses. Plant new herbaceous perennials and lift and divide congested clumps.

● Replace rockery plants.

● Hard prune shrubs grown for their winter bark colour.

● Rake the lawn to remove old thatch. You may also be able to mow.

● Lay turf lawns unless the soil is frozen.

● Trim winter flowering heathers as soon as they finish flowering.

● Towards the end of the period, plant gladioli.

● Plant lilies outside if the weather's favourable. If not, pot them up for planting later.

● Feed all plants in the borders not forgetting the hedges.

Greenhouse, windowsill and potting shed
● Ventilate freely on sunny days but still close up almost completely at night. Check frames and cloches on sunny days and ventilate if necessary.

● Sow begonias and geraniums in a heated propagator.

● Pick over rooted cuttings, removing diseased leaves.

● Take cuttings of chrysanthemums, dahlias, fuchsias, geraniums and most tender perennials.

● Towards the end of the period sow cucumbers, melons and tomatoes for growing in the cool greenhouse.

● Sow half-hardy annuals.

● Repot fruit plants if necessary.

● Take basal cuttings of perennials.

● Sow seeds of perennials for flowering later this year.

● Sow tender perennials like salvia, eccremocarpus and rhodochiton for flowering later this year.

● Take cuttings of heathers.

General
● Put down tiles or slates to catch slugs and turn them over each morning.

SPRING

Kitchen garden
● Sow maincrop varieties of beetroot, broad bean, carrot, chicory, florence fennel, french beans, kohl rabi, lettuce, onion, pea, radish, salad onion, salsify, scorzonera, spinach, summer cabbage, summer cauliflower, swiss chard and turnip.

● Thin out or transplant seedlings as necessary.

● Continue to plant early potatoes.

● Prune cherries and plums.

● Plant onions raised in the greenhouse or frame.

● Mulch with compost or manure around rhubarb.

● Apply water in dry weather.

● Sow dill, hyssop, parsley, rue, marjoram and thyme.

● Plant asparagus.

● During the day remove cloches from strawberries to allow the entry of pollinating insects. Tuck straw underneath ripening fruit.

● Towards the end of the period sow swedes.

● When weather conditions permit, plant courgettes, tomatoes, cucumbers, french beans, runner beans and squashes under cloches and sow the same vegetables outside.

● Pinch out tops of broad beans attacked by blackfly.

● Protect carrots, parsnips, celeriac, hamburg parsley and parsley against carrot fly attack.

● Put out codling moth traps.

● Earth up potatoes and protect them against frost if necessary.

● Plant leeks and brassicas from the seed bed.

● Plant self-blanching celery and protect against carrot fly.

● Take cuttings of mint and rosemary.

● Take measures to control apple and pear scab.

● Tie in new growth of briar fruits as they develop.

Flower garden
● Thin out hardy annual seedlings sown earlier.

● Remove flowers of bulbs as they fade to prevent seeding unless self-set seedlings are required.

● Plant acidanthera, crocosmia, galtonia, gladioli, nerine and ornithogalum.

● Plant evergreens and shift large plants if necessary.

● Plant sweet peas.

● Plant our crysanthemums, argyranthemums and euryops.

● Mow the lawn regularly and feed and weed.

● Take conifer cuttings.

● Finish lifting, dividing and transplanting hardy perennials.

● Continue turfing and sow new lawns.

● Prune spring-flowering deciduous shrubs as soon as they finish flowering.

● Stake hardy herbaceous perennials as they grow.

● Plant aquatic and bog plants and remove blanket weed from the pond.

● Towards the end of the period sow hardy perennials and biennials in a seed bed outside.

● Prune early flowering clematis after it's finished flowering.

● Lift, divide and replant polyanthus.

● Lift bulbs that have finished flowering where space is needed and heel them into a corner of the vegetable plot.

● Plant out hardy perennials raised from seed in the greenhouse.

● Trim alpines if they're spreading beyond their allotted space.

● Tie in climbers regularly.

Greenhouse, windowsill and potting shed
● Ventilate the greenhouse as much as possible and keep floors and staging moist to create humidity.

● Sow sweet corn and tomatoes for planting outside.

- Continue to prick out and repot plants as necessary.

- Continue sowing half hardy annuals for outside planting and for pot plants.

- Take dahlia cuttings.

- Take conifer cuttings.

- Plant tomatoes and cucumbers in the border or in growing bags and pot up peppers and aubergines all in the cold greenhouse.

- Control whitefly.

- From the middle to the end of the period, shift half-hardy plants to the cold frame to harden off before planting out.

- Cover frame if frost is threatened.

- If you have room towards the end of the period, plant up hanging baskets and tubs and keep them inside until all danger of frost is gone.

- Remove sideshoots from tomatoes and start feeding them together with the cucumbers, peppers and aubergines.

- Sow calceolarias, cinerarias and primulas for pot plants.

- Start to prune grapes.

- If plants waiting to be planted begin to look yellow, give them a liquid feed.

General
- Keep topping up the compost heaps. If both become full, empty out the one that's most rotted and stack it outside until use.

- Keep on top of the weeds by regular hoeing or hand pulling.

- Check all new plantings and water regularly.

EARLY SUMMER

Kitchen garden
- Plant out runner beans, tomatoes, cucumbers, courgettes, marrows and sweet corn.

- Continue sowing radish and spinach but now in a shady spot.

- Peg down runners of strawberries to make new plants for forcing.

- Control greenfly and other pests.

- Continue sowing beetroot, carrot, chicory, endive, lettuce, swedes and turnips.

- Sow chicory for forcing and spinach beet for autumn use.

- Sow chinese cabbage, french beans, swiss chard, rhubarb chard and some spring cabbage in a seed bed.

- Net fruit bushes against birds.

- Pick the first gooseberries for ripening and leave some to eat fresh later.

- Protect newly planted brassicas from cabbage root fly.

- Harvest and store shallots and harvest early potatoes.

- Remove flower spikes from rhubarb.

- As tomatoes grow, take out the

sideshoots from the upright growers and tuck straw underneath the bush varieties.

● Pick and dry herbs as they become ready.

● Sow carrots, turnips and beetroot for winter storage.

● Harvest globe artichokes before the flowers start to open.

● At the end of the period start to sow some early varieties of vegetables for lifting in autumn.

● Sow a few broad beans for the harvest of green tops they provide in autumn.

● After strawberries have finished cropping, cut off the old leaves and clean the beds.

● Pinch out the tips of runner beans when they reach the top of the canes.

● Harvest and prune raspberries as they ripen.

● Summer prune pears.

Flower garden
● Plant out half hardy annuals and tender perennials.

● Put out planted tubs and hanging baskets and start watering daily and feeding weekly.

● Take softwood cuttings of shrubs.

● Prune brooms that have finished flowering.

● Continue to trim and tie herbaceous plants cutting them down after flowering unless you intend to save seed.

● Divide and replant Iris germanica rhizomes.

● Plant corms of Anemone coronaria.

● Take stem cuttings of pinks. Tie in climbers regularly.

● Top up the pool and bog garden in dry weather.

● Propagate climbers by layering.

● Plant perennials and biennials sown earlier into a nursery bed.

● Stake gladioli and other tall summer bulbs.

● Disbud chrysanthemums and dahlias for larger blooms.

● Mound up alpines that are going bare in the middle, dropping a little compost into the bare areas.

● Prune summer-flowering deciduous shrubs.

● Dead head roses and annual bedding to extend flowering.

● Take cuttings of hydrangeas.

● Layer border carnations.

● Collect and sow seed of some perennials.

● Take half-ripe cuttings of shrubs.

● Cut back straggly growth of arabis, aubrieta and violas.

● Plant autumn-flowering bulbs.

Greenhouse, windowsill and potting shed
● Ventilate freely, all night if necessary and keep damping down

the floors and stagings. Shade the glass.

● Prick out seedlings of pot plants sown earlier.

● Trim and feed cucumbers and tomatoes regularly and feed peppers and aubergines.

● Put those greenhouse plants that prefer lower temperatures outside but don't forget to water.

● Pinch back vines regularly and feed fruits in pots.

● Take cuttings of regal pelargoniums.

● Sow more half-hardy annuals for pot plants.

General
● Keep the sprinkler going if it's allowed.

● Turn the compost heap to accelerate rotting.

● Continue hand weeding.

SUMMER

Kitchen garden
● Prune raspberries and tie in new canes.

● Support autumn fruiting raspberries with a single string round the whole row.

● Sow an autumn variety of lettuce.

● Prune cordon gooseberries, redcurrants, apples and pears.

● Cut off potato haulm showing

symptoms of blight and harvest the crop.

● Remove old wood of briar fruits after harvesting and tie in new.

● Sow winter-hardy salad onions, winter-hardy spinach or spinach beet and winter radish.

● Sow spring cabbage in a seed bed if not already done.

● Towards the end of the period sow early carrots, lettuce, raddish and turnips in the cold-frame.

● Harvest early apples and use.

● Support heavily laden branches of fruit trees.

● Protect autumn-fruiting raspberries and strawberries from birds.

● Allow a few french beans to ripen and collect and bottle them.

● Plant strawberries and pot up runners for forcing.

● Cut and dry herbs.

● Begin harvesting onions.

● Set up marrows in the sunshine to ripen.

● Begin to lift and store root vegetables.

● Remove debris from peas and beans to the compost heap but leave the roots in the ground to release nitrogen.

● Prune peaches and nectarines.

● Continue picking apples and pears.

● Earth up celery, celeriac and leeks to blanch them.

● Control cabbage white butterflies.

Flower garden
- Take clematis cuttings.

- Take cuttings of alpines, especially those that are short-lived.

- Trim conifer hedges and cut back those that have reached the required height.

- Sow and turf new lawns but be prepared to water.

- Continue mowing but leave the grass longer in dry weather.

- Sow biennials where they are to flower.

- Plant narcissi.

- Continue to feed plants in pots and baskets but change to a high nitrogen feed.

- Cut gladioli but leave some foliage to build up the corm.

- Take half-ripe shrub cuttings and softwood cuttings of geraniums, fuchsias and other tender perennials.

- Continue to dead-head roses, annuals and herbaceous perennials unless you wish to save seed.

- Continue to cut back herbaceous perennials after flowering but also continue to harvest seed where required.

- Prune rambler roses after flowering.

- Early in the period plant autumn flowering bulbs.

- Plant evergreen shrubs towards the end of the period.

- Pot up a few narcissi to fill gaps next spring.

- Greenhouse, windowsill and potting shed

- Maintain continual night ventilation and damp down to keep up the humidity.

- Harvest vegetable fruits regularly, keep up the regular feeding and remove dying leaves from the bottoms of the plants.

- Sow calceolarias, schizanthus, cyclamen and primulas for pot plants.

- Pot up prepared hyacynths for Christmas flowering and plunge them outside.

- Sow winter lettuce for growing in the cold or slightly heated greenhouse.

- Repot cyclamen corms that have been resting.

- Towards the end of the period, remove shading.

- Take stem cuttings of coleus, begonias and impatiens.

AUTUMN

Kitchen garden
- Harvest and store onions, garlic and root crops.

- Plant lettuce for later cloching and spring cabbage outside.

- Harvest and store apples and pears.

● Bring ripened marrows inside to store.

● Take hardwood cuttings of gooseberries.

● As patches of soil become vacant, manure and dig them.

● Prune blackcurrants and gooseberries.

● Prune plums when they've finished cropping.

● Protect the last of the autumn-fruiting strawberries with cloches.

● Check tips of apples and pears for mildew and cut it out.

● Divide and replant rhubarb.

● Plant garlic.

● Take hardwood cuttings of currants.

● Start lifting and forcing chicory.

● Cut down tops of Jerusalem artichokes.

● Cut down asparagus and mulch with compost.

● Put greasebands round apple and cherry trees.

● Continue to pick and store apples.

● Remove yellowing leaves from brussels sprouts.

● Sow broad beans.

Flower garden
● Plant herbaceous perennials and evergreen shrubs.

● Plant deciduous trees and shrubs as soon as leaves have fallen.

● Lift, divide and replant perennials.

● Remove and compost summer bedding and replace with spring-flowering biennials.

● Replant polyanthus.

● Lift gladioli and dahlias and store the corms/tubers.

● Lift tender perennials and box them up for winter storage.

● Plant spring-flowering bulbs and lilies.

● Continue laying turf but stop mowing.

● Take cuttings of fuchsias, chrysanthemums, heathers and hydrangeas together with tender perennials.

● Rake out the thatch from the lawn, spike and topdress.

● Cut down all perennials that are over and clear away debris.

● Clean up the pool and cover with netting to prevent leaves falling in.

● Prune climbing and rambler roses and weeping standards.

● Cut back the old leaves of hellebores.

● Clip over loose growing conifers like Chamaecyparis pisifera 'Boulevard'.

● Pick up fallen rose leaves to remove any infected with blackspot.

● Take hardwood cuttings of deciduous shrubs.

● Sow sweet peas in the cold-frame.

● Plant containers with bulbs and biennials for a spring display.

Greenhouse, windowsill and potting shed

● Start to close the greenhouse at nights and reduce watering and damping down.

● Pot up a few root cuttings of mint and sow a pot of parsley for the windowsill to give a winter supply.

● Alternatively, bring a tub of herbs into the greenhouse.

● Pot up and plunge bulbs for spring flowering.

● Bring inside any plants that have been standing out for the summer.

● Clear out all vegetable fruits and give the greenhouse a good clean with a solution of household bleach.

● Start a regular inspection of pot plants and remove leaves attacked by fungus.

● Pot up a few roses for early cut flowers next year.

● Pot up some early-flowering herbaceous plants from the garden to make good cheap pot plants.

● Bring in pot-grown chrysanthemums and feed regularly.

General

● Clean up the garden as much as you can for the winter, removing dead leaves and weeds to the compost heap.

● Spread compost or manure on vacant soil and prick it in with a fork.

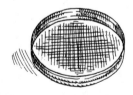

Climates

E ven though this is a relatively small country, there are dramatic climate variations across it. The effect of the Gulf Stream keeps the west of the country quite warm while cold northerly winds bring harsher conditions to the north. Easterlies often bring cold weather from the Russian continent and from Europe while the prevailing south-west wind tends to bring wetter weather from the Atlantic. It follows, therefore, that the east of the country is generally drier and colder than the west and the north is normally colder than the south. Height above sea level also makes a great difference to temperature and wind-chill.

So, giving accurate timings for gardening operations just isn't possible. These maps will show the differences. Gardeners living in the coldest areas should be at least two weeks behind the temperate zones while those in the warmer spots could be a fortnight ahead. If you're new to the area, take advice from the locals.

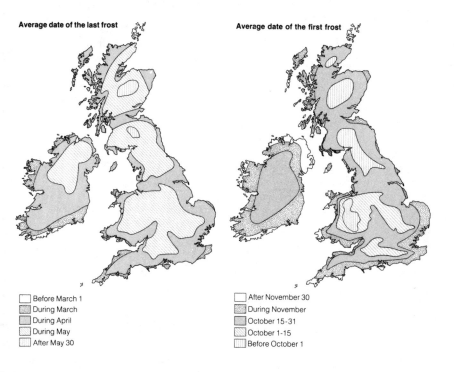

Average date of the last frost

Average date of the first frost

Before March 1	After November 30
During March	During November
During April	October 15-31
During May	October 1-15
After May 30	Before October 1

Temperature zones across Europe

EUROPE

FINLAND
NORWAY
SWEDEN
Estonia
Russia
Latvia
Lithuania
Belorussia
DENMARK
GREAT BRITAIN
HOLLAND
GERMANY
POLAND
BELGIUM
Lux.
Ukraine
CZECHOSLOVAKIA
FRANCE
SWITZER-LAND
AUSTRIA
HUNGARY
ROMANIA
(formerly) YUGOSLAVIA
PORTUGAL
SPAIN
ITALY
ALBANIA
BULGARIA
GREECE

Zone 4 −34 to −29°C (−30 to −20°F)	**Zone 8** −12 to −7°C (10 to 20°F)
Zone 5 −29 to −23°C (−20 to −10°F)	**Zone 9** −7 to −1°C (20 to 30°F)
Zone 6 −23 to −17°C (−10 to 0°F)	**Zone 10** −1 to 4°C (30 to 40°F)
Zone 7 −17 to −12°C (0 to 10°F)	

Weathercall Map

Gardeners sometimes need a weather forecast which is more accurate than the national one given on radio and television. Is it going to rain hard enough to delay the trip to the open garden? Will it freeze tonight and catch my dahlias? Should I cancel the readymix concrete because it's going to snow? There are all kinds of reasons.

You get a very accurate and up-to-the-minute forecast from Weathercall on the number for your area.

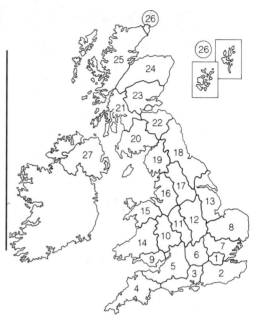

Weathercall Map

Dial 01891 500 followed by the area number below.

National	400
1 Greater London	401
2 Kent, Surrey, Sussex	402
3 Dorset, Hampshire, Isle of Wight	403
4 Devon, Cornwall	404
5 Wiltshire, Gloucestershire, Avon, Somerset	405
6 Berkshire, Buckinghamshire, Oxon	406
7 Bedfordshire, Hertfordshire, Essex	407
8 Norfolk, Suffolk, Cambridgeshire	408
9 South, West and Mid Glamorgan, Gwent	409
10 Shropshire, Hereford, Worcestershire	410
11 Central Midlands	411
12 East Midlands	412
13 Lincolnshire, Humberside	413
14 Dyfed, Powys	414
15 Gwynedd, Clwyd	415
16 North West England	416
17 West and South Yorkshire, Yorkshire Dales	417
18 North East England	418
19 Cumbria, Lake District	419
20 South West Scotland	420
21 West Central Scotland	421
22 Edinburgh, South Fife, Lothian, Borders	422
23 East Central Scotland	423
24 Grampian, Highlands	424
25 North West Scotland	425
26 Caithness, Orkney, Shetland	426
27 Northern Ireland	427

The Environment and Conservation

All good gardeners are naturally conservationists at heart. It's difficult to be as close to nature as we get without becoming concerned for the wider issues. The Gardeners' World team is becoming increasingly involved with organizations like Butterfly Conservation and the Royal Society for the Protection of Birds simply because gardens are becoming more and more important as habitats for wildlife these days.

If you're concerned about any aspect of the environment, you'll find the appropriate organization here. They'll be pleased to help you and could certainly do with your support too.

Environmental Groups

Association of the Conservation of Energy
9 Sherlock Mews, London
W1M 3RH
Tel: (0171) 935 1495

Association for the Protection of Rural Scotland
Gladstone's Land, 3rd Floor, 483
Lawnmarket, Edinburgh
E11 2NT
Tel: (0131) 2257012

The Barn Owl Trust
Waterleat, Ashburton, Devon
TW13 7HU
Tel: (01364) 653026

The Bat Conservation Trust
c/o Conservation Foundation
1 Kensington Gore, London
SW7 2AR
Tel: (0171) 240 0933

British Association of Nature Conservationists
36 Kingfisher Court, Newbury,
Berkshire RG14 5SJ
Tel: (01635) 550380

British Isles Bee Breeders Association
11 Thomson Drive, Codnor, Ripley,
Derbyshire DE5 9RU
Tel: (01773) 745287

The British Butterfly Conservation Society Limited
PO Box 222, Dedham, Colchester,
Essex CO7 6EY
Tel: (01206) 322342

British Trust for Conservation Volunteers (BTCV)
36 St Mary's Street, Wallingford,
Oxfordshire OX10 0EU
Tel: (01491) 839766

British Trust for Ornithology
The Nunnery, Thetford, Norfolk
IP24 2PU
Tel: (01842) 750050

Campaign for Lead-Free Air (Clear)
3 Endsleigh Street, London
WC1 0DD
Tel: (0171) 387 4970

Campaign for the Protection of Rural Wales
Tygwyn, 31 High Street, Welshpool,
Powys SY21 7JP
Tel: (01938) 552525

Centre for Alternative Technology
Llwyngwern Quarry, Machynlleth,
Powys, Wales SY20 9AZ
Tel (01654) 702400

Centre for the Conservation of Historic Parks and Gardens
The Institute of Advanced
Architectural Studies, University of
York, The King's Manor, York
Y01 2EP
Tel: (01904) 433966

Common Ground
Seven Dials Warehouse, 44 Earlham
Street, London WC2H 7LA
Tel: (0171) 379 3109

The Conservation Foundation
Lower Lodge, 1 Kensington Gore,
London SW7 2AR
Tel: (0171) 235 1743

The Environment Council
21 Elizabeth Street, SW1W 9RP
Tel: (0171) 828411

Council for the Protection of Rural England (CPRE)
Warwick House, 25 Buckingham
Palace Road, London SW1 0PP
Tel: (0171) 976 6433

Country Council for Wales
Plas Penrhos, Ffordd Penrhos,
Bangor, Gwynedd
LL57 2LQ
Tel: (01248) 370444

Countryside Commission
John Dower House, Crescent Place,
Cheltenham, Gloucester
GL50 3RA
Tel: (01242) 521381

English Nature
Northminster House, Northminster
Road, Peterborough, Cambs
PE1 1UA
Tel: (01733) 340345

Fauna and Flora Preservation Society
1 Kensington Gore, London
SW7 2AR
Tel: (0171) 823 8899

Friends of the Earth (FoE)
26–28 Underwood Street, London
N1 7JQ
Tel: (0171) 4901555

Friends of the Earth (Scotland)
Bonnington Hill, 70–72 Newhaven
Road, Edinburgh EH6 5QG
Tel: (0131) 554 9977

Greenpeace
Canonbury Villas, London N1 2PN
Tel: (0171) 354 5100

Henry Doubleday Research Association (HDRA)
National Centre for Organic
Gardening, Ryton-on-Dunsmore,
Coventry CV8 3LG
Tel: (01203) 303517

Joint Nature Conservation Committee
Monkstone House, Peterborough
PE1 1JY
Tel: (01733) 62626

London Wildlife Trust
80 York Way, London N1 9AG
Tel: (0171) 278 6612

Marine Conservation Society
(now incorpoating the COASTAL
ANTI-POLLUTION LEAGUE)
9 Gloucester Road, Ross-on-Wye,
Hereford & Worcester
HR9 5BU
Tel: (01989) 66017

**National Federation of City Farms
(NFCF)**
The GreenHouse, Hereford Street,
Bedminster, Bristol BS3 4NA
Tel: (0117) 923 1800

**National Society for Clean Air
(NSCA)**
136 North Street, Brighton
BN1 1RG
Tel: (01273) 326313

National Trust
National Trust for Northern Ireland,
Ireland, Scotland
see *Organizations*

Plantlife
Natural History Museum, Cromwell
Road, London SW7 5BD
Tel: (0171) 938 9111

Ramblers Association
1–5 Wandsworth Road, London
SW8 2XX
Tel: (0171) 582 6878

**Royal Society for Nature
Conservation (RSNC)**
The Green, Witham Park, Waterside
South, Lincoln LN5 7JN
Tel: (01522) 544400

**Royal Society for the Protection of
Birds (RSPB)**
The Lodge, Sandy, Bedfordshire
SG19 2DL
Tel: (01767) 680551

Scottish Natural Heritage
12 Hope Terrace, Edinburgh
EH9 2AS
Tel: (0131) 447 4784

Soil Association
86 Colston Street, Bristol
BS1 5BB
Tel: (0117) 929 0661

Tidy Britain Group
The Pier, Wigan WN3 4WX
Tel: (01942) 824620

Tree Council
35 Belgrave Square, London
SW1X 8QN
Tel: (0171) 235 8854

Urban Wildlife Trust
Unit 81B, Jubilee Trades Centre,
130–133 Pershore Street, Birmingham
B5 6ND
Tel: (0121) 666 7474

**The Women's Environmental Network
(WEN)**
Aberdeen Studios, 22 Highbury
Grove, London N5 2EA
Tel: (0171) 354 8823

Woodland Trust
Autumn Park, Dysart Road,
Grantham, Lincs NG31 6LL
Tel: (01476) 74297

World Wide Fund for Nature (WWF)
Panda House, Weyside Park,
Godalming, Surrey GU7 1XR
Tel: (01483) 426444

Recycling Addresses

Aluminium Can Recycling Association
Suite 308, 1 Mex House, 52 Bulcher
Street, Birmingham B1 1QU
Tel: (0121) 633 4656

British Glass Manufacturers Federation
Northumberland Road, Sheffield
S10 2UA
Tel: (0114) 268 6201

British Plastics Federation
6 Bach Place, Rivington Street,
London EC2A 3JE
Tel: (0171) 457 5000

British Waste Paper Association
Alexander House Business Centre,
Station Road, Aldershot, Hants
GU11 1BQ
Tel: (01252) 344454

Weights and Measures Conversion Tables

Length

10 millimetres = 1 centimetre
1,000 millimetres = 100 centimetres =
1 metre
mm = millimetres
cm = centimetres
m = metres

6mm = ¼in
13mm = ½in
2cm = ¾in
2.5cm = 1in
4cm = 1½in
5cm = 2in
6.5cm = 2½in
7.5cm = 3in
9cm = 3½in
10cm = 4in
11.5cm = 4½in
12.5cm = 5in
14cm = 5½in
15cm = 6in
16.5cm = 6½in
18cm = 7in
19cm = 7½in
20.5cm = 8in
21.5cm = 8½in
23cm = 9in
24cm = 9½in
25.5cm = 10in
26.5cm = 10½in
28cm = 11in
29cm = 11½in

30.5cm = 12in
30.5cm = 1ft
61cm = 2ft
91cm = 3ft
0.9m (91cm) = 1yd
1.8m = 2yd
2.7m = 3yd
3.6m = 4yd
4.6m = 5yd
9.2m = 10yd
23m = 25yd
46m = 50yd
92m = 100yd
400m = 440yd (¼ mile)
800m = 880yd (½ mile)
1200m = 1320yd (¾ mile)
1600m = 1760yd (1 mile)

Weight

1000 grams = 1 kilogram
g = gram
kg = kilogram

7g = ¼oz
14g = ½oz
21g = ¾oz
28g = 1oz
42g = 1½oz
57g = 2oz
71g = 2½oz
85g = 3oz
99g = 3½oz

113g = 4oz
128g = 4½oz
142g = 5oz
156g = 5½oz
170g = 6oz
184g = 6½oz
198g = 7oz
213g = 7½oz
227g = 8oz
241g = 8½oz
255g = 9oz
269g = 9½
284g = 10oz
298g = 10½
312g = 11oz
326g = 11½oz
340g = 12oz
354g = 12½oz
369g = 13oz
383g = 13½oz
397g = 14oz
411g = 14½oz
425g = 15oz
439g = 15½oz
454g = 16oz
454g = 1lb
907g = 2lb
1.36kg = 3lb
1.81kg = 4lb
2.26kg = 5lb
4.54kg = 10lb
11.34kg = 25lb
22.68kg = 50lb
45.36kg = 100lb
6.35kg = 1 stone (14lb)
12.70kg = 1 quarter (28lb)
50.80kg = 1 cwt (112lb)
1016kg = 1 ton (2240lb)
1 gram = 0.035oz
1 kilogram = 2.20lb

Area

10000 square centimetres = 1 square metre
10000 square metres = 1 hectare
sq.cm = square centimetre
sq.m = square metre

6.5sq.cm = 1 sq.in
13sq.cm = 2 sq.in
19sq.cm = 3 sq.in
26sq.cm = 4 sq.in
32sq.cm = 5 sq.in
39sq.cm = 6 sq.in
45sq.cm = 7 sq.in
52sq.cm = 8 sq.in
59sq.cm = 9 sq.in
65sq.cm = 10 sq.in
71sq.cm = 11 sq.in
77sq.cm = 12 sq.in
930sq.cm = 1 sq.ft
1860sq.cm = 2 sq.ft
2790sq.cm = 3 sq.ft
3730sq.cm = 4 sq.ft
4650sq.cm = 5 sq.ft
5570sq.cm = 6 sq.ft
6500sq.cm = 7 sq.ft
7430sq.cm = 8 sq.ft
8360sq.cm = 9 sq.ft
9300sq.cm = 10 sq.ft
8360sq.cm = 1 sq.yd
1.7sq.m = 2 sq.yd
2.5sq.m = 3 sq.yd
3.3sq.m = 4 sq.yd
4.2sq.m = 5 sq.yd
5.0sq.m = 6 sq.yd
5.9sq.m = 7 sq.yd
6.7sq.m = 8 sq.yd
7.5sq.m = 9 sq.yd
8.3sq.m = 10 sq.yd
21sq.m = 25 sq.yd
42sq.m = 50 sq.yd
84sq.m = 100 sq.yd
1012sq.m = ¼ acre

2024sq.m = ½ acre
3036sq.m = ¾ acre
4047sq.m = 1 acre
8094sq.m = 2 acre
1.2 hectares = 3 acres
1.6 hectares = 4 acres
2.0 hectares = 5 acres
4.0 hectares = 10 acres
10 hectares = 25 acres
20 hectares = 50 acres
40 hectares = 100 acres

Capacity

1000 millilitres = 1 litre
ml = millilitre

142ml = ¼ pint
189ml = ⅓ pint
284ml = ½ pint
378ml = ⅔ pint
426ml = ¾ pint
568ml = 1 pint
852ml = 1½ pints
1.13 litres = 2 pints
1.42 litres = 2½ pints
1.70 litres = 3 pints
1.98 litres = 3½ pints
2.27 litres = 4 pints
2.56 litres = 4½ pints
2.84 litres = 5 pints
3.12 litres = 5½ pints
3.41 litres = 6 pints
3.69 litres = 6½ pints
3.98 litres = 7 pints
4.26 litres = 7½ pints
4.55 litres = 8 pints
1.15 litres = ¼ gal
2.27 litres = ½ gal
3.41 litres = ¾ gal
4.55 litres = 1 gal
9.09 litres = 2 gal
13.6 litres = 3 gal

18.2 litres = 4 gal
22.7 litres = 5 gal
45.5 litres = 10 gal
114 litres = 25 gal
228 litres = 50 gal
455 litres = 100 gal
28ml = 1 fluid oz
57ml = 2 fluid oz
85ml = 3 fluid oz
113ml = 4 fluid oz
142ml = 5 fluid oz
284ml = 10 fluid oz
568ml = 20 fluid oz
(1 pint)
142ml = 1 gill (¼ pint)
1.13 litres = 1 quart (2 pint)
1 millilitre = 0.0017 pint
1 millilitre = 0.035 fluid oz
10 millilitre = 0.017 pint
10 millilitre = 0.35 fluid oz
50 millilitre = 0.085 pint
50 millilitre = 1.75 fluid oz
100 millilitre = 0.17 pint
100 millilitre = 3.5 fluid oz
1 litre = 1.75 pint
1 litre = 35 fluid oz

Temperature

C = Centigrade
F = Fahrenheit
Freezing points: 0°C 32°F
Boiling points: 100°C 212°F

32°F = 0°C
35°F = 2°C
40°F = 4°C
45°F = 7°C
50°F = 10°C
55°F = 13°C
60°F = 15°C
65°F = 18°C
70°F = 21°C

75°F = 24°C
80°F = 27°C
85°F = 29°C
90°F = 32°C
95°F = 35°C
100°F = 38°C
105°F = 40°C

1°C = 34°F
2°C = 35°F
3°C = 37°F
4°C = 40°F
5°C = 41°F
10°C = 50°F
11°C = 52°F
12°C = 54°F
13°C = 55°F
14°C = 57°F
15°C = 60°F
16°C = 61°F
17°C = 63°F
18°C = 65°F
19°C = 66°F
20°C = 68°F

Conversion methods

TEMPERATURE
For accurate conversion of fahrenheit readings into centigrade, take away 32, multiply by 5, then divide by 9.

For accurate conversion of centigrade readings into fahrenheit, multiply by 9, divide by 5, then add 32.

WEIGHT/AREA
To convert ounces per square yard to grams per square metre, simply multiply the ounces by 34.

Thus, 4 ounces per square yard is equal to 136 grams per square metre.

DILUTIONS
To convert fluid ounces per gallon to millilitres per litre, multiply the fluid ounces by 6.

Thus 6 fluid ounces per gallon is equal to 36 millilitres per litre.

Botanical Names

Latin names can be quite daunting but you should try to get to grips with them. You can see from this list that they can tell you a great deal about each particular plant. What's more, if you use the Latin name of a plant in China, Russia or Timbuctoo, they'll understand you perfectly.

Because of the peculiarities of Latin, I'm afraid that the endings of the words sometimes vary a bit. For example, *californica* means exactly the same as *californicum* and *californicus* while you might find a green leaf described as *viride* or *viridis*. Don't let that put you off any more than the pronunciation. Like any foreign language, provided you get it near enough right you'll be understood. And that's really all that matters.

Names which are geographical

atlanticus – of the Atlas mountains (North Africa)
australis – southern
borealis – northern
californicus – of California
cambricus – of Wales
capensis – of the Cape (South Africa)
europaeus – of Europe
himalaicus – of the Himalaya
hispanicus – of Spain
japonicus – of Japan
lusitanicus – of Portugal
nipponicus – of Japan
occidentalis – western
orientalis – eastern
sinensis – of China

Names describing habitat

alpinus – alpine, of the Alps or growing in alpine regions
alpestris – of mountains
arvensis – of fields or cultivated land
aquaticus – of water, or growing by water
campestris – of plains or flat areas
littoralis – of sea shores
maritimus – by the sea
montanus – of mountains
muralis – growing on walls
palustris – of swamps or marshes
pratensis – of meadows
rivularis – of streams and brooks
rupestris – of rocks or cliffs
saxatilis – rock-dwelling
sylvaticus – of woods
terrestris – of the earth
uliginosus – growing in marshy places

Names describing habit

alatus – winged
arachnoides – spider- or cobweb-like
arboreus – tree-like
baccatus – berried
caespitosus – tufted
columnaris – columnar
compactus – compact
compressus – compressed
contortus – twisted
erectus – upright
fastigiatus – erect, the branches
frutescens – bushy
fruticosus – shrubby
giganteus – big
gramineus – grassy
horizontalis – horizontally-spreading
humilis – low-growing
major – greater
maximus – largest
minimus – very small
minor – lesser
nanus – dwarf
parvus – small
patens – spreading
pendulus – pendulous, weeping
procerus – very tall, high
procumbens – procumbent, creeping
prostratus – prostrate, hugging the
  ground
pumulis – dwarf
pygmaeus – dwarf
radicans – rooting
ramosus – branched
rectus – straight
repens – creeping and rooting
sarmentosus – producing long runners
scandens – climbing
spicatus – spiny
stoloniferus – suckered
suffruticosus – woody at base
vagans – wandering

Names describing leaves

acanthifolius – prickly-leaved
angustifolius – narrow-leaved
argutus – sharp
bifoliatus – two-leaved
buxifolius – box-leaved
cordatus – heart-shaped
coriaceus – coriaceous, leathery
crassifolius – thick-leaved
crispus – curled
deciduus – deciduous, dropping its
  leaves
disectus – dissected
glabrus – glabrous, without hairs
hederaceus – ivy-like
heterophyllus – variable-leaved
hirsutus – hairy
incanus – grey-downy
incisus – deeply-cut
integerrimus – without teeth
laevigatus – smooth and polished
lanatus – woolly
latifolius – broad-leaved
macrophyllus – large-leaved
maculatus – spotted, blotched
marginatus – margined
microphyllus – small-leaved
mollis – soft
nitidus – shining
oppositifolius – with opposite leaves
orbicularis – rounded
ovatus – oval
parvifolius – small-leaved
pictus – painted, coloured
pinnatus – pinnate
platyphyllus – broad-leaved
quintuplinervis – five-ribbed
reticulatus – net-veined
rotundifolius – round-leaved
saponarius – soapy
sempervirens – always green,
  evergreen
serratus – sawed

splendens – glittering, shining
tomentosus – covered with a short
  dense pubescence
trifoliatus – three-leaved
triplinervis – three-ribbed
undulatus – wavy
variegatus – variegated, two-coloured
velutinus – velvety

Names describing flowers

barbatus – bearded
calyciformis – calyx-like
campanulatus – bell-shaped
cornutus – horned
duplex – double
farinosus – floury
ferox – fertile
fimbriatus – fringed
flore-pleno – double-flowered
floribundus – free-flowering
fragrans – scented
grandiflorus – large-flowered
labiatus – lipped
macropetalus – many-petalled
nudiflorus – naked, without leaves
nutans – nodding
octandrus – with eight stamens
paniculatus – flowering in panicles
parviflorus – small-flowered
pauciflorus – few-flowered
pectinatus – comb-like
pedunculatus – stalked
pleniflorus – with double flowers
plumosus – feathered
polyanthus – many-flowered
punctatus – finely-spotted
racemosus – flowers in racemes
spicatus – flowers in spikes
stellatus – starry
tigrinus – spotted
triflorus – flowers in threes
umbellatus – flowers in umbels
uniflorus – one-flowered

Names describing colours

aethiopicus – black
albus – white
albicans – nearly white
albidus – off white
argenteus – silvery
ater – black
atro-coccineus – crimson black
atro-purpureus – purple black
atrovirens – deep green
aurantiacus – orange
auratus – gilded
aureus – golden
bicolor – two-coloured
caeruleus – blue
candicans – becoming white
cardinalis – cardinal red
carneus – flesh-coloured
chlorinus – yellow green
cinereus – ash grey
citrinus – lemon yellow
coccineus – scarlet
coloratus – coloured
concolor – of the same colour
cupreus – copper-coloured
dealbatus – whitened
discolor – two-coloured
erythrinus – red
ferreus – iron grey
ferrugineus – rusty brown
flavus – pale yellow
flavissimus – intense yellow
galanthus – milky white
glaucus – sea green
hepaticus – liver-coloured
igneus – flame-coloured
incanus – grey
juniperinus – blue brown
lacteus – milky white
lilacinus – lilac
lividus – grey purple
luteus – yellow
lutescens – becoming yellow

marginatus – edged with another colour
melleus – honey-coloured
nigellus – nearly black
niger – black
nivalis – pure white
ochraceus – yellow ochre
pallidus – pale
primulinus – sulphury yellow
puniceus – crimson
purpureus – purple
roseus – rose-coloured
ruber – red
sanguineus – blood red
sulphureus – sulphur yellow
tricolor – three-coloured
variegatus – variegated two-coloured
versicolor – variously-coloured, or changing colour
violaceus – violet
virens – green
viridis – green

Names describing aromas and scents

aromaticus – aromatic
citriodorus – lemon-scented
foetidus – strong-smelling, unpleasant
fragrans – fragrant
fragrantissimus – most fragrant
graveolens – smelling unpleasantly
odoratus – sweet-scented
odoratissimus – sweetest-scented
moschatus – musk-scented
suaveolens – sweet-scented

Names alluding to other plants

bignonoides – bignonia-like
jasmineus – jasmine-like

liliiflorus – lily-flowered
pseudoplatanus – false plane
quercifolius – oak-leaved
rosaceus – rose-like
salicifolius – willow-leaved
tulipiferus – tulip-bearing

Names which are commemorative

delavayi – after the Abbé Delavay
douglasi – after David Douglas
fargesii – after Père Farges
farreri – after George Farrer
forrestii – after George Forrest
foryunei – after Robert Fortune
fraseri – after John Fraser
harryanus – after Sir Harry Veitch
henryanus – after Dr Augustine Henry
hookeri – after Sir Joseph Hooker
mariesii – after Charles Maries
thunbergii – after Carl Peter Thunberg
veitchii – after John Gould Veitch
vilmorinii – after Maurice de Vilmorin
williamsianus – after Mr J C Williams
willmottianus – after Miss Ellen Willmott
wilsoniae – after Mrs E H Wilson

Miscellaneous names

acaulis – stemless
aestivus – summer
affinis – related (to another species)
amabilis – lovely
ambiguus – doubtful (identity ?)
amoenus – charming, pleasing
bellus – pretty
biennis – biennial

brilliantissimus – very brilliant
bulbiferus – bulb-bearing
calceolarius – slipper-shaped
ceriferus – waxy
communis – common, occuring in plenty
confusus – confused (identity ?)
crenatus – scalloped
crispus – curl
cristatus – crested
cruciformus – cross-shaped
cuneatus – wedge-shaped
cuspidatus – pointed
cylindricus – cylindrical
cymbiformis – boat-shaped
decorus – handsome
deformis – misshapen
dentatus – toothed
dependens – hanging down
dissimilis – unlike
dulcis – sweet
echinatus – spined
edulis – edible
elatior – higher
elegans – elegant
exiguus – small, scant
fibrosus – fibrous
flabellatus – fan-shaped
flaccidus – weak
floridus – free-flowering
formosus – handsome, beautiful
fragalis – fragile
frigidus – cold
glabellus – smooth
gracilis – slender
gladiolus – little sword
globosus – ball-shaped
glutinosus – sticky
grandis – large
gutatus – spotted
hortensis – of gardens
hybridus – hybrid

insignis – outstanding
integerrimus – whole
intermedius – intermediate
laciniatus – fringed
laevigatus – smooth
lanuginosus – downy
laxus – loose
lentus – pliable
lineatus – finely-lined
littoralis – of the sea shore
lucidus – clear, shining
maculatus – spotted
medius – middle, midway between
mollis – tender
nervatus – of the shop (herbal)
officinalis – of the shop (herbal)
oxalis – acid (taste)
perennis – perennial
plicatus – folded
praecox – early
praestans – excellent
pulchellus – beautiful
rigens – rigid
rugosus – wrinkled
sativus – sown, planted or cultivated
scaber – rough
speciosus – splendid
spectabalis – showy
splendens – brilliant
squamatus – scaley
sterilis – barren
striatus – striped
terminalis – terminal
tuberosus – tuberous
tubularis – flat
tulipus – turban
utilis – useful
validus – strong
ventricocus – swollen
vernalis – spring
vulgaris – common
zebrinus – striped

A Glossary of Gardening Terms

All occupations that have a professional side to them develop a specialist jargon and gardening is no exception. Often it's confusing to new gardeners (for example, we pot-on, we pot-off, we pot-up and sometimes we even pot-down. But we *never* pot-*in*!). On the *Gardeners' World* programme we do try to avoid jargon but sometimes, I admit, it does slip in. The list below, while by no means complete, explains some of the most-used terms.

Acid. Soil with pH below 7.

Activator. A chemical used to speed up the composting process.

Adventitious. A plant organ that appears in an unusual place. Ivy, for example, produces adventitious roots above ground.

Air laying. A propagation technique where roots are induced to form on a stem above rather than in the soil, without severing it from the parent.

Algae. Microscopic plants that turn pond water green and also appear on top of composts etc.

Alkaline. The opposite of acid (having a pH of over 7).

Allee. A walk or ride lined with trees and shrubs.

Alpines. Plants from mountainous areas which are grown in rock gardens.

Alpine meadow. Mountainous areas growing grass and alpines or a representation in a garden.

Anaerobic. Living without air. (The bacteria that turn grass-cuttings slimy are anaerobic.)

Annual. A plant that lives for one season, sets seeds and then dies.

Anther. The male, pollen-bearing sexual organ of a flower, usually on a stamen.

Aphid. Greenfly and blackfly.

Apical dominance. The passing down of growth retardants from the growing tip of plants to ensure that the topmost bud grows fastest and so reaches the light quickly.

Aquatic plant. One that lives in water.

Arboretum. A collection of trees and shrubs.

Arris rail. The horizontal bars of a close-board fence.

Auxin. A chemical hormone present in plants and affecting growth.

Axil. The angle between the leaf and the stem.

Axillary bud. One that grows from the axil.

Balled. The roots of trees and shrubs which have been lifted from the field and wrapped in hessian or plastic mesh.

Bare-rooted. Plants lifted from the field.

Bark ringing. Removing a section of bark from a tree to reduce the flow of sap and thereby slow growth.

Base dressing. Fertilizer applied before sowing or planting.

Bastard trenching. Double digging.

Beard. A tuft of hair on the lower petals, particularly in irises.

Bedding. Plants used for a short period to give a very colourful display. Usually annuals, biennials and tender perennials.

Bed system. Growing vegetables in 120cm (4ft) wide beds.

Bee plant. One that produces lots of pollen, and is therefore attractive to bees.

Biennial. A plant that is sown in one year, makes its growth the same year, flowers the following year and then dies. Wallflowers are biennials.

Biennial bearing. The habit some fruit trees adopt of producing a crop only every other year.

Bi-generic cross. A hybrid between two plants of different genera.

Blanching. Excluding light from some vegetables and fruits to make them whiter and therefore more tender. It's done with things like chicory, seakale and rhubarb.

Bletting. The over-ripening of fruits, especially medlars, in order to create a distinctive flavour.

Blind shoot. One that fails to grow.

Blueing. The process of making pink hydrangeas blue, using a special chemical blueing agent.

Bog plant. One that grows in soil that is always wet.

Bolting. Early running to seed.

Bonzai. Trees and shrubs dwarfed by root restriction and pruning.

Bottom heat. Warmth provided normally by a propagator to encourage the rooting of cuttings and rapid growth of seedlings.

Bract. A modified leaf that's often highly coloured and looks like a flower. The red parts of poinsettias are bracts.

Brassica. A member of the cabbage family including cauliflowers, kale, brussels sprouts etc.

Break. New growth produced by pinching back the growing tip of a plant.

Bridge graft. A method of repairing a damaged plant by grafting a shoot above and below the damaged area.

Broad-leaved. Description of a tree other than a conifer.

Budding. A propagation method by which the bud of the desired variety is transferred to a rootstock of another variety to impart vigour. It's done particularly with roses.

Bud wood. A shoot containing several buds of the variety to be budded onto the rootstock.

Bulb scaling. A method of propagating bulbs by removing and rooting separate scales.

Bulb. An underground stem made of fleshy scales, which is used to store food.

Bulbil. A small bulb found in the axils of the leaves of some bulbous plants such as lilies.

Calcicole or calciphile. Description of a plant that thrives on limey soil.

Callus. Hard tissues formed over a wound to help the healing process.

Calyx. The outer ring of the flower parts made up of sepals.

Cambium. The region of active growth immediately below the bark.

Capillary bed. A bed that holds water, often with a sand base, on which to stand potted plants that will suck up the water.

Capillary mat. Fibrous matting for the same purpose as a capillary bed.

Capping. The formation of a hard crust on the surface of soil.

Capsule. The seed-carrying pod.

Carpel. The female sexual organs containing the ovary, style and stigma.

Catch crop. A quick-maturing vegetable crop grown between plants that take a long time to mature.

Chit. The process of putting seed potatoes and other seeds in a light, occasionally moist place to produce sprouts prior to planting. The sprouts too are called 'chits'.

Chlorophyll. The green pigment in plants necessary for photosynthesis.

Chlorosis. Yellowing of leaves often caused by nutrient deficiency.

Cloche. Originally a bell-shaped cover to protect plants from low temperatures. Now available in many shapes.

Clone. Several identical plants propagated vegetatively from the same parent.

Contact pesticide or weedkiller. A chemical that kills pests, diseases or weeds on contact.

Container-grown. A plant grown from the propagation stage in a pot as opposed to those grown in the field and potted up.

Controlled release fertilizer. A new development whereby fertilizer pellets are coated to allow them to release their nutrients slowly. Generally affected by temperature.

Cordon. Method of training a fruit tree as a single stem.

Corm. A swollen stem which resembles a bulb but has no fleshy, onion-like layers.

Cotyledon. Seed leaf – the first to appear.

Cristate. A crested leaf form found mainly in ferns and cacti.

Crock. Drainage material which is placed at the bottom of pots.

Cross. A hybrid.

Crown. The part of the plant where the leaves arise from the roots. Also applies to a root of rhubarb.

Cultivar. A variety raised in cultivation.

Cutting. A shoot rooted in compost to make a new plant.

Damping down. Watering paths and stagings in the greenhouse to increase humidity.

Damping off. A fungus disease of seedlings.

Dead-heading. Removing faded flowers.

Deep bed. A 1.2m (4ft) wide bed for growing vegetables.

Deciduous. Plants that lose their leaves in winter.

Dibber. A tool for making planting holes.

Dibble. Describes the use of a dibber.

Dicotyledon. A plant with two seed leaves.

Dioecious. Bearing male and female flowers on different plants.

Disbudding. The removal of buds to concentrate energy into one, selected bud to increase its size.

Disc. Central mass of small flowers or florets, as in daisies.

Diurnal. Flowers that open in the day and close at night.

Division. Propagating plants by

splitting the roots into more than one piece.

Dormancy. Resting period of seeds in particular but also applied to plants.

Dot plant. A single tall plant in a border of otherwise short ones, added to give height.

Double, semi-double. Flowers with more than the usual number of petals.

Double digging. Bastard trenching.

Draw-hoe. A hoe with the blade set on a curved tang used with a chopping motion.

Drawn. Elongated and weak stem.

Drill. A shallow furrow used to sow seeds.

Dutch hoe. A hoe with a flat blade used by pushing it with short movements while walking backwards.

Dutch light. A glass or plastic frame used on cold-frames and greenhouses.

Dwarfing rootstock. A rootstock on which fruit trees normally are budded and which reduces the eventual height of the tree.

Dwarf pyramid. A method of fruit-tree pruning which makes a shape like a Christmas tree with successively shorter horizontal branches.

Earthing up. Drawing soil round the stems of plants. Used mainly on plants like potatoes and celery.

Edging iron. A half-moon shaped tool for cutting straight lawn edges.

Emasculation. The removal of the male sexual parts from a flower to prevent self-pollination during breeding work.

Epiphyte. A plant attached to another but not taking nourishment from it.

Ericaceous. Describes acid-loving plants.

Escape. A plant that has naturalized itself in the wild after having been introduced into gardens. Often a weed.

Espalier. A method of training fruit trees in horizontal tiers of branches.

Etiolated. Drawn due to poor light.

Evergreen. A plant that loses only a few leaves at a time, rather than all at once, in autumn.

Everlasting flowers. Flowers that hold their colour after drying.

Eye. Growth bud, particularly in a potato.

F1. A first generation cross resulting from the hand-pollination of two selected parents.

F2. Second generation cross resulting from crossing two F1's.

Falls. The outer petals of irises which hang vertically.

Fan-trained. A method of training fruit trees with radiating branches like the ribs of a fan.

Fasciation. A freak condition where often two stems are welded together and flattened.

Feathered. Describes a young tree with unpruned branches so that, instead of a bare stem like that of a traditional standard tree, the branches start from the bottom of the main stem.

Festooning. A method of training fruit trees by tying branches down.

Fibrous roots. A much-divided root system consisting of masses of thin roots.

Fillis. Softs string.

Fimbriate. Fringed petals.

Flocculation. The binding together of

clay particles by chemical action induced by the application of lime.

Florets. Small flowers making up a larger flower head.

Foliar feed. A liquid fertilizer sprayed onto and absorbed by leaves.

Forcing. Accelerating plant growth, generally by raising the temperature.

Forking. Digging with a fork, but also applied to root vegetables that divide below ground.

Form. A variation or different strain of a plant.

Frame. A wooden (or aluminium) and glass (or plastic) structure used to grow some early crops and to acclimatize plants to lower temperatures before planting out.

Friable. A description of soil that's crumbly, light and moist and breaks down well.

Frost pocket. A depression in the landscape where frost collects.

Fruit bud. One that will grow out to produce a fruit as opposed to a wood bud.

Fruit cage. A structure carrying netting to protect fruit from birds.

Gall. An abnormal swelling on a shoot caused by a burrowing insect or a bacterium.

General fertilizer. One containing all necessary main plant nutrients.

Genus. A group of plants with similar characteristics making up a family.

Geotropism. The growth or movement of a plant in response to gravity.

Germination. The emergence of roots and shoots from a seed.

Graft. The joining of two pieces of stem or root to form one plant.

Grease band. A sticky band put round fruit trees to catch crawling insects.

Green manure. A crop grown to be dug in to add organic matter to the soil and retain nutrients.

Ground cover. Low growing plants forming a weed-suppressing mat.

Growing point. The tip to the stem.

Ha-ha. A deep ditch, often with a hedge in the bottom to form a boundary without interrupting the view.

Half-hardy. Describes a plant that won't survive low temperatures.

Half pot. A flower pot which is half the normal depth.

Half-ripe. A shoot that has begun to harden.

Hand-light. A small, individual cloche.

Hardening off. Gradually acclimatizing plants to lower temperatures before planting out. This is normally done in a cold frame.

Hardwood cutting. A cutting of ripened wood taken in autumn.

Hardy. Describes plants able to withstand frosty conditions.

Haulm. Top-growth of vegetables like peas and potatoes.

Heading back. Drastic pruning of trees or shrubs.

Heel. A small strip of bark torn from the parent when a heelcutting is taken.

Heeling-in. The temporary storage of bare-rooted plants by covering the roots with soil.

Herbaceous plant. One with a non-woody stem.

Herbicide. Weedkiller.

Hollow-tine fork. A fork with hollow prongs designed to remove a core of soil from lawns to aid aeration.

Hormone rooting compound. Growth-regulating substance in powdered or liquid form, used when rooting cuttings.

Hose-in-hose. A flower where one appears to be inside another, found notably in primulas.

Host plant. A plant that supports a parasite.

Hotbed. A heap of manure that gives off heat as it rots down, warming a bed of soil on top. Used to grow early vegetables.

Humus. The final stage of the decay of vegetable matter.

Hybrid. The offspring resulting from crossing two plants of different species.

Hydroponics. Growing plants in nutrient solutions without soil.

Hypertufa. A mixture made by mixing sand, cement and peat used to make imitation stone troughs and to coat glazed sinks. Use 2 parts sharp sand, 2 parts sieved coir compost and 1 part fresh cement.

Incurved. Describes petals that curve inwards, generally on chrysanthemums.

Inflorescence. A flower head composed of several flowers.

Inorganic. Generally applied to chemical pesticides and fertilizers.

Internode. The position between two leaf joints.

Insectivorous plants. Those that live by trapping and digesting insects.

Intercropping. See catch crop.

Irishman's cutting. A basal cutting taken with a little root attached.

Jardiniere. An ornamental container for houseplants.

John Innes Composts. Soil-based composts made to a recipe devised by the John Innes Institute.

King fruit. The large, dominant fruit in the centre of a cluster.

Knot garden. A formal garden laid out in clipped box, lavender, santolina etc.

Laced. Describes flowers of garden pinks which have a band of different colour round the edge.

Lateral. A sideshoot.

Layering. Propagation method where a shoot is pegged to the soil to induce rooting.

Leaching. The draining away of nutrients through the soil.

Leader. The terminal shoot that will grow out strongest to form the main stem of the plant.

Leaf-bud cutting. A cutting consisting of a single leaf with a piece of shoot attached.

Leafmould. The result of rotting down leaves.

Legume. A member of the pea family.

Loam. A balanced mixture of soils with clay, sand and humus to form a good, easily worked soil.

Long-day plant. One that flowers when the days are lengthening.

Long tom. A deep, narrow plant pot.

Lute. A type of rake used for working top-dressings into lawns.

Maiden. A one-year-old tree.

Maincrop. Crop of vegetables that is allowed to mature. Generally applied to potatoes, peas and carrots.

Marginal plant. One that grows at the water's edge.

Mattock. A tool similar to a pick axe with one flattened blade and one axe-like blade used for grubbing out trees etc.

Meristem. Plant tissues capable of producing new cells.

Meristem culture. A method of propagating in the laboratory.

Microclimate. A particularly localized climate.

Mist unit. A device for automatically spraying plants with water at intervals during propagation.

Mixed border. A border where trees, shrubs, herbaceous plants and bulbs grow together.

Module. A plastic tray divided into a series of separate cells used to raise seedlings without the extra process of pricking out.

Monocarpic. A plant that dies after flowering and fruiting.

Monocotyledon. A plant with one seed-leaf, i.e. onion and grass.

Monoecious. A plant carrying male and female flowers.

Moraine. A plant habitat consisting of coarse, gravelly rock chippings suitable for alpines.

Mother plant. One used exclusively to provide propagation material.

Mulch. A top dressing normally of bulky organic matter used to prevent evaporation of water and to restrict weed growth.

Multistemmed. Describes a tree with several, (normally 3), main stems coming from the base.

Mutation. A charge in a plant's inherited genetic structure.

Mycelium. The vegetative growth of fungi consisting of fine thread-like strands.

Naturalize. A method of planting (using bulbs in particular) in grass to look as if they're growing wild.

Neutral. A soil with a pH of exactly 7.

Nicking and notching. The technique of cutting a small nick above a bud to divert growth retarding substances sent down from the apical bud, thus making the bud below grow out. Notching is making a nick below the bud to concentrate the growth retardant.

Nitrogen-fixing bacteria. Bacteria which live in the roots of some plants and have the ability to capture and use nitrogen from the air.

Node. A leaf-joint.

Nodule. A swelling in a root caused by the presence of nitrogen-fixing bacteria.

NPK. The chemical symbols for nitrogen, phosphorus and potassium that make up the major nutrients in a balanced fertilizer.

Nursery-bed. A bed used to plant out young plants that are growing on, prior to planting in their permanent positions.

Nutrient film technique. A method of growing plants without soil or compost by allowing a film of nutrient solution to run over their roots.

Obelisk. A tapering, ornamental structure used either as a piece of statuary or to grow climbing plants over.

Offset. A small bulb or shoot

growing from the stem of the parent plant.

Onion hoe. A small hoe used in one hand to accurately hoe round plants (originally, of course, onions).

Open-pollinated. Seeds that have come from plants which have been pollinated naturally in the field.

Organic. Usually refers to fertilizers and pesticides derived from plant or animal materials.

Overpotting. The mistake of putting a plant in too big a pot and thereby surrounding it with a mass of wet, cold compost.

Oxygenating plant. A submerged pond plant that helps to add oxygen to the water.

Pan. A compacted soil layer usually caused by constant cultivation at one depth or by building work on new houses.

Parasite. A plant that grows on and derives nutriment from another.

Parterre. A formal garden in the French style, somewhat resembling a knot garden but with flowers growing inside the hedged enclosures.

Pathogen. An organism causing disease.

Pelleted. Refers to seeds which have been covered with a coating to aid sowing and germination and to fertilizers which have been processed to form small pellets for easier and more accurate distribution.

Peat-bed. A raised bed containing soil and a high proportion of peat to enable acid-loving plants to be grown in otherwise alkaline soil.

Peat block. A hard block of peat used to build walls.

Peat pot. A pot made with peat and wood-fibre which decomposes after planting out.

Perennial. Generally refers to a herbaceous plant that flowers annually.

Pergola. An arched walk over which climbing plants are grown.

Perlite. Heat-expanded minerals used in potting composts.

Pesticide. A chemical used to control pests or diseases.

Petiole. Leaf stalk.

pH. The unit of measurement of acidity with pH7 being neutral and anything below acid and above alkaline.

Photoperiodism. The control of plant growth by altering the day-length.

Photosynthesis. The process by which plants convert carbon dioxide and water into growth-promoting sugars using the energy of sunshine through chlorophyll in the leaves.

Phototropism. The movement of plants in response to light.

Physic garden. A garden devoted to the growing of medicinal plants.

Picotee. A petal with a different coloured band round the edge.

Pillar. A method of training fruit trees to form a columnar shape.

Pinching out. The removal of a plant's growing tip to encourage the growth of lower shoots, making the plant bushier.

Piping. A cutting, usually of pinks or carnations, made by pulling a shoot from the leaf-joint.

Pistil. Female organs of flowers comprising ovary, style and stigma.

Pleaching. The pruning and intertwining of branches, generally on the upper part of trees, to form a narrow shape. Used normally on trees either side of an avenue.

Plug. A young plant grown in a module.

Plumule. The first shoot of a seedling.

Plunge-bed. A bed of organic matter or sometimes sand into which pots are sunk to keep roots cool and moist or to encourage rooting in bulbs.

Pollarding. The removal of branches of a tree or shrub hard back to the trunk.

Pollen. Male fertilizing agent.

Pollination. The transfer of pollen from the anther to the stigma.

Pollinator. A variety, most commonly of fruit tree, used to provide pollen to ensure fruiting of others.

Pompon. Small, ball-shaped flower.

Pore space. The spaces between soil particles which provide necessary aeration.

Porous tube; porous pipe. A plastic hosepipe which leaks water along its whole length used for under-soil irrigation.

Potager. A formal vegetable garden like a parterre but with vegetables and fruit growing within the hedged compartments.

Potato fork. A fork with flat tines used to dig potatoes.

Pot-bound. The state of a pot-grown plant that has filled the space with roots.

Pot-thick. The arrangement of pots generally on a greenhouse staging, where the pots are touching.

Potting-on. The transfer of a pot-grown plant into a bigger pot when the space for roots has become full.

Potting-off. The transfer of small plants from seed-tray to pot.

Potting-up. As above.

Predator. The enemy of a pest.

Pre-emergence. Describes a weedkiller used to kill weeds before they emerge.

Prepared. Describes bulbs which have been treated with a special temperature regime to induce early flowering.

Pricking out. Transferring young seedlings to wider spacings in seed trays.

Propagating case. See propagator.

Propagator. A glass or plastic box used to provide bottom heat and to increase humidity to aid rapid rooting of cuttings and germination of seeds.

Propagule. A plant used for propagation.

Prostrate. Describes a plant that grows flat to the ground.

Puddling. Now generally refers to the heavy watering-in of plants after planting.

Radicle. The first root of a seedling.

Recurved petals. Upward or downwardly curved petals.

Reflexed. A flower with sharply curved petals.

Remontant. Flowering and/or fruiting more than once in a season.

Residual. Describes herbicides that remain active in the soil for a period.

Reversion. A condition in which a plant with variegated leaves produces plain green ones. They're generally cut out. Also refers to a disease of blackcurrants.

Rhizome. A swollen, root-like stem which acts as a storage organ and grows both roots and shoots (i.e. flag irises).

Riddle. A wide-meshed sieve.

Ridging. A method of cultivation in which the soil is thrown up into ridges to expose a bigger area to the effects of weathering. Some plants, like potatoes, are also ridged up after planting, covering the planted tubers with a ridge of soil.

Ring culture. A method of growing tomatoes in bottomless pots on a bed of gravel.

Ripe wood. A young shoot that has started to harden and mature.

Rogue. A plant that does not conform to normal characteristics.

Rogueing. The removal of rogues from a crop, especially a seed-crop.

Root ball. The mass of roots in a pot-grown plant.

Root cutting. A piece of root induced to form adventitious roots as a means of propagation.

Rooting compound. See hormone rooting compound.

Rootstock. A plant on which a variety is budded or grafted. It's generally used to control vigour or sometimes to impart disease resistance.

Root hairs. Tiny hairs on roots, responsible for the uptake of water and nutrients.

Root pruning. The pruning of roots by trenching round a plant, used to restrict growth.

Root-run. The area through which a plant's roots extend.

Rotation. A method of growing vegetables to make best use of resources. (See p.266).

Runner. A shoot growing along the ground and rooting at intervals (i.e. strawberries).

Saprophyte. A plant living on decaying organic matter.

Scarify. To rake moss and dead grass from a lawn. Also refers to the scraping of the hard seed coat of a seed in order to allow water to enter more readily.

Scion. Shoot or bud grafted onto a rootstock.

Scorch; scorching. The drying and desiccation of leaves due to lack of water, excess sunlight, salt spray, strong winds, frost, pesticide damage or nutrient deficiency.

Scoring. A method of propagating bulbs by cutting into the base plate.

Scree. A bed of small stones and gravel used to grow alpine plants.

Seed drill. See drill.

Seed dressing. A chemical coating used to protect seeds from fungus attack.

Seed leaf. The first leaf or cotyledon.

Selective weedkiller. One that attacks one type of weed but not others.

Self-fertile. A flower capable of fertilizing itself without the need of pollen from another plant.

Semi-ripe. See half-ripe.

Sepal. Separate leaf of the calyx.

Set. A small onion or shallot bulb used instead of seed. The term also refers to the successful fertilization of flowers and initiation of fruit.

Sheet composting. Laying out of vegetable matter, weeds etc. on soil to compost *in situ*.

Shield budding. A method of propagation involving taking a shield-shaped piece of tissue including a bud and inserting it into a slit cut into the bark of the rootstock.

Shoddy. Wool waste used to add organic matter to soil.

Shrub. A woody plant without a trunk.

Sideshoot. A shoot growing out of the main stem.

Sideshooting. The removal of sideshoots.

Single. Describes flowers with the normal number of petals as opposed to double and semi-double.

Slip. An old-fashioned term for a cutting.

Slitting. Making short cuts in turf for aeration.

Slow-release fertilizer. See controlled release fertilizer.

Snag. A short stub left by pruning or breakage.

Soft fruit. Fruit from bushes or canes as opposed to top or tree fruit.

Softwood cutting. One taken using the current season's growth before it ripens.

Soil conditioner. Organic matter added to soil to improve its condition.

Soilless compost. Compost consisting of organic or inorganic materials but excluding soil.

Soluble fertilizer. One that's dissolved in water and added as a liquid.

Species. Plants of the same specific type within a genus.

Specimen plant. A single plant placed for maximum visual impact.

Spiking. Making aeration holes in lawns with a fork, a hollow-tine fork or a machine.

Spit. A spade's depth.

Spores. The equivalent of seeds on non-flowering plants like ferns and fungi.

Sport. A mutation. An accidental mix-up in genetic characteristics resulting in a change. This often affects flowers and is the source of many new varieties.

Sprout. See chit.

Spur. A collection of short shoots generally on fruit trees. It's these that bear fruits on trained trees like cordons.

Stamen. The male, pollen-bearing reproductive organ.

Standard. A tree with a single, bare stem on top of which is the crown of branches.

Sterilization. A means of using chemicals, steam or heat to clean soil of pathogens.

Stigma. The female reproductive organ of the flower, where the pollen is received.

Stipule. A leaf-like sheath at the base of a flower, where the pollen is received.

Stock. See rootstock.

Stolon. See runner.

Stomata. Minute pores in leaves enabling the exchange of gases.

Stone fruits. Fruits like plums and peaches that contain a hard stone.

Stool. The base of a bushy plant, usually used to provide cuttings.

Stool back. To cut back a bushy plant to encourage the growth of young shoots for cuttings.

Stop. To pinch back the growing point of a plant to induce bushy growth.

Stove house. A greenhouse kept at very high temperatures.

Straight fertilizer. A fertilizer containing only one nutrient.

Strain. Seed-produced plants, all the same, emerging from a common parent.

Stratify. To put seeds into sand or some other material and expose them to winter cold to trigger germination.

Striated. Striped.

Strike. To root a cutting.

Style. Female reproductive organ linking the stigma to the ovary.

Subsoil. The layer of soil below the topsoil containing no organic matter.

Substrate. Any material in which plants can be grown.

Successional sowing. Sowing seeds at intervals to produce a continuous harvest.

Succulent. A plant with fleshy leaves.

Sucker. A shoot arising generally from a rootstock.

Swan-necked hoe. See draw-hoe.

Symbiosis. A mutually beneficial relationship between two plants or animals.

Systemic. Refers to a pesticide that enters the plant's system attacking pests and diseases through the sap.

Tap-root. The long, central main root.

T budding. See shield budding.

Tender perennial. A perennial plant needing frost protection.

Tendril. A thread-like shoot by which climbing plants cling.

Terminal bud. The bud at the end of a shoot.

Thatch. The accumulation of dead grass on the surface of lawns.

Thinning. Removing surplus plants from a row to allow others room to develop.

Thong. A root cutting, especially applied to seakale and globe artichokes.

Tiller. A shoot arising from the base of some plants, grass in particular.

Tilth. Soil broken down to a fine consistency.

Tine. The prong of a fork or rake.

Tip-bearing. A fruit tree that only bears fruit at the tips of each branch.

Tip-layering. A method of propagation where the tip of a climbing plant is put into the ground, i.e. blackberry.

Tissue culture. A laboratory method of propagation.

Tomentose. Hairy or woolly.

Top-dress. To add fertilizer to a growing crop or organic matter plus fertilizer to lawns.

Top fruit. Fruit that grows on trees, e.g. apples and pears.

Topiary. The art of clipping plants into decorative shapes.

Topsoil. The fertile top layer of soil.

Total weedkiller. One that will kill everything it touches.

Trace elements. Plant nutrients essential to healthy growth but required in tiny amounts.

Transpiration. Loss of moisture from leaves.

Transplant. Move a plant, generally a seedling, from one position to another.

Treading. Consolidating soil by walking over it thoroughly.

Treillage. French for trellis, generally applied to structures like arbours and obelisks.

Trenching. Deep digging to grow crops like celery.

Trompe-l'oeil. A method of deceiving the eye with a device like a mirror or a mural.

True leaves. Adult leaves appearing after the first seed leaves.

Trug. A shallow basket, traditionally

of wood, used to carry tools or harvested produce.

Truss. Cluster of fruit.

Tuber. Food-storing, swollen root or stem.

Tufa. A very soft rock, which is used a lot in alpine houses and roof gardens because of its lightness.

Turgid. Erect after watering.

Umbel. An umbrella-shaped flower head with all the stalks of the florets originating from one place.

Underplanting. Growing low-growing plants underneath taller subjects.

Variegated. A leaf or flower of two or more colours.

Variety. A variant of a species.

Vascular system. The conductive and supporting tissue of plants.

Vegetative propagation. Increasing plants by cuttings, division, layering, budding or grafting as opposed to seed.

Vermiculite. A heat-expanded rock used in potting and propagation mixes.

Vernalization. A method of treating bulbs etc. with an artificial temperature regime to speed development.

Viability. The ability of seeds to germinate and grow.

Vine-eye. A flat metal nail with a hole in it used to hammer into walls to carry wires used to support plants.

Virus. A highly contagious organism causing plant and animal diseases. Often transmitted by insects.

Viticulture. The art of growing grapes.

Wall nail. A strong nail with a lead tag on the head used to train plants against walls.

Wardian case. A glass and wood container used originally to transport plants from expeditions and now as a decorative way of growing them.

Water shoot. A useless, sappy shoot arising after drastic pruning.

Wattle fencing. Fencing panels made with young willow or hazel shoots woven together.

Weaning. The gradual removal of seedlings from an atmosphere of high humidity and temperature to a cooler climate.

Weep holes. Holes left at the bottom of retaining walls to prevent a build-up of water pressure behind the wall.

Weeping tree. One whose branches trail downwards.

Whip. A young, generally single stemmed tree.

Wood bud. One that will grow out to produce a shoot as opposed to a fruit bud.

Wounding. Removing a sliver of bark from the base of a woody cutting to encourage root formation.

Xerophyte. A succulent with a special water storing system.